Road to Survival

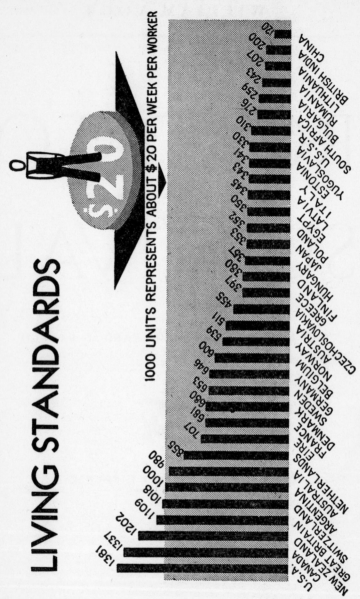

LIVING STANDARDS

1000 UNITS REPRESENTS ABOUT $20 PER WEEK PER WORKER

$20

U.S.A.	1381
NEW ZEALAND	1337
CANADA	1202
GREAT BRITAIN	1109
SWITZERLAND	1018
ARGENTINA	1000
AUSTRALIA	980
NETHERLANDS	855
EIRE	707
FRANCE	681
DENMARK	680
SWEDEN	653
GERMANY	646
BELGIUM	600
NORWAY	539
AUSTRIA	511
CZECHOSLOVAKIA	455
FINLAND	391
GREECE	380
HUNGARY	357
JAPAN	353
POLAND	352
EGYPT	350
ITALY	345
LATVIA	343
ESTONIA	341
YUGOSLAVIA	330
U.S.S.R.	310
SOUTH AFRICA	276
BULGARIA	259
RUMANIA	243
LITHUANIA	207
BRITISH INDIA	200
CHINA	120

Based on *Global War*, An Atlas of World Strategy by Edgar Ansel
Mowrer and Martha Rajchman, copyright 1942 by William Morrow &
Co., Inc. By Permission.

WILLIAM VOGT

ROAD TO SURVIVAL

with an introduction by BERNARD M. BARUCH

Illustrations by STUART I. FREEMAN

WILLIAM SLOANE ASSOCIATES, INC.
Publishers, New York

The author wishes to thank the publishers for permission to quote from *Aztecs of Mexico* by George C. Vaillant, copyright 1941, *Vanishing Lands* by R. O. Whyte and G. V. Jacks, copyright 1939, published by Doubleday & Company Inc.; also *Asia's Lands and Peoples* by George B. Cressey, published by Whittlesey House, copyright 1944, by McGraw-Hill Book Co., Inc.; and *Streamlines* by Christopher Morley, copyright 1933, 1934, 1935, 1936, published by J. B. Lippincott Co.

First Printing

Published simultaneously in Canada by George J. McCleod, Ltd.
Manufactured in the United States of America
By The Haddon Craftsmen, Scranton, Pa.

To

MARJORIE

Contents

Table of Illustrations

Introduction

THE COST OF MODERN WAR, AS WELL AS THE COST OF peaceful living, has risen so sharply that we have built a structure of indebtedness that is a danger to our entire economic structure. Our outstanding bills comprise national, state, and municipal debts, including legal obligations to veterans, and implied promises to pay for growing, government-sponsored social responsibilities. Since our real wealth—as opposed to the product of government printing presses—is drawn from the earth, in always limited quantities, as minerals, food, wood, water, and wildlife, destruction of the earth's surface, and waste of its products have a cogent meaning that touches the life, today and tomorrow, of every human being.

Because of the great abundance of the earth's resources we have taken them for granted. But now, over most of the globe, as this book shows, we are face to face with a serious depletion of "resource capital." More than one country is already bankrupt. Such bankruptcy has wiped out civilizations in the past; there is no reason for thinking we can escape the same fate, unless we change our ways.

The productivity of much of the earth, through man's mistreatment of it, has fallen to such an extent that what one man-hour of labor could formerly produce, now requires ten, fifty, or even a hundred man-hours. Agricultural lands in the Far East and Puerto Rico are examples; some of our forests, where we are painfully culling out scattered saw-timber, and many an exhausted "old field" in our southeast are others. It has been humorously, but not entirely inaccurately, said that on some of our overgrazed western ranges cattle must run so fast and so far to get enough to eat, they wear themselves out; here the land abuse affects cow-hours of work.

One of the chief reasons we have let ourselves become involved in such a maze of difficulties is that throughout history we have seldom tried to understand man as a part of his environment. It has taken the medical profession more than two thousand years to learn it must cure not the organ, nor even the disease, but the *patient*. We are only beginning to comprehend that it is not enough to improve political and economic systems; mankind must reach a sound, healthy relationship with its *total* environment, not only if it is to survive, but also if it is to raise its standard of living, to give every individual the most complete opportunity to realize his own potentialities. The need is especially pressing to reach a favorable biophysical relationship with the earth.

It is imperative that business, intellectual, and governmental leaders—throughout the world—understand the dependence of man on his environment, and the complex, ever-changing relationships within that environment. For, whether or not they act in response to people's mandates, these leaders profoundly influence our destiny today, and by their decisions chart its course for tomorrow. In common with the rest of mankind, they have tended to ignore critical aspects of man's place in the world he has helped to make. I hope they will read this book, and give serious consideration to its analysis of man's situation in his world.

Road to Survival is, I believe, the first attempt—or one of the first—through carefully chosen examples, in large part drawn from wide first-hand experience—to show man as part of his total environment, what he is doing to that environment on a world scale, and what that environment is doing to him. It is no dry-as-dust study; it deals with the raw stuff of living, how more than two billion men and women and children—including you and me—are to be fed, and sheltered, and clothed, and whether or not they are to live in peace, tomorrow, and next year, and in the year 1975.

It asks more questions than it answers, as any scientific book must. While I may not agree with Mr. Vogt in all his conclusions, I believe his work not only deserves but requires careful thought and evaluation at this troubled period of the world's history.   BERNARD M. BARUCH

Foreword by the Author

WE LIVE IN A WORLD OF SUCH RAPID AND DYNAMIC change as man, in his hundreds of thousands of years of existence, has never known. What we today believe to be a fact may tomorrow prove to be illusion. Many of the truths men have lived by must be accepted as delusion in a new frame of reference; and, though we may find it difficult to adjust our nervous systems to different circumstances, the modern world is continuously changing the old frames of reference. Even during the brief span that has been required to write and publish this book, some of history's most dramatic and fateful pageants (including Hiroshima) have rolled upon the stage.

We must accept change, and adjust our lives to it, if we are to survive. To do this, we must look for the order, the principles within the seeming chaos. Our understanding of these principles also changes, but we may be sure they are there, even in chain-reactions let loose by atomic fission. The interactions of "cause" and "effect" are orderly, and if we understand their relationships we are prepared to control them, or at least to adapt ourselves to them.

This book was written in the hope that it would clearly set forth certain relationships—of man with his environment—that have powerfully shaped many of the dilemmas and quandaries in which we find ourselves today. They are inevitably exerting a gargantuan impact upon the human world of tomorrow. Disregarded, they will almost certainly smash our civilization.

There is nothing maleficent about these phenomena. If man will find a harmonious adjustment with them, as he surely can, this adjustment should make possible a greater flowering of human happiness and well-being than the human race has ever known. This is not to suggest that a sound relationship with our environment is an easy, or even sure way out of our multiplex difficulties; there is no simple solution. But ecological health is one of the indispensables.

Anyone reading this book should share the author's conviction, deepening ever more as the book was written, of how extremely fortunate we are to be Americans. I hope I may help this realization to grow, and that with it there will also grow the recognition of the opportunity and responsibility we all have, not only to be effective members of our own national community, but also of the world community. We have not treated our own country well; only its lush bountifulness has made possible the richness of our lives in the face of our abusive wastefulness. We still have much wealth left; as we prudently husband it to avert our own rainy day, we must, in human decency as well as in self-protection, use our resources to help less well-endowed peoples. But it is high time our thinking about such sharing be guided by our heads and not, in Lincoln Steffens' phrase, "with our hips".

Some readers may find parts of this book objectionably critical. I can only hope that, like Latin American friends who have been shocked by my reports on their countries, they will recognize that I am trying to paint an honest picture in colors that will convey an adequate image. If a patient is flushed with tuberculosis, no one will be benefited by pretending it is the high color of robust health. Besides, criticism is implicit in progress; to advance we must re-evaluate in order that we may create. Science, especially, rolls forward on the bearings of free criticism. Conservation, as an applied science, grows only through a continuous, critical correction of past errors.

My debt for material included in this book is so extensive that it cannot possibly be itemized. I have talked with trappers in Manitoba and sheepherders in Patagonia; and, in between, with scientists, labor leaders, fishermen, sea captains, farmers, peasants, millionaires, presidents, cabinet ministers, diplomats, newspapermen, lumbermen, engineers, etc. From most of them I have been able to learn something. The reading of books and scientific papers too numerous to mention has provided much of the background.

My story is not complete or final; none can ever be. If flaws are found in it, as I am sure there will be, I hope they may be measured against the whole thesis and its development, and judged not too significant. It must be emphasized that viewpoints advanced in this book are my own and do not necessarily represent those of any organization with which I am associated.

I am most grateful to Mr. Bernard M. Baruch, whose understanding of these problems has long seemed to me to excel that of any other leader in public life, for his sympathetic introduction.

To the following publishers and authors appreciation is due for permission to quote lengthy excerpts or drawings from copyrighted material:

Dr. Rodolfo Barón Castro for population data from his *La Población de El Salvador* (Instituto Gonzalo Fernandez de Oviedo, Madrid, 1942).

The Brookings Institution, Washington, D. C., for excerpts from *The Formation of Capital,* by Dr. Harold G. Moulton.

Doubleday and Company, for excerpts from *Aztecs of Mexico,* by Dr. George C. Vaillant, and *Vanishing Lands* by R. O. Whyte and G. V. Jacks.

Dr. Karl Brandt, of the Food Research Institute, Stanford University, for excerpts from a 1944 speech before the Council on Foreign Relations.

Alfred Korzybski, for the structural differential from his *Science and Sanity* (Science Press, Lancaster, 1941).

The University of Illinois Press for excerpts from Dr. Avery O. Craven's *Soil Exhaustion as a Factor in the Agricultural History of Virginia and Maryland.*

The University of Pennsylvania Press for excerpts from their 1941 volume, *Conservation of Renewable Resources.*

Whittlesey House, of McGraw-Hill Book Company, for excerpts from Dr. George B. Cressey's *Asia's Lands and People*.

William Morrow and Co., Inc., for the chart from *Global War, an Atlas of World Strategy* by Edgar Ansel Mowrer and Marthe Rajchman.

And to the authors and publishers of a number of other works, listed in the bibliography, for brief citations without special permission.

I am particularly indebted to several individuals. Foremost among these are M. Jean-Paul Harroy, whose brilliant book, *Afrique—terre qui meurt*, has provided most of the material for my chapter on Africa, with his permission; and Guy Irving Burch, who not only granted permission to quote from *Human Breeding and Survival* (originally published as *Population Roads to Peace or War*), of which he is co-author, but who has also been extraordinarily helpful with advice, bibliographic suggestions, and critical discussion. He, Mrs. F. R. Eldridge, Edward H. Graham, Charles F. Sarle, Robert C. Cook, and Joseph J. Hickey have read parts or all of the manuscript, and made constructive and valued suggestions. The responsibility for any errors remains, of course, my own.

Mrs. Annette L. Flugger brought to the labor of preparing the index her unusual understanding of the subject matter, and the editorial currycombing administered by Helen K. Taylor of William Sloane Associates was such a contribution as would be welcomed by any author; to both of them my thanks.

Most of all, I am indebted to my wife whose counsel helped to clarify and increase the interest of many parts of the manuscript; without her cooperation as researcher and amanuensis, it would have been impossible to complete this book, in the press of other responsibilities. W. V.

Washington, D. C.
April, 1948

Road to Survival

Chapter 1

The Earth Answers Back

THE GRAY COMBERS OF THE TASMAN SEA RACED PAST the ship from astern and with a slow rhythm, like that of a long pendulum, they lifted its screw to race futilely in the air. Captain Martins, after rising early as was his custom, stepped into the pilothouse to check the vessel's course, and then out onto the bridge. The low sun burned with a strange coppery yellow such as farther north might presage a typhoon. He looked anxiously about the horizon and estimated that the wind from the west was blowing with a force of five on the Beaufort scale. The sky did not look stormy, but he went once more into the pilothouse to check the glass. The barometric pressure was high, with no indication of trouble ahead.

Again he stepped out onto the bridge and scanned the sky. Then he became conscious that in the sheltered recesses of the bridge there was a thin overlay of brown dust. He muttered to himself in momentary irritation at the slackness of his crew, and looked again at the sky. He realized that, almost like a soft mist, a film of dust was falling through the air. In six hours he would be in Auckland. There was no land astern for more than a thousand miles. With a feeling of unbelief, he again checked the wind direction. His observation confirmed that the wind was coming from the west, and the fact that the dust must be blowing all the way from Australia.

He watched the sky a half hour before going in for his morning coffee. In Sydney he had heard talk of trouble in the back country, of hundreds of wells from which the windmills were sucking only air, of sheep dying of thirst or having to be slaughtered by hundreds of thousands. He had a cargo of wheat for England but this, too, was reported in short supply.

The soft dust was still raining down, and the reddening sun showed that the cloud was thickening. Martins shook his head and thought grimly to himself, "The whole damn continent must be blowing away."

MARIA

A few hours later, on the other side of the world in the Mexican State of Michoacán, a little woman trotted along a dusty road, with the swinging Indian gait that eats up the miles. On top of her head she balanced a rusty five-gallon tin that had not carried gasoline for many years. It was filled with her day's supply of water, precious water that had to be carried five miles to her pueblo. Ten miles every day she trotted, to have the liquid for tortillas and occasional tamales, for cooking her black beans and watering her few chickens. She weighed less than a hundred pounds and the can on her head was heavy, but the weight of her burden passed unnoticed in the heaviness of her heart. Until a few days ago she would also have been carrying a baby on her back, but now the rebozo was empty. As babies are so apt to do, in regions where water is scarce and polluted, hers had died early.

The ten-mile trip every day, under the beating sun of August or through the cold dry winds of January, did not seem in any way unusual to the woman. Didn't her husband have to walk even farther to till his little patch of maize and beans? She could neither read nor write, and she had no way of knowing that when her pueblo was built the people had gathered there because it was near a clear cold spring that gushed from the hillside. The sterile landscape about her, gray-stained with sparse grass and clumps of maguey, told her nothing of the rich forests that had once built soil for leagues about her town. She was tired, and her heart was heavy, but with the fatalism of a people that rarely knows surcease from a precarious existence, she sighed and muttered to herself, *"Se aguanta"*—one must bear with it. No phrase is more common on the lips of the women of her people.

Tom Cobbett

Tom Cobbett sat with his elbows on his desk and his face buried in his hands. He had come a long way since the first day he began to cut at the shining coal in the Yorkshire mines, but he was not thinking of the past, of the years on end when he had hacked out coal sixteen and eighteen hours a day nor of how he had forced himself to study night after night, pulling himself painfully up the ladder of books—the only escape he could find from the mines.

Tom should have been the happiest man in Great Britain tonight. He had just won a by-election with one of the greatest majorities piled up by any Labor candidate in England's history. His triumph was a tribute to himself and a rousing vote of support for the Labor party's program of socialization. For four hours he had put on an act for his friends and supporters, displayed a jubilation he did not feel. Far down in the honest recesses of his mind, Tom had to admit to himself that he wished it had not happened.

He was, he realized, a sort of way station in an historical process. He had begun to fight for this election twenty years before, and he could not have avoided the victory without betraying his people and his country. But the weight of the prize was heavy on his mind. He, too, knew nothing of events in the Tasman Sea, nor on the dusty hillsides of Michoacán. If he had known of them, the orientation of his mind might have given him an inkling of their significance and increased the weight of the responsibility that lay so heavily upon him.

He was now a member of one of the oldest legislative bodies on the earth, charged for a time with participation in the ruling of a great empire. He and his party were committed to one of the most courageous and high-minded efforts man had ever made to better his lot.

Over two decades before the war, Cobbett had been fighting for this chance. Then the pattern he had been following was suddenly twisted out of shape by world revolution. Few members of the party saw this, but to Cobbett it was painfully clear. The Parliament to which he had just been elected ruled fifty million people who lived on two islands with an area of 95,000 square miles, the size of Oregon. By the most heroic efforts of men and women together, utilizing every yard of available land, these people had not been able to produce much more than half of the food they needed.

Before World War I this had not mattered—much. The coal he had hewn from the dripping seams had been used to buy the beef that meant so much to England, and the corn, as the English called it, for their bread. The remarkable skills of British workers had fashioned the raw products of all the world into a multitude of things that five continents would purchase with food.

But now the mines were playing out and British skills had been duplicated, with varying degrees of success, around the world. The British worker's horizon had broadened, and he looked to the prosperity of the American worker and the economic organization of the Russian, and claimed them for his own. Cobbett, along with his party, had taken on the responsibility of satisfying this claim. Indeed he felt an intuitive kinship with the Australia of the blowing earth, with the Argentina of the rich lands, with the North America of failing waters. The hungers and desires of his crowded island would somehow have to be meshed with the rest of the world but now, faced with a driving reality, Cobbett knew that a political and economic solution would not be enough.

FOSTER RAMSEY

From far above, in the deep-blue sky, came the vagrant trumpeting of homing geese. There was not another sound in the still prairie night, and Foster Ramsey put down his pen and listened. As always, he felt a tug at his heart when the geese passed over. Across the high plains, the black spruce, the tamarack bogs, and the tundra, the flock would drive northward until it split over isolated pools, to set up the season's housekeeping.

He took off his glasses, rubbed his tired eyes, and shook his head ruefully. Wild geese to income taxes—it was a long jump! "Not a chance," he said to himself. "The twins will have to make do here."

He was president of a college but it was a small college, a "cow college." His salary would not have impressed an automobile salesman in New York. If there had been only the two older children to consider, things would have been much simpler. The twins had been a surprise, and the extra burden they brought with them had been enormously complicated by the war. The high school in the little town where they lived was not much good. How could it be, when the teachers received only $1,500 a year? Ramsey had hoped the children might go away to boarding school, but even with the scholarships he could count on, he knew he could not swing it.

He looked down again at the tax form, and wryly signed his name. Then he wrote a check. Taxes this year, including the hidden ones, would take nearly a third of his income. "Seventeen weeks out of the year," he said to himself, "I worked for the government. Thank God, it's the American government, and not the Nazi government!" In a sense he was grateful to be paying these taxes, glad he was able to, but as he looked at the form in front of him he could not help thinking what pleasure it, and millions like it, would have given the defeated Nazi hierarchy.

Germany had organized the greatest system of slave labor the world had ever known. Few people, Ramsey knew, realized that this slavery was not yet at an end. The major part of his taxes was helping to pay for the war and its aftermath. With luck he would have thirty years more of work ahead of him. If the national debt were ever to be paid, if there were not to be repudiation or disastrous inflation, he knew there could not be much hope that his tax load would be reduced. Seventeen weeks a year for thirty years—ten years of his life dedicated primarily to paying for the adventures of Mussolini, Hitler, and the Japanese war lords. Multiply his lot by that of tens of millions of other American workers, and it added up to a greater force of slave laborers than had ever struggled under the Nazi lash in Europe.

Ramsey did not know of the sea captain, the unhappy Tarascan woman, the English politician, but if he had, his well-organized mind, used to thinking in terms of the land, would have readily related them to the papers on his desk. Because he understood the land, had watched the degeneration of his state's cattle ranges, had seen failing springs break more than one rancher, he would have recognized that a gullied hillside in Szechwan or a hollow-eyed miner in the Ruhr was a factor, although a hidden factor, in his tax form.

He had already recognized the substantial decrease in his living standard. He knew that for the rest of his life he would not only be carrying his share of the burden of the war but contributing increasingly to what he mentally called the "gimme boys." Some of them wore union badges, some of them carried cards of the American Farm Bureau, some of them wore the little blue cap of the American Legion to which service in World War I entitled him. He might have added to them worried government officials in capitals in many foreign countries.

No, the kids wouldn't get much of a high school education. He and Janet would have to see what they could do to fill in the gaps at home.

Jim Hanrahan

Jim Hanrahan stood in front of the mirror in his bathroom door. He tugged speculatively at the tire around his middle. It was many a year since he had pulled a peavey and he knew he looked it; but he shrugged his shoulders and thought to himself, "What the hell!" From now on peaveys would be handled for him by other men, and they would get one-fiftieth of what he made from their work.

He went to the window and looked across at the magnificent spectacle of the snow-capped mountains, unusually clear this afternoon. He poured himself a stiff highball and sighed contentedly. In a couple of hours he would eat the best dinner to be had in the city, and after that there would be the little girl at the Waikiki night club.

Tonight was a celebration, and he was going to make the most of it. He had cleaned up on war contracts—working eighteen hours a day—and now he had cashed in. True, he had had to pay a politico $8,000, but even so he had been able to get timber covering five entire mountains for less than a fifth of what it would have cost him in the States. His plant was well capitalized and his engineers would be on the ground within two weeks.

In cold dusk the night before he had stood among the mighty trees and looked out over another city below. He was buying the city's water supply, and he knew it. But he had a lumberman's conscience, with calluses so thick that he no longer felt even cynical about these deals. It was their country. If they wanted to sell it, it was O.K. with him. This one job would leave him sitting pretty for at least fifteen or twenty years. What would happen to the town without water at the end of that period he did not even consider. After all, business is business!

The Nameless

The ship was running without lights. The skipper would be damned glad to get rid of his cargo; but even so he kept the screw turning at only quarter speed. On the decks, small groups of huddled forms clung together and prayed. They knew that before morning some of them would probably be dead.

Death was nothing new to this human cargo. Most of them had lived with it as a familiar for ten years or more. Battered about from town to town, from country to country, they had wandered in an almost unbroken wilderness of dislike, of distress and stupid hatred. Not one of the men, women and children aboard but had lost someone close and dear to him. Some of these had died in concentration camps, others had been shot in cold blood as hostages, still others had been ripped apart by the whistling bombs. Hundreds of miles these people had walked, and many had left bloody tracks behind them on stony roads and in the snows. For years they had roamed, almost without hope, but now they were coming out of the wilderness—truly into a promised land.

For most of their lives, it seemed, they had lived as human contraband, and they were still human contraband. Armed guards lay in wait for them but some of them, perhaps most of them, would be able to slip ashore in the darkness. The guards might well shoot them down, although they themselves had no reason to feel any hatred against these tired wanderers. The guards themselves were mere puppets manipulated by a politician's mistake. Lies had been spoken twenty-five years before, and these guards were set, somehow to turn the lies into truth.

The promised land to which every man and woman and child in this group hoped to win through was no land of milk and honey, such as their ancestors had found. It was a worn-out desert that once had been a rich landscape, that once had supported towns and industries and sent its ships to the edge of the known west. Man's abuse had wrung most of the life out of it, and now man's intelligence and backbreaking toil were slowly bringing it to life again. Grueling labor, harsh rations, little rest, were the best these few score people could hope for if they managed to scuttle past the whistling rifle bullets. But in the heart of every one of them there was high hope and confidence. They knew what their people had done and they knew what they could do. Here, although they might eventually have to fight for it, they were sure they could work in peace.

To these pitiful wanderers through the storms of a hostile world there was no word more precious than "peace."

Wong

Wong sat by the side of the dusty road, almost too weak to hold himself upright. Carts with shouting drivers, wheelbarrows piled high and pushed by silent men, occasionally rickshaws, passed by, often within a few inches. It seemed as though they must strike him, but he did not move.

Wong no longer cared. He knew he was going to die, because he had seen hundreds dying all about him. He felt no pain. This had passed days ago. He no longer even felt hungry, and this was such a new experience to him that it almost made him welcome his approaching death. He looked sixty and was thirty-four. Hardly a day since he had been weaned had he known what it was to escape the hunger pains that gnawed at his middle. His bones stuck out through a yellow skin even more parchment-like than usual.

Three weeks before, or four, or five, he did not remember, he had left his wife and baby in the western provinces and started to walk toward the sea, in the hope of finding something for them to eat. So far as he knew, he did not have a friend or a relative within hundreds of miles. One by one he had sold the garments off his back, until he was all but naked. Once in a while he had been able to scrape together a few grains of rice, but for days now he had known that he was losing the struggle. There had not been enough to keep him going, and in that great world of famine where hundreds and thousands and tens of thousands were dying as he was, no one cared. To a European or an American this might have seemed the ultimate sadness. To Wong it was meaningless, since he was dying as he had lived most of his life.

The sun seemed like an incandescent dome clamped atop the world. Not even in the great river bed was there a trickle of water. Eight months ago it had raged with floods that broke into the towns and stormed away with hundreds of victims. Now he would have to sell his last garment even to get a drink. The steep, bare hillsides, completely denuded of vegetation, towered above him. The cold wind flung towers of dust before it, dust that powdered into the corners of his mouth.

Halfway around the world men and women were trying to scrape together such grain as they could, to keep the ember of life glowing in Wong and millions like him. But he knew nothing of this. If he had, it would have made no difference. He knew now, when he had finally given up all hope of life, that nowhere in the world could there be enough food to feed so many hungry mouths.

JOE SPENCER

Joe Spencer's hand trembled as he moved the slide back and forth under the microscope's objective. Over and over again he checked the blood smear. There was no trace of plasmodium.

He sat back in his chair and let his eyes wander about the laboratory. The monkeys and the birds played in their cages, quite unconcerned at having a date with history. All through the war Joe had worked, as had hundreds of other researchers, to find a certain and harmless protection against malaria for United Nations troops. Now with the war, technically, at least, over, he apparently had it.

He had had 100 per cent success in protecting the experimental animals with a few grains of white powder. Over and over again he had run tests on them, and all had been negative. Then, after dosing with the compound, he had deliberately inoculated himself. It was not at all certain that this chemical, whose molecules he had been shuffling for nearly two years, would work the same way on him as it had on canaries. He had waited two weeks for a positive reaction—and there had been none. He had tried again, with negative results. Three more checks indicated that he was completely immune. Then Marion, his wife, insisted that he try it on her before saying anything to anyone else about it. A slide smeared with his wife's blood lay in front of him. If this was negative, he would be 99 per cent certain. He slipped the slide onto the stage of the microscope and with practiced fingers ran over it rapidly. Not a thing to be seen. Then he settled down and checked it with infinite care, by minute fractions of a millimeter. Still nothing!

He sat back in his chair, and realized that he had broken into a heavy sweat. Unless he was most improbably wrong, he had a sure and harmless preventive for one of the worst man killers of all time. Its manufacture would cost less than aspirin, and millions of suffering men and women would find immediate surcease from racking pains. What would this mean to the hordes of India and China? What would it mean to the world?

Joe knew that in the test tubes of his laboratory there was confined a power that was perhaps as dangerous as that of the atomic bomb. He had walked the cobblestone streets of Rumanian towns, of muddy byways in Italy, and seen hundreds of coffins carried on the shoulders of men, coffins that had been filled by the bites of mosquitoes. From afar off he had seen the burning ghats of India, had watched them across stinking pools of standing water from which the winged death had silently flitted away. His fingers had searched for the swollen spleens of children in Guayaquil and Manáos, and all over northern South America. He had watched the dragging gait of men and women who spent their nights burning with the fire they called "paludismo."

Then he had spent two weeks in Puerto Rico, where the miracles of American medicine had been worked, with the chief result that more people were kept alive to live more miserably. He knew India had grown by some fifty millions in ten years, and even before the first of those fifty millions was born there was not enough food to go around. Was there any kindness in keeping people from dying of malaria so that they could die more slowly of starvation? Could there be any end of wars, and rumors of wars, while such people as the prosperous Americans had far more than they needed and the

millions of India and China and Java and Western Europe—
and perhaps Russia—did not have enough? Few men of his day,
Joe knew, had had the power to shake so profoundly the future
of the world.

"WE BE OF ONE BLOOD—"

None of these human beings, sharing similar hopes and
despair according to his individual lot, is aware of the others.
None of them, except the scientist, sees himself as part of a
great world drama in which each plays his part as both cause
and effect. This gallery of portraits of people today, of the
troubled or contented, could be multiplied millions of times.
They are not all of humanity, but they are a sample of all of
humanity. They are fictional, but it would not be difficult to
find living equivalents.

All of them have one thing in common. The lot of each,
from Australian sea captain to biochemist, is completely dependent on his or her global environment, and each one of them
in greater or less degree influences that environment. One common denominator controls their lives: the ratio between human populations and the supply of natural resources, with
which they live, such as soil, water, plants, and animals. This
is a highly unstable relationship, changing from moment to moment, continually conditioned anew by human acts.

Before the great age of exploration at the end of the fifteenth
century, this relationship was a simple matter. Man lived in a
series of isolated cells. What was done in Britain had little
influence on what was done in China. What was done in the
great Mississippi Basin made no impact on the rest of the world.
Then Columbus set in motion forces that only a few people
have yet begun to comprehend.

Columbus, more than the atomic scientists, made this one
geographic world. Woodrow Wilson saw that we all live in
one world in a political sense, and Wendell Willkie popularized
the concept for the man in the street. However, few of our
leaders have begun to understand that we live in one world in

an ecological—an environmental—sense. Dust storms in Australia have an inescapable effect on the American people; they set mutton prices soaring, and our own western sheep raisers, not looking beyond their own depleted ranges to the starving peoples of El Salvador and Greece, are content.

The little Indian woman, whose forebears were robbed by the cupidity of early Spanish miners, is a drop in the great pool of deprivation that is threatening to overwhelm the world. She is an integral part of our own Latin-American relations; whether or not she and her twenty-three million compatriots have enough to eat and drink and wear is rich in meaning for the foreign policy of the United States.

The English politician haunted by the chimera of high American living standards, is, though he may not see it, the resultant of forces that stirred into life the day the "Santa Maria's" lookout cried "Land!" to his mutinous fellow sailors.

The American lumberman, riding high, wide and handsome, neither knows nor cares that he is stretching the slow fingers of death throughout the New World; he is a true worshiper of that sacred cow Free Enterprise.

The refugees, who have suffered perhaps more greatly than any other group of people in history, give no thought to the fact that their fate has its roots deep in the cotton lands of the Mississippi Delta, the black loam of Iowa cornfields, the forests of the Appalachians. They only see, with hope high in their hearts, that they are returning to rebuild a land devastated by their ancestors some three thousand years ago.

Wong, dying by the side of the road, cannot possibly comprehend that he is being killed by an unexpected genie that spiraled out of the test tubes and cultures of Louis Pasteur. Nor does he see himself as part of an explosive pressure rapidly building and threatening someday to burst all bonds.

The biologist sees his role more clearly. Engaged in a mission of mercy, he realizes that his little white grains of powder may turn into dragon's teeth. He hesitates as to whether he should loose this new, uncontrolled force upon the world. If he is like most scientists, he is not politically minded and has little idea about ways and means of guiding the forces of science.

Political leaders are trying to solve the infinitely complex problems of the modern world while literally ignoring most of that world. They assume, perhaps because most of them are city men and therefore urban minded, that man lives in a vacuum, independent of his physical environment. They are seeking the solution of an extraordinarily complex equation and almost completely neglecting major factors.

Perhaps a bio-equation, that takes into account man's physical universe, will help us to clear our thinking and even to regulate the forces that bemuse our political leaders. Here is a simple formula, no more complicated than the relationship of the family budget to the family income.

This formula is $C = B:E$.

Here C stands for the *carrying capacity* of any area of land. In its simplest form this means its ability to provide food, drink, and shelter to the creatures that live on it. In the case of human beings, the equation finds complicated expression in terms of civilized existence.

B means *biotic potential*, or the ability of the land to produce plants for shelter, for clothing, and especially for food. Only plants are able to synthesize food from the raw materials of the earth and the air in a form assimilable by animals. This is the only way in which food exists for animals.

E stands for *environmental resistance*, or the limitations that any environment, including the part of it contrived and complicated by man, places on the biotic potential or productive ability. *The carrying capacity is the resultant of the ratio between the other two factors.*

The equation is, perhaps, oversimplified, but it expresses certain relationships—almost universally ignored—that every minute of every day touch the life of every man, woman, and child on the face of the globe.

Until an understanding of these relationships on a world scale enters into the thinking of free men everywhere, and into the thinking of rulers of men who are not free, there is no possibility of any considerable improvement of the lot of the human race. Indeed, if we continue to ignore these relationships, there is little probability that mankind can long escape the searing downpour of war's death from the skies.

And when this comes, in the judgment of some of the best informed authorities, it is probable that at least three-quarters of the human race will be wiped out.

Chapter 2

Energy from Earth to Man

MAN, QUITE AS MUCH AS ANY FORD OR PACKARD, requires refueling. No one would expect to drive along our highways with an empty gasoline tank. We have recently had unpleasant evidence, in China, India, and Europe of what happens to the man and woman and child whose fuel tanks are not replenished.

All the energy with which man refuels himself is derived from the sun. From the instant the struggling sperm meets the waiting ovum until the last drop of blood dribbles out from the dying heart, man is burning fuel from this one source. His power to move, to grow, to think, to digest, and to beget his kind has the same origin. The hydroelectric power that he uses to reduce the drain on bodily energy—and to make available the energy locked in the atom—is drawn from falling water that was lifted to the clouds by the heat of the sun. The wind that raises water to his farm tanks blows because the heat of the sun causes inequalities in atmospheric pressure on the surface of the earth. Coal and petroleum hold only solar energy captured by plants millions of years ago. Even the great forces in the nucleus of the atom were hurled off from the sun at the world's birth.

Man's bodily energy can reach him only through the slender channels of millions of green plants. Despite his growing comprehension of natural laws and command of natural forces, he has not learned to take the raw materials of the earth and air—carbon, nitrogen, hydrogen, phosphorus, etc.—and synthesize them into the foods he needs to build his bone and muscle. This can be done only through the alchemy of the chlorophyll that paints our landscape green. Like the amoeba, the starfish, the crocodile, the hummingbird, and the tiger, man is a biological creature subject to biological laws, and the first of these is that he cannot live without plants. The carnivorous animal, such as the lion and the short-eared owl, secures its food second-hand through the bodies of herbivores; the lion feeds on the herbivorous zebra, the owl on herbivorous field mice, which serve in this food chain as a means of passing on the energy stored in plants.

Unless we realize this fact, there is no possibility of approaching a full understanding of man. The end of the Babylonian Empire is usually written in terms of wars with the Persians. Little or no weight is given to the fact that Ur, the great city of Abraham and once a thriving seaport, now lies 150 miles within a sterile desert.[1] * The goat and the ax, driving the sands down to the coast, were far more destructive weapons than the horses and javelins of the conqueror Cyrus. Hannibal had an empire worth fighting for, and the means of supporting a powerful army. Today the very habitat of the elephants that were his tanks and half-tracks has been overwhelmed by desert sand, and even the elephants are no more.[2] Cato, in his bitterest brooding, could not have foreseen such utter destruction. The history of Babylon, Assyria, Carthage, China, Spain, Britain—and of the United States—is meaningless unless it is related to the way the peoples of these countries have treated the plants on which they depend. Indeed, most of the history that has been written of these areas gives a picture as distorted as a Picasso drawing, because it blindly ignores the part that plants and their habitats have played in man's story.

CYCLE OF THE PLANTS

Plants, except marine forms economically inaccessible to man, cannot exist without soil and water. Although they draw

* Superior numbers refer to bibliographic sources, given by chapters at the end of the book.

principally on the carbon dioxide of the air, they are inevitably dependent upon other minerals that are found in soil. They get water through their root systems, which are spread for the most part through the upper few inches of soil. It has been suggested that man can feed himself "hydroponically"—that is, independently of the soil—on plants grown in chemically charged water. Indeed, this was done during the war on such strategically important areas as Ascension Island. There, however, the requisite water had to be distilled from the sea through the medium of petroleum—plants again—and the high cost of such distillation places it beyond the reach of all but a few people. Should we try to depend generally on hydroponics, we should still need enormous, vegetated catch basins to supply the necessary water.

It is conceivable that a more complete command of nuclear energy will permit distillation of water from the sea. This might tend to concentrate populations along the seaboards of continents and make habitable areas that now support no life, such as the Peruvian and Chilean deserts. It has also been airily asserted by technicians, who ought to know better, that "science" can solve the problem by synthesis of chlorophyll and, therefore, of food. But here is what one biochemist has to say about it:

"Unless our devices are to be much more efficient than the green plants and unless we are willing to spoil with ugly machinery an acreage now covered by beautiful forests and pastures, artificial photosynthesis is not only utopian but impractical. Even assuming we were to discover some sort of artificial photo-chemical reduction of carbon dioxide into a digestible carbohydrate with an overall efficiency surpassing that of the plants which use on the average 2 per cent of the incident radiation, it would not help us much, since we need, not one product of plant metabolism, but a thousand . . ." [3]

The bare possibility of such developments certainly lies many decades in the future, and it is literally true that we do not have time to wait for them. We need more and better production of life-giving plants now. Newspaper headlines tell us that, nearly every day. As this book is written, and read, men and women and children are dying of starvation.

Carrying Capacities

Each piece of land has its own unique productive capacity. No two pastures, no two cornfields are exactly alike. This productive capacity—*the biotic potential*—varies as to the *quantity* of vegetation it can produce, and as to its nutritive and other *qualities*. This is a fact well known to every farmer, although it seems to have escaped the leaders who shape our destinies. The hard-working victory gardener found it out when he tried to raise corn and tomatoes on the harsh soil of a city lot, long since robbed of its organic matter; he looked enviously at a fellow toiler whose rich plot lay on alluvial soils along a river bottom.

Just as the productive capacity of individual gardens varies, so do the productive capacities of nations and continents. The gardener working his city lot could expect only a low yield from his land. So, too, must the Canadians and the Russians; most of their territory, lying within the subarctic frost line, has thin and acid soil, or soil as subject to wind erosion as our Great Plains, and they are capable only of low production. Though the Ukraine and Canadian prairies produce heavy yields per acre, these rich areas represent small fractions of the vast extent of the countries. Even here, environmental resistances are subject to sharp, uncontrollable increases.

The productivity of any piece of land varies considerably with time. The high crop yields that attracted settlers to what later became our Dust Bowl vanished with the recurrence of the dry cycle, a period of deficient rainfall. Floods and drought sharply reduced our corn crop in 1947, with world-wide repercussions. Drought in India has caused repeated crop failures, which, by bringing famine, have sharply cut back human populations. Since these droughts have occurred before, they must be expected again. From the national and world point of view it is imperative that we recognize such variations as these and adjust our populations and economies to them. *For it is the least favorable conditions, not the most favorable, that determine the ability of the earth to support human beings.*

The biotic potential of any piece of cultivated land has an absolute or *theoretical* ceiling that is never reached, except under extraordinary conditions. The cornfields about Iowa State College, with its great financial, technical, and intellectual resources, probably produce, within the limits of 1948's knowledge, the utmost quantity of foodstuffs of which they are capable. The three or four bushels of corn per acre grown by the Mexican Indian are undoubtedly far below the biotic potential of his land. Nevertheless, it is important to remember that even with optimum farming conditions the three inches of soil on which these peasants are often trying to produce food could not possibly approach the fifty bushels or more raised on the rich, deep soils of Iowa.

At varying distances below the theoretical ceiling of production lie a very large number of *practical* ceilings. And it is the practical ceilings, in most of the world dropping lower every year, with which man must concern himself; for it is these that determine the amount of food—the amount of energy —and the amount of fibers for clothing and shelter that man is able to make available to his rapidly increasing populations. Whether man likes it or not, he must live within his means— and these are shrinking.

The practical ceiling is imposed by the *environmental resistance*, which is the sum of varying but always great numbers of limiting factors acting upon the biotic potential. Where it is possible to reduce the number and effectiveness of these limiting factors, the environmental resistance is decreased, the biotic potential is more nearly realized, and the carrying capacity of the land rises. Irrigation and insect control are two methods of doing this. When the carrying capacity of the land rises, the possibility of higher living standards increases for limited numbers of people, or a lower living standard for excessive numbers.

THE PHYSICAL BOUNDS

The most obvious limiting factor with which man must cope is climate. Where the summer season is too short to permit the growth of plants, thus making agriculture impossible, man must, like the Eskimo, turn to the sea. By eating polar bear, seal, and the delectable mollusks scooped out of the seal's belly, he takes advantage of the production of plants in the more stable environment created by large masses of water. He can depend only on such land animals as the caribou, which are able to subsist on such cold-tolerant plants as lichens. Or, like the Canadian, he must concentrate his population along the southern edge of his country and from it draw the food with which he may purchase the minerals, pelts, and timber of the northern reaches.

If, by contrast, he lives in equatorial lowlands where temperatures of well over a hundred degrees rapidly break down the organic matter in his unprotected soils and rains leach out minerals, he must either cultivate each patch of earth briefly, so that the land is rested as much as thirty years after one or two years of use, or he must depend largely on tree crops that are well adapted to the soil they shelter.

Aridity makes uninhabitable, or nearly so, vast areas of the globe, such as northern Africa and much of the Soviet Union. Without sufficient water, plants cannot be grown to supply food. If there is any precipitation at all, and temperatures are not excessively high or low, wild plants have invaded even semiarid areas and made possible the survival of small numbers of pastoral nomads. According to Ackerman, 18 per cent of the earth's agricultural land consists of arid or subhumid areas on which it may be assumed there is often deficient and highly unpredictable precipitation.[4] Our own Great Plains are one example; Argentina's Patagonia is another.

Excessive precipitation may be quite as effective in limiting the development of agricultural land. In such areas as southern Chile, with some ten feet of rain a year, or parts of India, with *forty* feet, the life-giving minerals are so rapidly washed out of the upper layers of the soil that agriculture can be carried on for only short periods. On the coasts of Central America and Mexico the cycle from virgin forests through banana cultivation to abandoned land is in many places only seven or eight years.

Evaporation through many daily hours of high temperatures and dry winds will function as a limiting factor in some areas. Precipitation, considered alone, is meaningless. It is significant only in relation to temperature, wind, underlying soils, and other factors limiting the amount of water available for plant growth. Where dry winds blast such an area as the interior Soviet Union or, at times, our own wheat and corn belts, they sharply reduce the usefulness of the little water that falls.

The influence of climates over a large region is complicated by the climates of small areas, or microclimates. The mean temperature of the soil beneath tropical forests will be more than 60 degrees F. lower than would be the temperature of the same soil if the tree canopy has been removed; extreme temperatures will vary even more widely.[5] The coffee grown on the slopes of Central America and northern South America can survive only under the microclimate created by a heavy growth of shade trees. The trees help to protect the slopes against rainfall that would otherwise sweep away the soil, and thus create a microclimate that is as favorable for soil as for coffee. Grasshopper outbreaks that annually destroy millions of dollars' worth of crops are, in large part, probably caused by man's disturbance of microclimates, through his destruction of vegetation. Off the coast of Peru, where millions of birds produce the guano indispensable to that country's agriculture, the removal of the guano cap has so altered microclimates by reducing the amount of wind reaching large sections of the islands that, because of their high surface temperatures, they are no longer habitable by the birds; eggs are cooked in their shells, and the young die.

Orographic, or land-form, phenomena often act as powerful limiting factors. Deep soils built up on the slopes of Guatemala and other Central American countries have produced lush forests. When, however, these forests are cleared, the angle of repose of the soils is immediately altered and entire hillsides collapse into river valleys. Hard-scrabble farmers of New England have long recognized the value of southern slopes that enjoy the slanting rays of early spring suns. In the rainy tropics, slopes may also be an advantage to the farmer, albeit probably a temporary one, because they get rid of rain water; in regions of lesser precipitation he may be forced to interrupt the slopes with carefully constructed terraces, to break the incline and hold on the land as much water as possible.

In much of the world the relief of the land exerts so powerful an influence on its productivity that luxuriant vegetation and semidesert conditions may lie only a few hundred yards apart. This phenomenon is familiar to anyone who has traveled in Mexico, where land producing only cactus may be surrounded by rich forests or crop lands. As one flies over the Santa Marta Mountains between Barranquilla, in Colombia, and Caracas, in Venezuela, dramatic variations in carrying capacity, literally within two or three hundred feet of one another, may be seen beneath one's plane. Trade winds blow against the east slopes of the mountains and deposit rainfall that, even in the high altitudes, produces rich pastures. As the winds are forced to rise they expand, cool, and lose their moisture as rain. When they reach the leeward slopes, they are nearly dry, and these slopes may produce only cactuses and other drought-tolerant plants. The entire coastal area of Peru is affected by this adiabatic cooling; the great rampart of the Andes acts as a dike against rains that turn much of the Amazon Valley into a semiswamp.

The Peruvian coast, as well as the north Chilean coast, is further plagued by a phenomenon that is often observed on the west side of continents, as in southern California and south-west Africa. As the earth spins toward the apparently rising sun it sets up a drift of surface waters offshore from these western coasts. This ocean cap is replaced by cold waters from the depths, with a temperature, in the case of Peru, more than 40 degrees F. lower than that of the sea in the same latitudes of the Pacific, offshore. The cold surface waters condense moisture that might be brought in from the open ocean, and give Los Angeles the high fogs it does not like to mention and Lima the high fogs that are one of its chief topics of conversation.

Soils themselves impose sharp limitations on productivity of the land. If they are highly acid or highly alkaline, the survival of most food plants will be difficult or impossible. Soils may be so deficient in trace elements such as boron, magnesium, copper, etc., that the nutritive value of the plants produced will be low. Goiter, caused by lack of soil iodine, is common in the Alps, Andes, and parts of our Middle West. Soil structure may lock the door against the penetration of plant roots. Limestone foundations will drain off rain so rapidly that the indispensable layer of soil-water will be impoverished. Clay soils, on the other hand, may have such poor drainage that they drown or rot plant roots. Most soils in the United States are so subject to erosion that slopes of more than 5 per cent—a vertical rise of five feet for every hundred feet advanced—cannot safely be cultivated without special cultural practices that are often costly in terms of money and labor; slopes of more than 15 per cent cannot in general be cultivated. Less erodible volcanic soils, however, such as are found in Java and in much of Central America, may often safely be cultivated with proper agricultural practices on slopes of 50 per cent.

The organic content of soil, which is a determinant of its productivity, varies widely. In regions of low temperature and high rainfall, the top, or A-horizon, of rich organic soil is likely to be thin. This results in a low carrying capacity in the southern part of Chile, for instance, where that country is trying to expand its agriculture. The extremely productive chernozem soils of the central Soviet Union are rich largely because the rainfall is limited; the high winds of the region make the soils highly susceptible to erosion once the plow has broken the sod. The erodability of the A-horizon varies widely with its composition, the rainfall and wind, and the slope.

How Much Land?

Thus the mere presence of land, even in areas that would seem in general to have favorable conditions of temperature and precipitation, does not necessarily mean that the land can be used for agriculture. The United States Department of Agriculture estimates that in the entire world there are 4,000,-000,000 acres of arable land. Their figure is largely based on estimates from the respective countries. These estimates, frequently made without maps and with inadequate comprehension of the many factors that go to make up arable land—and perhaps inflated as a means of bolstering national amour-propre —are sometimes dubious. In my opinion, the USDA figure is almost certainly too high.

Judging by my own field experience, the calculations of Pearson and Harper would seem to be more reliable.[6] By combining the areas of the earth that possess favorable soil, topography, temperature, reliable and adequate rainfall, sunlight and carbon dioxide, they arrive at an estimate of 2,600,000,000 acres of land adapted to food production, or a little over one acre for each living person. In a later paper [7] Pearson refines his estimate still more and states: "The really productive areas of the world are so limited that there is only about two-tenths of an acre per person." This would be a patch about ninety feet on a side. These estimates, of course, omit many additional variables that function as limiting factors, some of which will be discussed below.

There has never been, so far as I am aware, a satisfactory definition of arable land. In the arable concept, the farmer is quite as important as the farm; some Japanese or Philippine farmers would undoubtedly cultivate successfully millions of acres that are now being destroyed by their owners. In many regions a shift from tenancy to ownership would certainly save large arable acreages that are becoming marginal, if not desert. In other areas, such a change might well tend to have the opposite effect.

THE BIOTIC LIMITS

The nitrogen-fixing bacteria in the soil might be called the soil's dynamo. Where man has destroyed the topsoil, he can often rebuild part of its fertility by planting members of the legume family, which carry on their roots bacteria that restore nitrogen to the soil. The soil fauna and flora, especially the microscopic forms, make soil minerals available to plants by breaking down organic material. On the milpas of Latin America the soil is repeatedly swept by fire and washed by tropical downpours, and is thus progressively impoverished through the destruction of its fauna and flora. Here fire and water are the limiting factors.

One of the most effective limiting factors is the insect. It is estimated that one-tenth of all crop plants are destroyed by insects in the United States every year. In other words, the farmer gives one day out of ten and one acre out of ten to feed the insects on his farm. The cost of the food we all buy is increased some 10 per cent by aphids, cutworms, scale insects, etc. The so-called Dutch elm disease, which seems surely to be destroying one of the loveliest features of the landscape of the northeastern United States, is insect-borne.

Insects that carry human diseases make large areas of the earth marginal for man's occupation. This hazard is not nearly so important as has been suggested by the proponents of malaria control. In many areas malaria has actually been a blessing in disguise, since a large proportion of the malaria belt is not suited to agriculture, and the disease has helped to keep man from destroying it—and from wasting his substance upon it. Oncocercosis, a fly-borne disease that causes blindness and an espe-

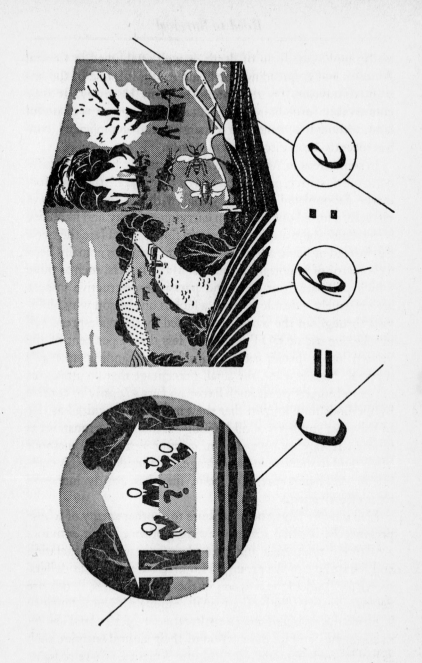

cially unpleasant form of death, is well established in Central America and is spreading north and south; it is one of the unwanted travelers on the Inter-American Highway. It may conceivably force human beings to avoid large areas of useful land, although a somewhat expensive and complicated cure has recently been discovered in Africa.

In some areas in Africa, where the tsetse fly has been locally controlled, native populations have overgrazed the land formerly depopulated by the fly and within a few years have virtually snuffed out its human carrying capacity and its ability to replenish the water table, restrain floods, etc. Here the tsetse fly, instead of being a limiting factor on man, has actually been a protector of important resources. Many insects, such as those which pollinate fruit trees and parasitize destructive insects, are extremely valuable to man, which is one reason why biologists throughout the world are alarmed by the widespread and unselective use of DDT. Probably less than 5 per cent of the known insect species can be considered a handicap to man's survival. Nevertheless, the small percentage that do attack his crops and forests wreak such havoc and are so costly to control by methods now known that they must be recognized as one of the most stubborn of all limiting factors. Unfortunately, as modern researches have shown, current agricultural methods often tend to increase insect damage. Furthermore, by his careless or unwitting spread of pests, man has greatly increased their effectiveness.

Man steadily pays a heavy tribute to another enemy of whose presence he is often scarcely aware—rodents. Their activities are largely nocturnal, and take place beneath the vegetation and the surface of the ground. Hundreds of millions of dollars' worth of food ($200,000,000 in the United States alone) are destroyed every year by these small mammals. Their abundance is often the result of man's maltreatment of the land—as by overgrazing—and his destruction of their natural enemies, such as hawks, owls, coyotes, etc. In Latin America, where peasants often leave their corn hanging on the bent stalk for want of corncribs, it is probable that rodents at times take up to 25 per cent of the crop. During periodic rodent population outbreaks, they are said to make farming impossible. Not a little of the hunger that now rides astride the world must be attributed to their excessive numbers.

Where human populations are so large that available land cannot decently feed, clothe, and shelter them, man's destructive methods of exploitation mushroom like the atomic cloud over Hiroshima. This may be seen in all parts of the world where demands exceed the carrying capacity of the land, from Italy to India. More and more land unsuitable for the production of crops is put under the plow.

Pressure of this sort may be political and economic as well as demographic. The grazing lands of the United States are being destructively overexploited; informed students estimate that 80 per cent of our range is overgrazed. Reducing herds and importing meat and wool from other countries might give the grass a chance to restore itself, but cattle and sheep interests are so powerful in Congress that they nullify such obviously sound attempts to relieve the strain on American ranges. Every year the environmental resistance against high productivity is piling up. Cattlemen themselves give evidence of recognizing this condition by their repeated attempts to take over the small amount of grazing land within our national parks, although the total area of these is only 71/100 of 1 per cent of the United States. They are quite willing to destroy this part of the nation's heritage, but they are not willing to draw on the ranges of Australia and Argentina.

Under primitive conditions, before man began to apply his intelligence and knowledge to understanding a *part* of the laws of nature, the ratio between biotic potential and environmental resistance reached a relatively stable equilibrium, which was altered considerably only over geological periods of time. Limiting factors operated but, within the framework of biophysical laws, the land produced its bounty in direct proportion to its basic richness. And probably no continent was richer than the North American. Nature had come to terms with itself, as it always must over long periods; its reach never exceeded its grasp.

Then, through a combination of circumstances discussed in Chapter 4, man rapidly increased his command of nature and, through a highly skewed development of this command, spawned a vast school of new limiting factors. A few rare individuals like Robert Malthus, Benjamin Franklin, and Thomas Jefferson had a partial comprehension of what was happening, but not even Malthus foresaw that in the core of increasing "production" there was hidden the worm Ouroboros, the worm that would finally consume the earth.

THE LAWBREAKER

During the nineteenth and twentieth centuries European man, partly because he thought in terms of the geography from which he had come, was largely spared the cutting rains characteristic of other parts of the world but, principally because he assumed that there was no end to his new riches and that he need not take measures to preserve them, spread desolation across Asia, Africa, and the Americas. Primitive man, and even some highly cultured groups of men, had destroyed environment before this but never with the seemingly calculated inexorability of a Panzer division. The destructive cultural forces that were developed and increased through our influence, have now crept around the globe until the Hottentot, the Malay, and the Ainu are spreading the plague.

One of the first and most destructive tools brought to the New World by the European was the steel ax. The forest seemed to him an enemy of man, as indeed it had been in Europe three centuries before, when the Scots deliberately burned their forests as their sole means of protection against wolves.[8] Axes flashed from Quebec to Georgia. Wood was often without value, and something to be got rid of.

The ax found a rampant ally in fire, and where there was

no time or labor to clear the forest with steel the torch could do it. "One man in one day with one match can clear a hundred acres!" according to a Nicaraguan proverb. Slopes were stripped and planted to corn which, like syphilis, has been one of the most potent contributions of the New World to civilization. It is probable that corn, under modern methods of cultivation, has caused more misery than the venereal disease.

Hard on the heels of the ax came the moldboard plow. This cut great gashes in the landscape, up and down the hills, and directed rain water toward most efficient destructiveness with such channeled force as could hardly have been improved by engineers; in the tropics, where a high proportion of farming is concentrated on highland slopes, it is perhaps the most devastating force introduced by man.

The pioneer brought the rifle and the fowling piece. He killed wildlife for food and for protection; later he began to kill for distant markets and for sport. Only within the past few decades has general recognition been given to the need of preserving a suitable environment and an ample breeding stock. Most of Latin America, Africa, and Asia still kills with complete lack of concern for the future. The roll of species that man will never see again is an unhappy testimony to his cupidity and stupidity.

Fire, the ax, the plow, and the firearm have been the four fundamental tools of our modern culture, and in some of the most fertile and productive regions of the earth they have raised the environmental resistance to such a height that the carrying capacity has been brought nearly as low as that of the Gobi or the tundras of Siberia. Hundreds of millions of acres of once rich land are now as poor as—or worse than—the city gardener's sterile plot.

Despoiled forests, erosion, wildlife extermination, overgrazing, and the dropping of water tables are unforeseen and unwanted by-blows of a vigorous and adolescent culture on the loose. Had intelligent precautions been taken, their development could have been prevented by a sort of ecological birth

control; but the occupation of the New World was such a head-
long, Paul Bunyan affair that there was no time for caution or
even for thought. Furthermore, the requisite knowledge to
permit harmonious living with the new environment was not
available—and still is not available.

Profits Are Loss

One of the most ruinous limiting factors is the capitalistic
system—and this is one of the gravest criticisms that can be
leveled against it. The methods of free competition and the
application of the profit motive have been disastrous to the
land. Railroads received great areas of land on which they settled the men and women whose grandchildren created the Dust
Bowl. Cutthroat competition in forest exploitation has long
since turned us from a creditor into a debtor nation in terms
of forest resources; we are forced to import timber and wood
pulp while our own lands best suited to its production are
being washed into the oceans and the Gulf of Mexico. Today
"free-enterprise" forestry is one of the greatest dangers to
Latin America.

Business has been turned loose to poison thousands of streams
and rivers with industrial wastes; and hundreds of cities are
spending millions of dollars so that they may safely drink the
waste dumped into the rivers upstream. Recently a new gadget
that grinds up garbage and washes it down the kitchen sink has
been promoted; there is, apparently, no way to hold its manufacturer accountable for the increased pollution he is introducing into inland waters. The augmented demand on oxygen
in the water, to permit bacteria to break down the organic
matter, is the final ruination of such fishing as is left in many
a river. The manufacturer cashes in—and the American citizen
pays the cost of increased environmental resistance.

Food prices rise and so does the world demand for food; the
farmer overstocks his pastures, plants every available inch of
marginal land to cash in "while the going's good." Prices fall

and he loudly cries that he cannot afford to improve his land; he must have a subsidy. Income that should have gone into permanent improvements has all too often gone into airplanes, cars, and fur coats—the "high" American standard of living.

Industry has been allowed to treat our underground water supplies as though they were inexhaustible, and the prosperity and possibly the existence of many of our cities have been jeopardized through waste of waters.

Commercial fishermen, assuming the pirate's prerogative to take whatever he can get, have reduced the populations of several important fishes to a point where it is no longer economically possible to take them. On the coast of California the sardine has been so overexploited that "the return per unit of effort on the part of fishermen in 1937-38 was less than half the return in 1932-33 . . . A reduction of the total catch by one-half seems, therefore, to offer the minimum of curtailment necessary to check the present population decline. To build up the population with any rapidity, an even more drastic cut to perhaps one-third of the present total may be necessary." [9] California fishermen continue to extend their exploitation ever farther from the United States, into the waters of Mexico, Central American countries, and Ecuador. Because they lack technically adequate departments of fisheries, these countries have little or no idea of how their resources are being depleted. When fishery technicians of the U. S. government began to give scientific aid to our Good Neighbors to the south, North American commercial fishermen brought pressure to bear to end the co-operation!

On the other side of our continent, "in 1934 the New England shad catch was 385,000 pounds, as against 2,000,000 pounds only fifty years ago. According to Ackerman, the annual catch was many times 2,000,000 pounds early in the last century, when the human population was only a fraction of what it has since become.

"In 1889 Maine marketed 25,000,000 pounds of fresh lobsters, much of the catch going to canneries at a price of two and a half cents a pound. Since 1905 the take has rarely exceeded 6,000,000 pounds, at a wholesale price of twenty-seven cents a pound, or more than ten times the old rate . . . Most of our supply of lobster now comes from farther and farther afield, but this means only that modern transportation is temporarily masking approaching exhaustion. [Before the recent war, tens of thousands of pounds of a spiny lobster were brought to New York, frozen, from the coast of South Africa!]

"The mackerel catch of the eastern United States was about 100,000,000 pounds a year from 1845 to 1885. Between the latter date and 1930 it averaged only 25,000,000 pounds, and this in the face of a rapidly expanding population and demand.

". . . In 1889, 173,000,000 pounds of menhaden were taken by New England fishermen. After 1900, however, a steady decline was evident and in 1933 only 1,000,000 pounds were caught in our waters. The menhaden tends to avoid regions of low temperatures. However, the summers of both 1936 and 1937 were abnormally warm in the Gulf of Maine and yet few of these herring appeared. They had been fished out, with no thought for the future." [10]

Whalers, treating the source of their wealth as though there were no limit to its abundance, have extended the range of their operations and the effectiveness of their attacks to ever more remote seas of the world; the largest mammal alive has been practically exterminated from most of its arctic range. The survival of the whales that are left probably depends on the observance of an international treaty that, as this book is written, has not yet been ratified by enough countries to make it operative. The power of commercial interests in a fat-hungry world and the intransigence of such nations as Russia make the future of these resources extremely doubtful.

The enormous guano resources of Peru, which a hundred years ago totaled more than 23,000,000 tons, were exploited on a competitive basis and by 1911 had been reduced to 30,000 tons. The most Peru has been able to harvest in any subsequent year was 168,000 tons in 1938. All the world, and especially

Latin America, is desperately in need of organic fertilizer, but the "saturnalia," as Peru has come to call the guano boom, built many fortunes under a system of "free enterprise." A literally invaluable means of restoring life to dying lands was knocked down to the highest bidder instead of being managed in such a way as to provide a sustained, maximum yield. The birds that produced the guano were driven from their nests because they got in the way of laborers.

Absentee landlordism, demanding its pound of the soil's flesh every year, has brought disaster to millions of acres. Many wealthy Latin-American landowners, with their interests oriented more toward Paris or New York than toward their haciendas, apply only one yardstick to their enormous holdings—this year's balance sheet. If their managers have to mine the land, as they often do to keep the balance high, the hacendado seldom knows or cares. In Africa the almost entirely extractive point of view of the colonial system results in land managers trying to make their pile and go home in as brief a period as possible. In the United States commercial combines are planting with wheat areas that are certain to lose their topsoil by wind erosion in the next drought. The chief interest is in profits, and these profits are set in a competitive market. Throughout virtually the entire world, land is used not to produce the crop best adapted to it on a permanent basis but to produce as much cash as possible, as cheaply as possible and as quickly as possible—the same system exalted by the manufacturer.

In other words, land is managed on the basis of so-called economic laws and in very general disregard of the physical and biological laws to which it is subject. Man assumes that what has been good for industry must necessarily be good for the land. This may prove to be one of the most expensive mistakes in history.

It Is Done with Mirrors

The rising living standard, as material progress is called, is almost universally assumed to be to the advantage of the human race. Yet its toll, in terms of erosion of the human nervous system, has given the United States one of the highest insanity rates in the world.* It has developed a parallel meretriciousness blatantly exemplified in the advertising "profession" and in the popular radio programs and magazines through which this profession flaunts its wares. Its enormous cost, in terms of the living and working hours that make possible the purchase of far-from-indispensable gadgets, has been frequently discussed. There are, nonetheless, few Americans who are not convinced that the *summum bonum* is a function of the sum of gadgetry.

This superstition, an integral part of American folkways, has never, so far as I know, been examined from the point of view of national physical welfare. What is the effect of our allegedly rising living standard on the natural resources that are the basis of our survival? Is the outpouring of the pulp-paper ordure of "love" stories, crime tales, and "comics" valuable enough to justify extirpation of the world's forests to fabricate the paper on which it is printed? Do unessential electrical knickknacks, industries, and the hydroelectric power necessary to operate them, justify the destruction of other values, the flooding of fertile farm lands in hydroelectric developments, and the exorbitant expenditures of public moneys required to build and maintain dams—moneys that, after all, came out of the hide of the American people?

The TVA has been viciously and stupidly attacked, and then defended as a crowning achievement of all but infallible men. It is certainly neither as good nor as bad as it is alleged to be. In view of the billions of dollars projected for similar de-

* While this book was in press, a friend called to my attention an interestingly parallel statement in *Streamlines*, by Christopher Morley, who, among us moderns, might be said to be notably cultivated on the contour: "We hear about the agricultural problem of soil erosion; hillsides denuded of fertile topsoil . . . or great regions of Middle Western richness scoured off by dust storms. Surely not less serious is the matter of mind erosion; the dust storms of daily excitement and of continual triviality can easily blow away the sensitive topsoil of the spirit. The result is a barren and shallow nervous credulity."

velopments, it would seem high time that we had a detached evaluation of all such work; this should include not only the power, navigation, and flood-control factors, but the total impact on our natural resources. Thus far there seems little doubt that TVA has been less than satisfactory as a method of *land* management. For years its officials virtually excluded the Soil Conservation Service from the Valley, and therefore conservation has lagged far behind much of the rest of the country. Its forestry program, according to reliable observers, has been badly fumbled, and its wildlife program—apart from fisheries —appears to be not much better. It has "controlled" floods, not by holding water in the soil where it will do most good, but by permanently submerging more than three-quarters of the land it was designed to protect! [11] Its much-touted recreational development has often been tawdry. Fishing or boating on its drawn-down waters, surrounded by miles of stinking mudbanks, is about as satisfying as playing basketball in a factory yard. Its so-called "multiple purpose" dams would be better named, as I point out elsewhere, "cross-purpose" dams.

The nineteenth century's enthusiasm for railroads paid little heed to what these were going to do to the land; the Dust Bowl was one of their contributions to modern living and the destruction of forests was, in part, another. We must avoid repeating such mistakes, now that the twentieth century is indulging its own enthusiasms for roads, airfields, and dams.

THE SUPERSATURATED LAND

There is an old Chinese saying that "one hill cannot shelter two tigers." This recognized a sound biologic fact. (And the Chinese would not even have conceived such a thing as piling tigers one upon the other in apartments with flush toilets and two-car garages.) Modern biologists have rediscovered the old Chinese principle and tell us that the mountain lion in our own West needs a radius of action of some forty miles; with any less land it cannot count on sufficient food resources. The deer, which form its principal food, may require forty acres each to sustain them in the cutover second-growth forests of the Northeast; and four hundred acres in the arid Southwest. Each quail requires approximately one acre, under certain conditions. When the overhunted bobwhites of Ohio were placed on the songbird list and relieved of hunting pressure, some years ago, they did not expand their population indefinitely, as the bird lovers had hoped; they increased up to the carrying capacity of the range for quail—and stopped. In some areas, two acres will feed a cow throughout the year; in others a square mile will be required.

Primitive man is subject to the same limitations of carrying capacity as the plants and animals on which he lives. The Indians of the United States probably never reached a population in excess of one million. Where they abandoned the hunting culture, turned to agriculture, and learned the rudiments of farming, they arrived at considerable population densities. In such centers as Mexico, Honduras, and Guatemala, their populations exceeded the carrying capacity of the land. They drew more from it than it was able to produce on a permanent basis. They destroyed forests, lost soil and water, and one after another their civilizations vanished. The Peruvian Indian suffered less from such disasters than did his northern neighbors. This may be because he learned to irrigate his lands and keep the soil in place; and because he possessed, in the guano of his coastal islands, the means of maintaining the fertility of the land.

The American farmer of two hundred years ago was essentially a peasant, although he would have resented the use of the European term. On a moderate-sized farm he could support himself, his wife, perhaps some indigent relatives, a hired man or so, and five or six children. They could be clothed mainly by the products of the farm, and entirely fed and sheltered. "Boughten" products were kept at a minimum, and—except in limited areas producing such destructive crops as tobacco and cotton—relatively low demands were made on the carrying capacity of the land.

Then came industrialization, railroads, the rise of cities with millions of inhabitants needing to be fed, and the concept of the American standard of living. Three of the chief identifying marks of the American standard of living are the automobile, the bathroom, and the radio. The farmer—like the industrial worker—is quite likely to feel that he should be entitled at least to these three. They must be purchased with profits derived from the farm. In other words, the farmer must sell his products to nonfarmers to secure the cash with which to buy his automobile. This immediately places a higher pressure on the carrying capacity of the land. A proportion of what it is able to produce is no longer available to the farmer and his family.

It is interesting to consider who and how many people must now be supported by the farmer's land. If he buys an automobile, the products of his soil, symbolized by money, go to pay the following: miners, metal workers, railroad workers, engineers, auto workers, union officials, machine tool manufacturers and workers in their factories, mining equipment manufacturers and workers in their factories, salesmen, advertising men, magazine publishers and staffs, printers, paper manufacturers, lumbermen who provide wood pulp, postal employees, railroad employees, manufacturers of railroad equipment, planters, rubber tappers, overseers, health officers, members of the rubber cartel, truckers to carry rubber to the piers, seamen and officers, shipbuilders, tire manufacturers and workers in their factories, members of their sales organization, oil well drillers, engineers, oil field workers, pipeline manufacturers and builders, the builders of tankers and their crews, stockbrokers, stockholders, garage builders and workmen, officials in auto license bureaus, traffic cops, builders and salesmen of motorcycles, justices of the peace, builders of superhighways and fabricators of the material of which they are constructed, surgeons, hospitals to handle traffic injuries, manufacturers and drivers of ambulances, insurance agents, undertakers, charity wards and orphan asylums to care for the victims of traffic deaths, wardens and the builders of jails, and a host of additional government employees such as legislators to frame traffic laws, the United States Maritime Commission to handle shipping, the Interstate Commerce Commission, State Department employees to watch over foreign oil resources—and perhaps the Army and Navy to fight for them, etc. This is only a partial list; but it gives an inkling as to the increasing demands that are being made on the American land.

Economists write of the "agricultural revolution," of greater productivity per farm worker, of the advantages of farm mechanization and the ability of the farmer to feed more people than he did prior to the nineteenth century. What most of them completely fail to recognize is that production-per-farmer is utterly meaningless divorced from production-per-acre. For a few decades the Western world was able to get along on this assumption—while it still had new lands to open up and while it produced by mining its topsoil. But modern agriculture has not raised the earth's biotic potential; except in very limited areas, it has not reduced environmental resistances. Over most of the earth it has enormously *increased* them, to the point of destroying hundreds of millions of productive acres. Discussion of the agricultural revolution in terms of increased production-per-farmer—or even in terms of pure agriculture, leaving aside the problem of water tables, forests, nonagricultural lands, fauna and noncrop plants, etc.—expresses a most fallacious and dangerous form of thinking. One man, under an improved technology, might be able to farm a full section; this would not bring into being more sections of agricultural land—nor raise or even maintain productivity on other acres.

The contribution of the individual farmer to any one of the people listed above is of course small; but 33 per cent of the automobiles, trucks, and tractors in the United States are registered from farms, and hundreds of thousands more are operated in the service of the farmer. Besides the millions of people in the auto industry and its satellites, there are the additional millions in the radio and other luxury industries. In the time of the Incas—to relate the problem to another part of the world—five or six acres could probably support an entire family; today, they would not buy a family car. Behind every farmer's chair, at the dinner table, stands a shadowy host of other families to which he is conveying energy resources by drawing upon his land, in order to maintain his American standard of living.

THE BOOKS MUST BALANCE

When the farmer is expert enough to manage his land well, where he can produce for his needs and desires without reducing the productive capacity—and where the land itself is of high enough quality to produce that much wealth on a sustained rather than an extractive basis—the economy is in balance. Where, however, because of poor soil or inadequate farming methods, the farmer can support his tractor, automobile, bathroom, and radio only by mining the land, it is difficult to defend his right to the so-called American standard of living; and if such land exhaustion is widespread it seems difficult even to justify the American standard of living. Actually, this is the situation over much of the United States. Land productivity is falling in many areas. The federal government has given tacit recognition to the unsoundness of the farmer's position by benefit payments in the name of soil conservation, and by subsidies. One example of this is the "floor" under wool prices; another, the "protective" tariff on wool. These amount to a government subsidy of soil erosion, since they support the overstocking of our western ranges. Were it not for such handouts, many woolgrowers would be forced out of business. And the grasses would be given a chance to recover.

So far as subsidy payments equalize the economic position of the farmer and subsidized industrialist (who is the first to protest any real attempt at free enterprise) they are certainly defensible. The farmer has been exploited for decades despite the fact that he is far more useful, productive, able, and hardworking a member of our society than the vast majority of businessmen. But it is difficult to see any justification for long-term support of extractive overcropping.

The payment of benefits over a short period is certainly preferable to letting the farmer so damage his land that it cannot be restored to productiveness within the lifetime of the nation. Perhaps it is justifiable as an injection of digitalis for a failing economic system. However, unless the national debt is to be repudiated or scaled down by inflation, such practices obviously cannot be continued indefinitely. Our economy cannot be permanently shored up with paper. Despite the theory of certain economists that the national debt is unimportant because we owe it to ourselves, it can be paid off only by means of taxes that are basically derived from our natural resources —taxes that represent working hours of American citizens and that express energy derived from our land. *It must be reiterated that there is no other source of this energy*. By the printing of paper, and other forms of postponing the reckoning, we create an illusion of wealth. By using up our *real* capital of natural resources, especially soil, we reduce the possibility of ever paying off the debt. To me it seems impossible to escape the conclusion that the relatively high material living standard we have set for our farmers cannot be realized in the long pull; and it is even more fantastic to seek it for the millions of nonproducers who are, in a very real sense, parasitic on the land.

Americans of good will have advocated an American standard of living, or something approaching it, for the entire world. "Freedom from want" was the carrot held before the noses of less prosperous peoples, to enlist their support during the war. What a monstrous deception this was, of ourselves and them, should be clear to anyone who thinks in terms of the carrying capacities of the world's lands.

A farmer in the Pennsylvania Dutch country will live comfortably and even become rich on 150 acres of land. He is probably using land that has been intensively farmed for two hundred years. His living standard is one of the highest to be found in any farm population in the United States, though he may religiously avoid gadgetry. On the other hand, in the western Dakotas, a descendant of the Swedes or Norwegians will require from two to three square miles to maintain a decent living standard for his family. He probably works quite as hard as the Pennsylvania Dutchman, is equally intelligent, and perhaps better educated. The fact that he needs so much more land is an index of its much lower carrying capacity. In the Dakotas the soil may be poor and the layer of topsoil thin; in many areas there has been considerable wind erosion, and the amount of precipitation necessary for crops is so variable that a farmer may have only six good years out of ten.

A recognition of the low carrying capacity of this land is mirrored in the exodus of people from the Dakotas. Whereas the national population is increasing, there has been a significant drop in populations in this region. (Mechanization of agriculture also has contributed to it.) In rural Georgia or South Carolina, where cotton and tobacco have combined to help build the rural slums so vividly portrayed by Erskine Caldwell, the living standard may be not much more than 50 per cent of what it is in Iowa. The carrying capacity was once far higher, but misuse of the land has been reducing it—raising the environmental resistance—since colonial times.

The carrying capacity differential exists, of course, throughout the world. No two cotton fields, no two pastures will produce even theoretically the same amount of food and fibers. With the various cultural complications, their productivity varies even more widely. It is interesting to ponder what a hand-picked group of Javanese farmers could do with an island like Puerto Rico. What would have been the fate of Mexico had it been settled by Swedes? What would have happened to North America had the Conquistadores come to dominate, in the early days, rather than a preponderantly North European stock? Carrying capacity is obviously a function of more than the land itself; and—no matter what the biotic potential may be—every area has a limited carrying capacity.

Chapter 3

As Mankind Thinketh

In China, THE IDEA THAT IT IS NECESSARY TO BE AN ancestor is a cardinal belief, despite the obvious fact that descendants are becoming more wretched with every generation. In starving India, the country is overrun by millions of cattle that cannot be used to satisfy human hunger because they are "sacred"; nor can they be killed and prevented from drawing from the land energy supplies desperately needed for human beings. The *idea* is dominant over the peristalsis of starving stomachs.

When mankind began the massive development of its forebrain, which is its greatest glory, it also began to lay up trouble for itself on the earth. The shackles of instinct, protectors of the amoeba and the ape, were largely discarded, and Plato became a possibility, and Moses, Aristotle, and Beethoven, and Darwin and Freud. Man was now on his own; he had the freedom to mold his own destiny. Unfortunately, the freedom did not always have its counterpart in wisdom. For this reason, ancient civilizations fell—and our own is tottering.

It has been the fashion, especially of modern years, to emphasize what man has done in the way of material accomplishments. But there has been a strong tendency to neglect what he has thought. For a nation whose founders left the blood of their bare feet in the snow at Valley Forge, we Americans are strangely blind to the power of ideas. We have recently fought our most desperate war, principally because the sick mind of an obscure Austrian so infected an entire nation that its idea of its relationship to Europe and the world was transformed into a virtual paranoia. In Russia we have watched an economic theory develop into a near psychosis that threatens modern nations with the fire and sword of a holy war.

The *idea* of the milpa farmer may be far more difficult to change than is the direction of the gullies through his land. To limit the desire of the Chinese for sons may be a problem more formidable than the provision of at least limited food for them. A slogan may twist the arm of Peace as dangerously as a new weapon. Faith in ancient precepts may be a more effective eroder of soil than two inches of rain in an hour.

Behind nearly every human act lies an "emotion" that sets the act going; and behind the "emotion" lies a "thought" or an "idea." If such survival-emotions as the desire for conservation are to become part of our daily existence, they must be based on knowledge and the thought that stems from it. If we are to make peace with the forces of the earth, that peace must begin in our minds—and we must seek, and accept, many new ideas. We must reject many old ones.

One of the strangest lacunae in human cultural development is the absence of understanding of man's relationship with his physical environment. So anthropocentric has he been that, since he began to achieve what we call civilization, he has assumed that he lives in a sort of vacuum. He has probably been an agriculturist at least a hundred centuries, yet it was only in 1944 that Dr. E. H. Graham published the first book on natural principles of land use.

Ignorance that runs through the entire social structure of the world, from leaders of all stripes to peasants and industrial laborers, is one of the limiting factors that will be most difficult to control. To change agricultural practices in areas of Latin America, Asia, and Africa, where the illiteracy rate is often 100 per cent, within a period short enough to save the land will require heroic measures. It is certain that, for all practical purposes, large areas of the earth now occupied by backward populations will have to be written off the credit side of the ledger.

THE DANGEROUS DOCTOR

The modern medical profession, still framing its ethics on the dubious statements of an ignorant man who lived more than two thousand years ago—ignorant, that is, in terms of the modern world—continues to believe it has a duty to keep alive as many people as possible. In many parts of the world doctors apply their intelligence to one aspect of man's welfare—survival—and deny their moral right to apply it to the problem as a whole. Through medical care and improved sanitation they are responsible for more millions living more years in increasing misery. Their refusal to consider their responsibility in these matters does not seem to them to compromise their intellectual integrity. They have been primarily responsible for making Puerto Rico, for example, one of the most miserable areas on the face of the earth, by expanding the population beyond all possible bounds of decent subsistence, and their present efforts to correct the situation are not much more than tokens. They set the stage for disaster; then, like Pilate, they wash their hands of the consequences.

Nationalism plays an all too effective part in reducing the carrying capacity of the world's lands. The attempts at national self-sufficiency, the movement to build local industries in areas that cannot support them, the protection given these industries by tariff barriers, the resultant drag on the free movement of raw materials and goods force man to exploit his land in increasingly ruinous ways. For a large and rich nation like the United States this nationalism is an effective, if temporary, defense against poverty. How long it can be maintained in the age of atomic and bacterial warfare is dubious. India has already begun to enunciate a Realpolitik that demands expansion.

UNSPEAKABLE REALITY

Finally, a factor limiting the sound use of natural resources is our Aristotelian heritage, so called because it originated with the great philosopher, and has been developed through the centuries by his followers.

The modern rejection of Aristotelian "logic" is without question as rich in promise of development and clarification for the field of ecology—and its application, conservation—as were the rejections of Euclidean and Newtonian limitations for mathematics and physics. Until we do reject antiquated notions we are likely to remain snarled in the confusion of inferences that are invalid—and the words that express the confusion.

Perhaps the clearest expression of a non-Aristotelian formulation is a graphic device, the "structural differential," [1] originated by Alfred Korzybski, and pictured here in somewhat modified form. It represents the physical world, and what we think, feel, and say about it. Let us relate it, for the sake of our discussion, to an area of land. (It is equally applicable to an apple, a chair, a painting, a blonde, a cathedral, etc.)

This land has an existence at a submicroscopic, colloidal, atomic, etc., level (A) much of which is (1948) unknowable. Space and time are not separated in it; modern physics has taught us that we must think of four-dimensional space-time. The land is constantly changing; it is different land June 1, 1948, and June 2, 1948. This is true if we consider only what happens on the submicroscopic level; it is also true, as we shall see later, on the microscopic and macroscopic levels. Therefore we should not think of the land—or a clod of earth in it—as a static object, but as a dynamic, ever-changing *process*.

By the use of scientific instruments, such as the microscope and pH meter, we can learn many things about the land—structure of the soil, hydrogen-ion concentration, chemical composition, kinds of protozoans present, etc.—as is graphically indicated by the dots in the diagram. What we learn, however, even with the most advanced scientific techniques, cannot be *all* the facts; so the microscopic level (B) has less dots than the submicroscopic level. With our scientific methods we have abstracted certain knowledge but inevitably we left something out. *We cannot know all!* (The "etceteras" so liberally used

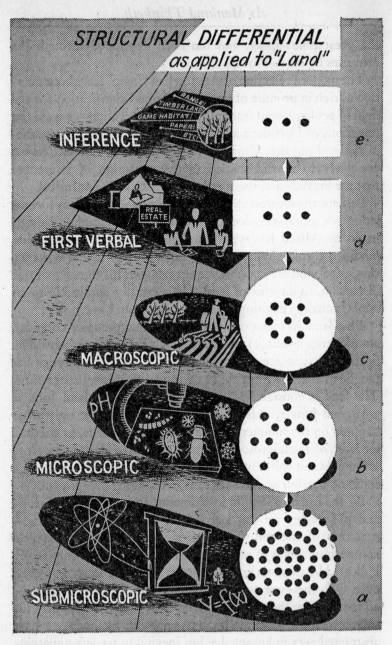

STRUCTURAL DIFFERENTIAL
as applied to "Land"

INFERENCE   *e*

RANGE! TIMBER LAND GAME HABITAT! PAPER! ETC

FIRST VERBAL   *d*

REAL ESTATE

MACROSCOPIC   *c*

MICROSCOPIC   *b*

pH

SUBMICROSCOPIC   *a*

$y = f(x)$

Based on chart from *Science and Sanity* by Alfred Korzybski, copyright by Alfred Korzybski.

throughout this book—a cardinal sin against rules laid down by all teachers of English composition I ever encountered—are a recognition of the impossibility of saying *all* about anything. To omit them would be to imply completeness of knowledge and expression, which would be impossible even were unlimited space available.)

As we pass to a still higher level of abstracting (*C*), the macroscopic or objective, where we depend on our unaided senses, our graph must include still fewer dots, showing that still more is left out. At each step we are further removed from *all* the "truth," even as it is currently understood. At this level we cannot possibly understand colloidal structure, chemical composition, functioning of organic matter, molds and their influence on plant life, etc. Still more is omitted; still greater is our ignorance. This is the nearest many of us will approach, in our abstracting, to the *process* that is the land. This is the level at which live most farmers and gardeners, some congressmen and teachers, and others who have firsthand knowledge. It is because we live at this level that we maintain soil surveys, agricultural experiment stations, agricultural colleges, etc. The people who work in them have a wider knowledge on the microscopic level; in their abstracting, they omit less.

These three levels might be called the levels of reality. They are limited to things that—someday, if not yet—may be weighed, or measured, or felt, or tasted, or seen. But they may not be *said*. They exist at what Korzybski calls the "unspeakable level." When we begin to talk about them we necessarily use a higher-order abstraction—leave out still more. And it is here that much of our trouble begins.

The first verbal level of abstraction is the label (*D*), the name, or description—"land." This does not smell sweet after a rain, or wash into our rivers, or raise fifty bushels of corn an acre, or stick to our boots. "The word is *not* the thing"—but many of us act as though it were. For businessmen, such as many real estate agents; for millions of asphalt-bound city dwellers; for many economists and national and international officials, there is no differentiation between the *word* land and the *process* or *object* land. The two are identified in thought and speech. This partially explains why thousands of unfortunate refugees are being dumped into tropical countries that do not have nonverbal land capable of feeding their own people.

(If this discussion of abstracting is not immediately understandable, it may be helpful to think of the structural differential in terms of the blonde. In one's abstractions, how much is necessarily omitted, and how many problems have complicated the lives of how many men because of their assumption of "allness"—that they know *all* about her. How many young men, scarcely aware of the "unspeakable" blonde, have fallen head-over-heels in love with the *verbal* level, including its luscious inferences, and identified it with the *object* level! Pin-up girls, wolf-calls, the popularity of certain movie stars —and of Reno—all bear witness to these identifications of levels of abstraction, the possible danger of "allness.")

Higher levels of abstraction are possible almost without limit —and they offer even greater opportunities for trouble. Let us look at a word like "forest" as applied to land. This is a still higher abstraction from level *A*. Miles of forest have been destroyed to make tons of paper on which to verbalize about "forest" land. But what is meant by it? The Woolgrowers' Association says it *is* range. The forester, even at this late date, is likely to say it *is* a source of timber. The wildlife manager says it *is* game habitat. The hydrologist says it *is* watershed protection. The Mexican politician says it *is* corn land. Etcetera. The word "forest," in this case, indicates an *inference* about the land, and each of these people abstracts something different—draws a different inference. Few of them speak with a consciousness of abstracting or a realization that much is omitted. In this way difficulties arise that often lead to tragic results, wasting billions of dollars, years of men's lives, and millions of acres of good land.

The lack of consciousness of abstraction, the assumption that one knows all, and says all, in a given situation, dams the minds of leaders and followers alike, leads to oversimplification, and "solves" extremely complex problems with many factors unconsciously omitted. This sort of thinking is especially characteristic of legislative bodies and world organizations. It leads to the writing and acceptance of documents like the Communist Manifesto and the Atlantic Charter. It tricks man into seeking political and/or economic solutions for problems that are political, economic, social, geographic, psychological, genetic, physiological, etc.; it is like the old application of the **clyster** as a cure-all.

THE BRAKE OF CONFUSION

The confusion of the levels of abstraction leads us to identify what happens on the purely verbal level with the process on the subverbal level. For example, a woman squeezes the breakfast oranges, sips the juice, and thinks, "How sweet they are." Her husband rushes out a few moments later, takes a few mouthfuls of flapjacks and maple sirup, and then drinks his orange juice. "Gosh, these are sour oranges!" he exclaims.

They are, for all practical purposes, the same oranges. It is the husband—including maple sirup—that is different. Or, more exactly, what has happened at the subverbal level—the relationship of the juice to taste buds, affected in one case by sirup, but not in the other—is the process; "sweet" and "sour" are merely words. Instead of considering the total situation as mapped by the structural differential, the husband has looked at only one isolated level—*one element.*

This leads us to consideration of what Korzybski has called "elementalistic thinking." The various individuals, in their reactions to forest land, mentioned above, have thought in elementalistic terms. This type of reasoning has been enormously harmful in our fumbling attempts to deal with the problems of human survival and decent living standards. It constantly bewitches sociologists into trying to settle "population" problems apart from the total environments in which populations live. It is partly responsible for the antics of such people as Army Engineers, who seem literally incapable of understanding the necessity of beginning flood-control work on the hilltops. It straps many of our foresters into the strait jacket of timber production, and isolates even the concept of multiple use of forest lands from the exceedingly pertinent implications of economics, sociology, hydrology, and national and international affairs. It holds the agriculturist, as he is often proud to state, "down to earth," and separates his thinking—and especially his education—from the undeniably related concerns of logic, economics, semantics, education, languages, broad land-use organization, history, anthropology, etc. It keeps many economists wandering in a symbolical cosmos situated somewhere between heaven and hell, as was the world of the thirteenth-century theologian. It leads international organizations to seek solutions in Economic and Social Councils that, by definition, omit from their calculations such indispensables as geography, climate, psychology, carrying capacities, folkways, and population developments, all of which are, themselves, dynamically interrelated. It is responsible for the self-satisfaction of the medical man, smug in his conviction that his chief responsibility is to postpone death as long as possible, under whatever circumstance.

The fact that most of us live mainly on the verbal level leads to verbal splitting that has no justification at the level of reality. We talk and think of "body" and "mind"—though modern physicians have begun to recognize their unity in psychosomatic medicine. "Space" and "time," "emotions" and "intellect" are separated in words, and we accept the separation as though it were characteristic of reality. (This discussion, separating "thought" from emotion and action, is defensible—in non-Aristotelian terms—merely as a matter of convenience. In reality, of course, thought, action, and emotion are more inextricably intertwined than Laocoön and the serpents.)

The Aristotelian, two-valued thinking has plagued even the most advanced technicians in fields related to the management of natural resources and problems of human populations. The terms "good" and "bad" are used as absolutes, without recognition that there is a gradation between them and that every good includes much bad, and vice versa. For example, the "good" hawk and the "bad" hawk have kept game commissions bemused, and Audubon societies excited, for decades. "Cause" and "effect" are used as explanatory terms without the realization that every "cause" is in itself an "effect," and every "effect" a "cause." Conservationists are prone to insist that they are "men of action" as opposed to "theorists" or "men of thought," despite the fact that conservation activity, divorced from sound thinking, has enormously wasted our funds and our resources. "Conservation" has been so long sterilized by isolation from "education"—when they are, in reality, inseparable—that many Ph.D.'s are ignoramuses in questions having to do with the land; and a shocking proportion of our State Conservation Commissions are guided by traditions that should have disappeared with the Model T.

Identification—what Korzybski calls "is-ness"—results in the failure to recognize that all phenomena, from individual cornfields to individual countries, are *unique* and (as processes) *constantly changing*. But the problems of Great Britain and those of Iran are analyzed on an identical basis. The same medicine, perhaps labeled Democracy, is prescribed for Albania and for the United States. Young men are brought from all over the world for training and indoctrination under the TVA, on the assumption that TVAs should be prescribed for their own particular brand of national or regional rickets. Soil conservation methods, of proved soundness in the United States, are transplanted bodily to Latin America, where they are a failure because of wide disparities in geographic and cultural conditions. Economists who will change their car every two years, their ideas on nutrition and child-raising every ten, cling to nineteenth-century concepts such as the fallacy of Malthusianism, as though they were divine revelation.

Finally, another source of recurrent confusion is our failure to recognize what Korzybski calls "multi-ordinal terms." These are terms indicating abstractions in varying degrees, terms that are meaningless apart from the context in which they are found. Such notions as "security" and "standards of living" are multi-ordinal terms. A high standard of living for the son of a successful insurance salesman in Chicago—that is, the reasonable satisfaction of his desires—is a very different thing from the high standard of living of a pottery maker in Tlaquepaque. A "national park" is not the same phenomenon in Venezuela as it is in Arizona. "Freedom from want" in Timbuktu has little relationship to "freedom from want" in Dubuque.

Identity, elementalism, "allness," etc.—direct descendants of Aristotle's logic—have so shaped our thinking and, therefore, our treatment of our land and associated resources that they often exert as powerful an influence as rainfall and soil structure. As the basis of sound resource management, the necessity of recognizing and rejecting these mistaken notions can scarcely be overemphasized.

Two decades ago, the oldest man in a little Hudson Valley town married the village idiot, many years his junior. His explanation was that he hated to get into a cold bed alone.

Most of us are in a comparable situation. Our ideas, evolved twenty centuries ago, may be idiotic in an overpeopled, atomic age, with much of the world a shambles. Yet we cling to them because of an instinctive fear of lack of support if we give them up.

They were magnificent concepts in their day; their survival through all these centuries is clear proof of that. But they can no longer serve us, except as millstones about our necks. We live in a world of change, a world of infinitely complex relationships. As relationships change, so do values. They are relative and (in the mathematical sense) functional. Static values, any kind of static thinking, are as obsolete as the Roman chariot.

Modern science has taught us that, in the realm of mechanics, of medicine, of physics, etc. We must also learn it in our relationships with the earth and each other—if we are to survive.

Chapter 4

Industrial Man—the Great Illusion

THE POPULATION OF THE WORLD AT THE TIME OF THE American Revolution totaled some 900,000,000. Of these, 180,000,000 lived in Europe, and 600,000,000 lived in Asia. Despite the highly developed agriculture that had existed during forty centuries in Asia, and an agricultural revolution that was well under way in Europe, they were unable to feed themselves.

A study in Nanking University "revealed that from 108 B.C. to 1911 A.D. there were 1828 famines in China, or nearly one every year. A famine in Bengal, India, is reported to have taken one-third of the population . . ." [1]

In Edmund Burke's famous Speech on Conciliation with the Colonies, delivered in Parliament in 1775, he cried: "For some time past the Old World has been fed from the New. The scarcity which you have felt would have been a desolating famine, if this child of your old age, with a true filial piety, with a Roman charity, had not put the full breast of its youthful exuberance to the mouth of its exhausted parent!"

At a time when it is being called upon by a still more exhausted "parent," these are facts it is well to ponder.

In the period from 1200 to 1600, according to William Farr, England suffered a famine on the average of every fifteen years [2] and at the time of George III was living, balanced on the brink of starvation, on what "we now call an Asiatic standard." [3] Crop failures in Ireland are reputed to have reduced the population two and a half millions. [4] There are no statistics on the numbers dying from famine in the British Isles, but the total must have been many millions. People were forced to eat cats, rats, fern roots, dogs, and even human flesh.[5]

This situation was not restricted to the British Isles. A great Continental leader said in a speech to his troops: "Let none of your possessions detain you, no solicitude for your family affairs, since this land which you inhabit, shut in on all sides by the sea and surrounded by mountain peaks, is too narrow for your large population; nor does it abound in wealth; it furnishes scarcely food enough for its cultivators. Hence it is that you murder and devour one another, that you wage war, and that frequently you perish by mutual wounds. Let therefore hatred depart from among you, let your quarrels and your wars cease, and let all dissensions and controversies slumber. Enter upon the road to the Holy Sepulchre; wrest the land from the wicked race and subject it to yourselves. That land which, as the Scripture says, 'floweth with milk and honey,' was given by God into the possession of the Children of Israel." This harangue, which might have set the pattern for Nuremberg and 1939, was addressed to the Crusaders in A.D. 1095, by Pope Urban II.[6]

Until about the time of the Industrial Revolution, mass transport of foodstuffs was impossible and storage facilities were almost nil. When crops failed, people died. When people outbred the capacity of the local land to sustain them, there was rarely any escape but death. An exception was ancient Greece. The wisdom of its people found an expression that is rarely commented upon; they were aware of the constant threat of overpopulation, and purposefully reduced the danger by prostitution, infanticide, emigration, and colonization. To many, the ethics of some of these measures are repugnant; they would prefer mass misery and starvation. In most of the "civilized" world, people simply died for want of food.

Down to the end of the eighteenth century, famine was the normal, periodic lot of most human societies, and it still is in some parts of the world.

Then two cultural revolutions, long brewing, burst with

full force upon mankind. The first was the Industrial Revolution. It multiplied opportunities for labor. It made it possible for one man to do the work of ten, fifty, a hundred, a thousand. It created vast cities, with such slums as the world had never before known. It gave birth to an entirely new concept of living.

The Industrial Revolution did not, of course, suddenly come into being like some mutant spore floating high in the heavens. It had shallow roots in the past, and sent thick, sucking taproots into the future—especially toward the west. Without the Agricultural Revolution that preceded it by about a century, it might well have been stillborn; the problem of raising, transporting, and storing enough food and other raw materials to support the mushrooming cities would probably have been a lethal factor.

The Parasite

Without the New World on which to draw, the Industrial Revolution would have been a stunted dwarf. For, although the work of man became more efficient and less workers were needed on the farm to raise food, thus releasing a surplus of labor to work the machine, *the amount of land* did not increase. Actually, it shrank, with the growth of cities and extension of highways. Environmental resistances were lowered by the new agriculture; within a period of about sixty years, improved methods of cattle and sheep breeding doubled the weight of animals reaching the market. The biotic potential was more nearly realized. But the total potential carrying capacity of Europe contracted, with the diminution of area.

The train had been laid for the Industrial Revolution in 1492. The well-publicized discoveries of the Genoese and the explorers who followed him set in motion westward a slow trickle of population, and a backwash of products from the New World. Galleons from the southern continent brought a relatively sterile cargo of gold and silver and jewels; these were what most interested the Spaniards and such freebooters as Sir Francis Drake. They also brought a humble treasure from the Andes—the potato—which has been worth to the Old World many thousand times as much as the treasure of Cajamarca and Tenochtitlán. The potato took kindly to the soils and climate of Europe, and still further reduced the environmental resistance, for man.

But not enough. Demand increased too fast. To satisfy her increasing numbers Europe began to draw more and more on the soils of the New World. The first considerable crop to be sent back was tobacco, a crop from which our soils have not yet recovered. Corn, wheat, cotton, timber, rice, indigo, wool —these and many more rushed in to fill an economic vacuum. In the late eighteenth century eight bales of cotton were confiscated because it was "impossible" that the American colonies could have produced so much, and it was assumed they must have come from other, proscribed areas. Within a few decades Europe was receiving from America hundreds of thousands of bales. The new marvel of transport, one of the early offspring of the Industrial Revolution, made the transfer possible.

The New World, especially the United States, was primarily an agrarian society, and England tried to keep it so. The export of her newly developing textile machinery was forbidden, under pain of death. The American Revolution put an end to that—but for many years America was an expanding market for Europe's, especially Britain's, manufacturers. For these and for a good deal of capital we exchanged the products of our land—which is to say, our land itself. Every time a million bushels of wheat crossed the Atlantic, incalculable numbers of tons of topsoil washed down our rivers.

Population pressures in the Old World continued to rise. It was soon discovered that it was easier and cheaper to export a 150-pound man than to import the hundreds of pounds of food needed to keep him alive for a year. Irish, Italians, and Poles moved from the slums of the Old World to the slums of the New; once here, most of them scrambled out without much difficulty. Free land, or the industries such as railroads dependent upon it, provided opportunities for almost anyone willing to work. Early in Victoria's reign, much of the Western world took on something of the aspect of a boom town. Stephenson, Arkwright, Fulton, speculators and entrepreneurs made the wheels spin faster—but it was the rich forests of New England, the prairie soils of Illinois, the red lands of Georgia and the Carolinas, the slopes of São Paulo, the black soils of the pampas that kept them from grinding slowly to a stop.

Then the French pharmacist, Louis Pasteur, gave to the world an understanding of microbes and their part in disease. In Europe life expectancies had been climbing, what with better diets, improved sewage disposal and water supply, more abundant food, a rising material standard of living. The control of a long series of diseases came within man's grasp, and the most effective remaining check on populations began to disappear. The Sanitary Revolution had arrived.

More Hungry Mouths

Populations increased ever more rapidly. Simple techniques of sanitation, such as boiling contaminated water, spread rapidly beyond Europe and North America to much of the rest of the world. This was all that was needed to spark the population explosion.

In the hundred years prior to 1940, the world population more than doubled—from 1,000,000,000 to 2,200,000,000.

The nineteenth century was, of course, Great Britain's. She had a head start on the Industrial Revolution; for decades she could write blank checks against the riches of her colonies, and she had guaranteed markets protected by such devices as a $1,000 fine imposed on her merchants for importing Calcutta calico.[7] Her position was one of almost unchallenged dominance in shipping and industrial exports. In 1870 "she accounted for 32 per cent of the world's manu-

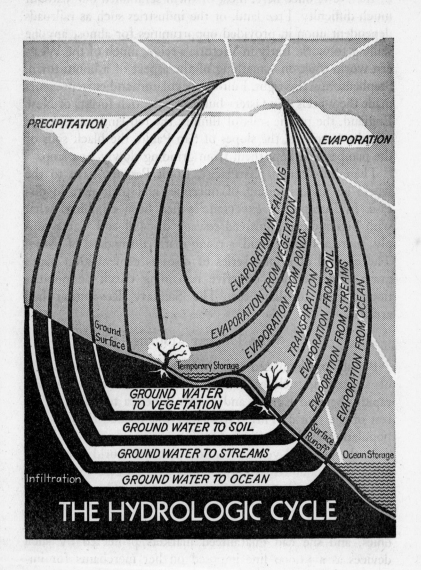

PRECIPITATION

EVAPORATION

EVAPORATION IN FALLING

EVAPORATION FROM VEGETATION

EVAPORATION FROM PONDS

TRANSPIRATION

EVAPORATION FROM SOIL

EVAPORATION FROM STREAMS

EVAPORATION FROM OCEAN

Ground Surface

Temporary Storage

GROUND WATER TO VEGETATION

GROUND WATER TO SOIL

GROUND WATER TO STREAMS

GROUND WATER TO OCEAN

Infiltration

Surface Runoff

Ocean Storage

THE HYDROLOGIC CYCLE

facturing production." [8] Her population, at that time, was 26,000,000.

Small wonder that she so vigorously espoused Free Trade! She was a contented parasite, drawing on the eroding hill-sides of New England, of Iowa, of Maryland, of Argentina and South Africa, of Australia and India. And most of these areas were more than willing to be parasitized—at a price. The famous steaks and chops at Simpson's carried with them the nitrogen, potassium, phosphorus, and other soil minerals from half the world.

It is, perhaps, not strange that the theories of Robert Thomas Malthus were buried beneath the bounty from the New World cornucopia. In 1798 he had warned that man's population tended to outstrip his food supply. Yet every day ships bearing the products of virgin soils provided not only better food for man, but more of it for more men. The economists, one after another, rejected the Gloomy Curate; popular opinion did not lag in following the economists, since Malthus's remedy lay in population limitation through continence. Why bother about populations? Living standards were rising everywhere. Excess numbers of people were welcome in the new lands. "Production," measured either in money or in quantities of food, was increasing. What matter if the erstwhile colonies had begun to abandon exhausted land long before the American Revolution—and continued to do so at an accelerated rate as progress really got going in the nineteenth century? What if sugar was wearing out the soil in the West Indies, and coffee was ripping down hillsides from Guatemala to Brazil? There was more land, wasn't there? The economists did not include in their concept of capital the highly vulnerable biotic potential. Money and wealth were equated, and the trade balances looked good to nearly every-body. The physiocrats had perceived the difference between the symbolic level and reality, but they were submerged in "progress" and "prosperity."

Despite her initial fumbling efforts Britain could not hope to monopolize industrial production, especially when many of her most vigorous and aggressive sons were seeking the democracy of the New World. Manufacturing spread across the Continent, and the cities of the United States began to expand.

We built our own industrial structure primarily for an internal market. True, the flush toilet is known in southern Peru as *"el chicago,"* but most of the cranky plumbing that has originated some extremely curious sanitary habits south of the Rio Grande came from Great Britain and the Continent.

During the period of great expansion our market was not only domestic but primarily rural. Before 1920 the majority of our people lived in country districts, and it was their purchasing power that built our industrial plant. They, of course, predominantly drew their wealth from the land.

The Source of Real Wealth

A clue to this relationship is given in the history of recovery from depressions between 1873 (when data are first available) and World War I, which added new factors.

In 1879 "the bumper crop of wheat [459,000,000 bushels!] accompanied by high prices [resulting from shortages elsewhere] gave to the very important wheat-farming sections of the United States a substantial expansion of purchasing power which stimulated, first, railroad expansion and, in due course, all phases of business activity. The additional income of the farmer was paid out in part for the purchase of consumption goods and in part for the purchase of capital equipment required on the farm. . . . The recovery movement in 1879 was also aided by the failure of the cotton crop in India. . . . The forward movement thus begun in agriculture spread in cumulative fashion throughout the entire industrial system. . . .

"The marked improvement in the agricultural situation [80,000,000 more bushels, with a 60 per cent price rise], which became evident by the middle of 1897, was quickly followed by a general expansion of business activity.

"In the closely associated field of railway equipment, purchases of freight cars and passenger cars were few in the first half of 1897, but increased thereafter . . . the agricultural improvement was a powerful aid; and it is not impossible that, had the agricultural situation been unfavorable in the autumn of 1897, the slight improvement noted would have flattened out as it did in 1895."

In a footnote in the same volume, the author observes: "In studying this period it is interesting to note that Russian recovery began in 1893, two years before any improvement began in Western Europe or the United States. Russia had exceptionally large wheat crops and large exports in 1893, 1894, 1895 and 1896, whereas the American crop was relatively small each year. In 1897 the situation was reversed—a small Russian crop and a bumper American crop.

"It may be noted in passing that the American revival of 1891-92, unmatched in European countries, was evidently the result of the extraordinary wheat crop of 1891, amounting to 678 million bushels, which was over 100 million bushels larger than the previous record crop. Owing to a relatively small world crop the price was fairly good and substantially higher than in the ensuing years. Exports increased from 109 million bushels in 1890 to 229 millions in 1891.

"Again in 1924, recovery from the sharp industrial reaction of the spring and summer appears to have been greatly stimulated by a very large wheat crop which was sold at high prices. The American wheat crop of 1924 was 840 million bushels, as against 759 million bushels in 1923; but the price on December 1 was $1.30 a bushel as compared with 92 cents the preceding year. As a result of a short world crop exports from the United States were increased from 132 million bushels to 255 million bushels." [9]

"Agriculture represents the largest, single purchasing unit for products of industry. There are 3½ times as many workers engaged in agriculture as in iron and steel and the automobile and mining industries combined. Thirty-six per cent of all wholesale and practically 50 per cent of all retail business deal in agricultural products. These groups employ 35 per cent of all wage earners in the entire wholesale and retail fields, and 40 per cent of the freight transported by railroads had its origin in the soil." [10]

Parenthetically, viewing the effect of the farmer's purchasing power upon our economy, it is interesting to consider the influence of increasing mechanization, the monopolistic trend toward large farms, and the resultant shrinkage in rural populations—with the growing concentration of farm purchasing power in the hands of fewer men and women.

The people who provided our rural markets drew their purchasing power from the land. Shifting from a self-sustaining, near-subsistence economy, they began to purchase textiles, farm implements, and vehicles of increasing complexity and cost, modern sanitation, and mechanized recreation—increasing amounts of consumer and capital goods. Many of the industries satisfying these wants of our rural population developed, economically speaking, into world forces. During the period when the greatest market was still our own rural areas, the purchasers of these products of American industry accumulated their buying power through farming practices that destroyed millions of acres of our land.

The late Leonard Salter told the story of the southern Wisconsin farmer who leaned against his barn and remarked contentedly, "I've got a hundred eighty acres, the house, barn and stock, and it's free and clear. It's cost me seventeen years of sweat and hard work—and six inches of topsoil."

EXPANDING WASTE

In view of the fact that our rural areas achieved such prosperity as they did only by mining the soil, it is difficult not to conclude that a large part of American prosperity—the

American standard of living—was bought by permanent destruction of this one-third of our topsoil. Had our farmers stayed off the slopes where plowing could only result in erosion, had they confined themselves to land-use practices that would not destroy the soil, there would have been far less agricultural land available in the United States. Much of it achieved a temporary, high carrying capacity only by being worn out. The new western Dust Bowl that is being built with the blessing of the U. S. Department of Agriculture is a case in point.

Considered on any sort of long-range basis that a nation must adopt if it is not to decay, millions of the acres whose destruction built our industrial empire had a low carrying capacity. But we were not satisfied by a yield of 1½ per cent. We were getting rich quick! The expanding economy, the necessity for which has become an Article of Economic Faith, has in hard fact been a contracting economy, since it developed at the expense of such irreplaceable capital goods as soils and minerals, and such theoretically renewable resources as water, forests, grasslands, and wildlife. Renewable resources, however, are renewable only if they are managed on a sustained-yield basis, with the crop restricted to replacement capacity. Since 1607 we have been living on our resource capital.

We have used the capital to buy expensive luxuries such as unnecessarily elaborate highway systems, an industrial organization so top-heavy that it requires constant shearing to keep it from tumbling over, and a material standard of living pasted together with pieces of paper money. We have produced a waster's psychology that would have appalled our frugal forebears and that is regarded as lunacy—even criminal lunacy—by people in other parts of the world. The supply of tin ore is limited, and it is conceivable that we might go to war to ensure access to tin sources; yet the reclamation of tin that was part of the war effort has been completely abandoned. West Coast lumbermen throw away timber that is two or three times the size of the saw logs being combed from eastern forests. The alert observer will agree that probably millions of dripping faucets are losing precious water; in the War Department's Munitions Building, wartime signs begged for water conservation, yet most of the washroom faucets leaked. Millions of unneeded electric lights burn, every year, untold thousands of tons of American coal. Our most prodigal wastage is, perhaps, of gasoline. We are an importing nation; and every day we waste hundreds of thousands of gallons. All manner of drivers let their motors run when they are not in use. Our tensions find outlets in racing motors and in traveling at high speeds that reduce the efficiency of our cars. We build into our automobiles more power and greater gas consumption than we need. We use the press and radio to push the sales of more cars. We drive them hundreds of millions of miles a year in pursuit of futility. With the exhaustion of our own oil wells in sight, we send our Navy into the Mediterranean, show our teeth to the U.S.S.R., insist on access to Asiatic oil—and continue to throw it away at home. Much of our resource capital has been used up, but we still have our yacht, our stable of horses—and quite a few breach-of-promise suits.

The Old World industrial structure was jerry built of the same laths. New lands—including Africa and Australia, as well as the Americas—provided the fuel to keep the population fires burning. From these lands came raw materials and food—wheat, corn, tobacco, cotton, wool, timber, oil, minerals, and a host of others.

Europe bought the products, trade balances were struck, the Reverend Thomas Malthus fell more and more into disrepute, and the governments, economists, and millions of people, content with this best of all possible worlds, enrolled under the banner of Dr. Pangloss. They shared, with our own pioneers, the illusion of "limitless" resources. What they did not understand, what most of them still do not understand, is that with their cotton and wool, tobacco and corn, they were also buying the land. They were buying gullies in Georgia, dongas in South Africa, barrancas in El Salvador, floods in Missouri, dust storms in the Tasman Sea.

· 68 ·

And they are still at it! We gloat over our recent wheat crops, as though they were not accidents of favorable weather —and the spark from which we may expect the new Dust Bowl to flare up. We are shipping carloads of grain overseas, at the cost of carloads of topsoil dumped into the Gulf of Mexico. We increase our tax load and/or our national debt to feed excess populations across two oceans, and in the process permanently damage our land, or at least injure it so that decades and many millions of dollars will be required to restore it to high productivity. Latin-American finqueros and lumbermen buy Packards, while peasants in the lowlands frantically run from sick rivers. Australian sheepmen fight for a tariff-free market while the good earth from their overstocked ranges blows a thousand miles across the Pacific.

Had the parasite of European industrial development not been able to sink its proboscis deep into new lands, world history would have been very different. Enormous populations, heavy industry, social and economic pressures could not possibly have developed into the great carbuncle that exploded as World War I. They would have developed local festers, come to a head on a small scale, and burst without ripping apart the entire world organism. Frankenstein's monster would still have been a monster, but a relatively ineffectual creature. But with all the world to draw on—he sucked in a hundred million acres of the best topsoil in the United States alone—he grew so great as to be uncontrollable. The bewildered British politician, the Jews who try to slip past hostile guns that are not of their enemy, the Tarascan woman mourning for her child— all these are, in a direct, historical sense, victims of that overfeeding.

The accidents of history are of unending fascination. If Columbus had arrived off the American coast two months earlier or later, as the late Frank M. Chapman pointed out, he would not have encountered the southward migration of the birds, might not have been able to control his mutinous crew. There might not be a Palestine problem, a United Nations—or perhaps a need for it. Fantastic? Of course, but justifiable fantasy if it helps to build a bridge of comprehension between the newer, now aging, lands and the multiplying, always-emptying stomachs.

THE FALLACY OF INDUSTRIALIZATION

The relationship between wealth and populations, on the one hand, and the land, on the other, is much more clearly seen if we examine some areas in which land hunger is more obvious than in the United States. One of the most tragic instances of a wide disparity between numbers of people and the carrying capacity of the land on which they live is twentieth-century Great Britain. Great Britain was ready to seek world markets decades ahead of her competitors. She early developed industrial skills that made it possible for her to sell at low prices and —one of her greatest assets—a considerable proportion of her manufacturers maintained a respect for quality that made British fabrics, British leather goods, and British machinery synonymous with the apparently unshakable worth of her pound sterling. Except for coal, she was almost without physical resources. Her chief resources were the industry and skill of her people—and the fact that she got there first. Her products were in demand wherever man had purchasing power, and it was easy for her to exchange her manufactured products for food and raw material.

In the latter part of the nineteenth century, however, she began to encounter sharp export competition from Europe, and later from the United States. More disastrous was the development of competing industries in nearly every country. Gandhi, who probably read British industrial history, was shrewd enough to try to break the British textile market in India. Nations all over the world, often with machinery imported from the British Isles, set up their own spinning mills and they established high tariffs to protect their own industries. As she lost the export market, Britain tried to meet the competition by cutting prices; in other words, by lowering the living standard of her workers. British shipowners keep down costs by paying wages to which our seamen would give the horse-laugh, and we have tried to meet the competition through exclusion of British shipping from our coastal waters and by giving shipowners and seamen subsidies that come out of the pocket of the American taxpayer. Cost of operation of American vessels is some 50 per cent higher than the costs of our competitors. And the rest of the world has won out in the struggle against Britain. Her share of manufacturing fell from 32 per cent in 1870 to 9.2 per cent before World War II.[11] And her population has nearly doubled. Even had there been no war, her plight would have been desperate by this time. There is little produced in the British Isles—except Scotch whisky—that is not available as cheaply elsewhere. British manufacturing quality has remained remarkably high but in a world in which mounting taxes first hit the people who can afford quality products, quality does not have the purchasing power it possessed fifty years ago.

Britain now has a population of twenty-five hundred people per square mile of arable land, which means that, despite superb agricultural techniques, she cannot possibly produce enough food at home to support what we consider a decent standard of living. She is perilously close to her condition in 1600. Indeed, because of her enormous population increase, she may well be in an even worse situation. Only now are her leaders beginning to understand her dilemma. In his Westminster College speech, that magnificent anachronism, Winston Churchill, in complete ignorance of the findings of Empire scientists, subscribed to the fatuous American statement: "There is enough for all. The earth is a generous mother; she will provide in plentiful abundance for all her children if they will but cultivate her soil in justice and peace."

The British people, stimulated by the presence of American GIs, have cast longing eyes toward the American standard of living. The Socialist government, counting on "economic" and "political" prestidigitation that hung in the air without any base on the land, promised to lift the United Kingdom by its own bootstraps, without recognizing that the bootstraps had been worn to the breaking point. Unless we are willing to place fifty million British feet beneath our dining-room table we may well see famine once more stalking the streets of London. And hand in hand with famine will walk the shade of that clear-sighted English clergyman, Thomas Robert Malthus.

A comparable situation exists within the island Empire of Japan. Here the population density is three thousand people per square mile of arable land, but the Japanese possess the not inconsiderable psychological advantage of being accustomed to a lower standard of living. They likewise possess, aside from coal, more mineral resources than do the British Isles. Also they have reached an understanding with their land that Western nations may well envy; in much of their area they can produce two crops a year. But with the introduction of modern industrial methods and modern sanitation, the Japanese population tripled in about seventy-five years, and it is clear that the Japanese cannot possibly feed themselves at a decent living standard.

Germany passed through the same cycle. She wanted what she considered a reasonable living standard—especially for her ruling classes. "The peoples of Central Europe were overcrowded. Each country needed room for expansion and desired additional markets and colonies where surplus peoples could be accommodated and food could be raised for the use of the homeland." [12] As in most countries that feel themselves threatened from without and desire to expand, especially dictatorships, she began deliberately to augment her population to provide soldiers, and thus made the situation worse. Two attempts to find a place in the sun were disastrous; but one can scarcely blame France for fearing a third. Germany is still not able to produce enough for a growing population.

Great Britain, Japan, and Germany were three of the most heavily industrialized nations in the world. None of them was able to maintain a high living standard through industrialization *without access to adequate areas of productive land.* Advocates of industrialization as the cure-all for poverty should ponder these cases well. A weakened and relatively peace-loving Britain now finds itself literally on the verge of starvation. Japan and Germany sought the solution advocated by Urban II. Through the rubble of their streets stalks starvation, and no means of providing their people with even two thousand calories a day have yet been suggested. They outbred the carrying capacity of their own land and lost the economic means of drawing on the land of the rest of the world for the food and fibers that are indispensable to modern man.

The fallacy of the theory that industrialization alone can produce high living standards, is clearly shown in Figure 3. This is largely based on studies by the Australian economist, Colin Clark, who has determined real income in terms of international units, or I.U.'s.[13] "An international unit is defined as the amount of goods and services which one dollar could purchase in the U.S.A. over the average of the period 1925-1934." It is highly significant that among the first ten, Canada, New Zealand, Argentina, and Australia were, before the war, countries in which industrialization had made but little progress; they were, however, all countries with small populations in relation to their land and other natural resources. On the other hand, the industrialized and overpopulated nations of Sweden, Germany, Belgium, Czechoslovakia, Japan, and Italy straggle all the way down to the twenty-fifth place. Great Britain, were she not today a pensioner of the United States, would have to drop far down the list. Switzerland, which maintained its rank by a combination of banking, tourists, and a near monopoly on the manufacture of precision instruments, as well as a small population, also has probably lost considerable ground. The Netherlands has maintained its position through the colonies she is now so loath to give up. Eire, where people once starved by the million, has halved her population in the past hundred years. And France, which possesses a peculiarly good balance between rural and urban distribution, is probably the only civilized country in the world today with a decreasing population. These ten countries, either because of the high carrying capacity of their own lands, or of lands to which they had access, *relative to their populations*, were in a favorable position that they would have lost immediately with an excessive increase in population; the carrying capacities served limited numbers well, rather than large numbers badly.

INSANE BIRTH RATES

In respect to the rate of population increases, the first ten countries in terms of living standards rank as follows, in a list of forty: [14]

United States	32nd
Canada	21st
New Zealand	25th
Great Britain	39th
Switzerland	36th
Argentina	17th
Australia	30th
Netherlands	22nd
Eire	27th
France	40th

It is plain that they are maintaining a relatively favorable relationship between carrying capacity and population (emptying stomachs!) by checking the increase of the latter.

The only one of the world's ten most "prosperous" countries with more than the median rate of population increase is Argentina, which is living on its resource capital. The ten with the highest rates of increase are China, India, Formosa, Mexico, Egypt, Puerto Rico, U.S.S.R., Chile, Philippines, and Albania —all overcrowded countries with extremely low standards of living.

During a limited period, when industrialists occupied a monopoly position, or something like it, and when there was an abundance of new land and unexploited resources, industrialization undoubtedly raised potential living standards—though concentration of wealth kept these benefits from the great masses of the people. Great Britain was an example of a near-monopolist on an international scale; the United States, with its vast internal market, an example on the national scale. But those days are as dead as the Emperor Nero. The smaller nations, such as those of Latin America, which are at present trying to raise their living standards by attempts at industrialization, have simply begun too late. Except for one or two, like Argentina and Brazil, their land—their national carrying capacity—is so poor that they do not possess any considerable internal purchasing power. Their land productivity is so low that they cannot export enough raw materials to provide a high standard of living for their growing populations. Absurd attempts at national autonomy unfortunately make the situation worse. The small countries of Central America, for example, are strapped into a stifling corset of restricted national boundaries.

Since industrialization, of itself, is clearly not the road to Freedom from Want, we should look briefly at two areas in which industrialization, for want of power and raw materials, has been impossible. El Salvador approaches China and India in terms of living standard. It is primarily an agricultural country, but it has so brutally maltreated its lands during more than four centuries that it has probably lost well over half its carrying capacity. It has almost no exports aside from coffee, plus small amounts of corn which it occasionally ships abroad despite hunger at home; and were the entire coffee crop to be socialized, as has been suggested by some of El Salvador's left-wing politicians, each inhabitant would receive one bag, worth approximately $15, a year. This little country is particularly significant to North Americans since it wears the shape of things to come in Latin America. The Salvadorians are hard-working, intelligent people of great integrity. Their workers seem to win universal respect in whatever country to which they emigrate. But they have outbred the capacity of their cultivable land to support them. They have left only about an acre each, and a considerable portion of these acres is of poor quality. As a result, thousands of them are dying of malnutrition—which is a polite way of saying starvation—and their *average* calorie intake is only about fifteen hundred a day. This means, of course, that many of them eat less than that.

OUR CHERISHED SLUM

Another area near at home, and one for whose miserable lot the people of the United States are largely responsible, is Puerto Rico. Here the population has doubled during the years since it became an American colony. For each inhabitant there remains *less than one-half acre of arable land*; [15] and much of the land remaining—Puerto Rico is badly eroded—belongs to continental sugar corporations which export its products for their own profit. If the present high rate of population increase continues, Puerto Rico will double its population in twenty-five years—and its people will possess less than a quarter of an acre of arable land! During its trusteeship (ironic word!) the United States has given Puerto Rico about one billion dollars in benefits of one kind or another.[16] Despite this drain on the American taxpayer—a drain, it must never be forgotten, that represents the loss of working hours and such benefits as a better educational system, more money for health, service and recreation, etc.—in 1941-42 the average family earning in Puerto Rico was $350! This income was swollen by war expenditures. "In 1937 the per capita income for Puerto Rico was only one-seventh as high as that of the United States, and only about one-third as high as that of Alabama, our poorest state." [17] Aside from the soil, Puerto Rico is poor in resources and almost without power—except the power to reproduce recklessly and irresponsibly.

Much of the increase of population in this island slum (and similar conditions may be found in some of our other dependencies) is the result of the U. S. government measures. We have deliberately taken many steps, such as improving sanitation, nutrition, and medical care, that have increased the population—and we have done virtually nothing to balance these measures. Latterly a birth-control law has been passed (welcomed by many Puerto Ricans) to help lower the birth rate but, according to Dr. Senior, "the application of the law has largely been entrusted to its enemies and it has been deliberately sabotaged."

The sum total of our activities in Puerto Rico has resulted in an appalling increase of misery for more people every year. The morals of such maltreatment seem not to be considered by those who would turn this ecological problem into a moral issue.

Industrialization would help Puerto Rico, for a time, at the expense of continental workers with a higher living standard but, unless the senseless proliferation can be checked, no substantial improvement can be expected. Puerto Rico is driving straight down the Chinese and Indian road, at a speed that is Asiatic.

So are El Salvador, and Haiti, and a host of other countries that, lacking the tariff-free outlets of Puerto Rico, cannot hope to find a reprieve through industrialization. Tariff barriers are not likely to be abolished. Nor does there seem to be any good reason why they should be. The overpopulated, low-standard countries would come into a free world market with coolie-produced goods, as Japan tried to do. Gresham's law applies to labor as it does to money: cheap labor tends to thrive at the expense of, and drive out, higher-priced labor. Why the United States, for example, should subsidize the unchecked spawning of India, China, and other countries by purchasing their goods is difficult to see. Until they adopt a rational population policy, these nations, it seems to me, have no right to expect aid from the rest of the world.

The same might be said of the highly industrialized nations of Europe. Their manufacturing, which made it possible through a hundred years or more to draw on the lands of other countries, was simply a stopgap, a means of postponing the day of reckoning. When probably every country in the world is trying to foster a protected textile industry, how can the nations with older industrial establishments, like Great Britain, expect to find a market through which they can exchange goods for food and raw materials? Industrialization, making it possible during a hundred years for the most powerful sector of the human race to live as though it were independent of the earth, kept alive the great illusion. The illusion is now vanishing, like a mirage in the desert air.

Heavy industries, and those producing durable consumer goods, can no longer be set up in small countries with limited internal purchasing power. We have reached a point of industrial saturation, as is evidenced by Great Britain and even by the United States, which is having nightmares at the thought of its agricultural and industrial surpluses. Purchasing power goes back, fundamentally, to natural resources—especially the land—and no amount of symbolical juggling of "capital" can help us to escape that hard fact. There are too many people in the world for its limited resources to provide a high standard of living. By use of the machine, by exploitation of the world's resources on a purely extractive basis, we have postponed the meeting at the ecological judgment seat. The handwriting on the wall of five continents now tells us that the Day of Judgment is at hand.

Not Bread, but Stones

Agricultural land, now amounting to little more than an acre per person and shrinking fast, as populations rise and the land is destroyed, is every year producing less food. The American surpluses are far from typical of the rest of the world; and unless we are willing to open our gates to a flood of competing manufactures, there is only one way for us to dispose of those surpluses—give them away. (Our agricultural surpluses, of course, are to a large extent illusory since they are achieved at the cost of wearing out and washing away the land itself—depleting our capital.) Except in a few, small Old World areas, forests are not being used on a sustained-yield basis; they are being inexorably wiped out. Grasslands are nearly everywhere being overgrazed; our own ranges have been critically hurt, and the "Cow Bloc," as a *Collier's* author called it, is doing everything in its power to give them the coup de grâce— to get rich quick. Water tables are falling, and more rivers are getting out of hand. Like a kitten playing with a ball of wool, we are yearly finding ourselves in a more difficult tangle.

There is, in all the world, not enough available untilled land to fill the net increase of 50,000 stomachs every day. And if we take care of our ecological DPs, additional space must be found for scores of millions now living. Outside the tropics, only the Soviet Union possesses sizable forest reserves, and Russia's forests are largely inaccessible; tropical forests can still not be exploited economically on a large scale. There are no untapped grasslands; we had better enjoy our steaks now, since there will be many less of them within the lifetime of most Americans.

As we look ahead toward a falling carrying capacity over most of the earth and toward a sharp increase in world populations, we must also look for a marked decrease in our material standard of living. In fact, though few people seem to realize it, the lower standard of living is here—and it is certain to go lower. Inflation in terms of real income is one symptom. The high cost of policing parts of overpopulated Europe and Asia is another. The vast loans with which we are trying to prop world economies, and which few people doubt are gifts— at the same time forfending our own depression—are another. Our out-and-out charity, as through UNRRA, is another. The need of feeding, clothing, and sheltering indigent millions from our own shrinking land resources is still another.

We are not likely, short of an open war, to approach the unhappy plight of the British, since our population is leveling off. But increasing expenses and mounting taxes are hitting most Americans. Hospitals are restricting their facilities. Our schools are being starved and the quality of our national education is dropping rapidly. Some of our essential governmental services are being wrecked in the name of economy. Eleemosynary institutions, such as museums, libraries, and colleges, are poorer every year. The purchasing power of the middle classes, especially the professional groups, is being more and more restricted to the necessities of life. The trend has been somewhat masked by the backlog of war savings, but these are shrinking fast. The impact of this shrinkage in purchasing power on our entire economy is certain to be a jarring one, to put it mildly; what its results may be, no one can foresee without an economic crystal ball.

Despite its unpalatability, a fall in living standards is unavoidable. To crawl into our still relatively downy couch and pull the covers over our head would ensure disaster. To ignore the breakers ahead would be equally disastrous, though not so quick. Never, in modern times, has there been a greater need for clear thinking removed as far as possible from emotionalism and traditionalism. Never has there been a greater need for high-minded leadership divorced from partisan self-seeking. Fortunately, we are armed with such knowledge as man has never before possessed; if we are intelligent and courageous enough to use that knowledge we may yet escape the crash of our civilization.

But we shall not do it by "political" and "economic" means alone. We must look at the whole man, and at his whole environment. Above all, we must realize that every grain of rice he puts into his mouth, every bit of potato, every piece of meat, and every kernel of corn, must be replaced by another bit from the earth—somewhere. We must realize that not only does every area have a limited carrying capacity—but also that this carrying capacity is shrinking and the demand growing. Until this understanding becomes an intrinsic part of our thinking and wields a powerful influence on our formation of national and international policies we are scarcely likely to see in what direction our destiny lies.

Chapter 5

That the Use Be Fitting

Probably no single factor has a more decisive influence on human beings than their relationship to the water that falls from the clouds. It has always bulked large in the consciousness of rural man, although usually he has not taken an intelligent attitude toward it. He has set up rain-gods and prayed for relief from drought and floods for which he himself has often been responsible. The countryman's limited comprehension has wasted millions of acres of land, caused sharp drops in crop yields, raised the crests of floods, starved cattle, spread deserts over the face of the earth, and launched ancient wars.

Urban man's unawareness of his relationship to rainfall has become a dangerous influence in our civilization. His lack of comprehension has shaped erroneous economic concepts, such as the belief that the European and American economic system is applicable to the rest of the world. It has confused his ideas on colonization and immigration, blinded him to the meaning of size and distribution of cities and industries. Failure to understand the limitations imposed by patterns of rainfall and its use has distorted his thinking about populations, and therefore about politics. It has even invaded the field of morals. In all these misunderstandings may well be germinating, at best, the hidden seed of future wars; and at worst the collapse of our civilization.

Man cannot live without water. Sixty per cent of his body is composed of water, which must be constantly renewed. His food consists largely of water; for example, three hundred tons of rainfall are required to grow one ton of corn. This is obvious, but what is not so obvious is the place of water in the total environment that determines man's survival and affects the development of his behavior and his cultures. Even less clear to most human beings is the way in which man's habits influence the supplies of water available to him, in relation to storage in the accumulated trash of the forest floor, the soil, wells, springs, marshes, and lakes. Indeed, many aspects of these relationships are still obscure even to scientific students of the subject.

All the water available to man is derived from the condensed vapor of the atmosphere. Some of it, like the moisture that forms on a cold glass of beer, is directly condensed at the surface of the earth by rapid cooling, as dew. Most of it condenses in the upper atmosphere, where it is visible in the form of clouds.

This condensation results, of course, from a decrease in temperature caused by rising, contracting air. At times the upward movement results from major shifts of large air masses. A cold air mass will wedge itself beneath a warmer air mass, and drive the latter upward. A warm air mass, flowing landward from an ocean, may overrun cold air and precipitate its moisture. Or convection currents, formed by the heat of the earth's surface, will mount rapidly, giving us the violent thunderstorms we know in the summer, and which are characteristic year-around in the tropics.

Every rise of three hundred feet causes a reduction in temperature of approximately one degree Centigrade. The colder the air is, the less moisture it is able to hold. Where mountains stand in the path of moving air masses, they will force winds to rise, cool, and lose their moisture. The movements of such air masses, with their far-reaching effects on human beings, were the theme of George Stewart's fascinating novel *Storm*, which may be recommended as a palatable introduction to an understanding of meteorology.

THE RAIN-GODS RULE

Most of the water dropped on the land is derived from the oceans by evaporation. This moisture dominates the hydrologic cycle, which is the circular movement of water from the atmosphere to the land and, through a large variety of processes, back to the atmosphere. Areas near the ocean and in the path of inflowing winds, as in Western Europe, the Northwest of the United States, and the monsoon region of India, receive an abundance of rain. Interior Asia, lying in the zone of eastward-trending storms but many hundreds of miles from the Atlantic, is for the most part crossed by winds that have long since yielded their humidity; this turns Central Asia into a desert. The Himalayas, spreading east and west, act as a dike against the monsoon winds. Our own coastal ranges and Rocky Mountains, running north and south, function in the same way and create in their lee what the geographers call a rain shadow. This is an area of low precipitation that sets the stage for the problem-dramas of the central Missouri Valley and our High Plains Dust Bowl.

Plants transpire, through tiny pores in their leaves, large amounts of moisture drawn from the ground. Climatologists are not yet in agreement as to the effect of this transpiration on rainfall. In areas flooded by air masses from the oceans it is probably insignificant. Where oceanic rainfall is limited, however, it seems likely that vegetation contributes materially to the hydrologic cycle. Where millions of acres of trees, as in the Amazon Basin, transpire hundreds of millions of tons of water a day to the atmosphere, from which it is reprecipitated, the climate must remain wetter than where most of the rain falls on dry earth and rushes into the sea. In the absence of protective vegetation, heat absorption by the bare earth is intensified, with the result that convection currents are more violent and rainfall more highly concentrated.

Rainfall varies enormously from place to place. In some parts of India it may total forty feet a year. On the coast of

Peru, in the rain shadow of the Andes, precipitation is measured in two-hundred-fiftieth's of an inch; more than one man, tramping through coastal valleys sheltered from the wind, has come upon his footprints made twenty or twenty-five years before. On the south side of the Paracas Bay, 125 miles south of Lima, pre-Conquest Indians dug in the earth a mysterious design that is variously known as the "Candelabra" or the "Three Crosses." In the four hundred years since the arrival of Pizarro so little rain has fallen that the trench is seemingly unchanged. In the "roaring forties" of southern Chile, where winds and heavy rain come from the west, the rain shadow is on the other side of the Andes, and Patagonia is semiarid.

As rainfall varies in space, it also varies widely in time. Fortunate areas, such as the British Isles, receive their precipitation well distributed over the year, with some one hundred fifty rainy days. This distribution, coupled with the fact that only about twenty-five inches fall, explains in part why Western Europe has been little bothered by soil erosion. In contrast with this rainfall pattern is that of large areas of the tropics, comprising about 13 per cent of the world's land areas,[1] where hot, dry seasons with an extremely high rate of evaporation alternate with concentrated precipitation rising to that reported from India. Besides the annual variation, there are complicated, longer-range variations that have profoundly influenced history; these probably set in movement the barbarian attacks both on old Chinese regimes and on European empires. Cycles of shorter duration first attracted farmers to our western Great Plains—and then starved them out.

LIFE UBIQUITOUS

Nature has responded to these dissimilar rainfall patterns with almost limitless variety and vitality. All habitable niches have been occupied by plants and by animals dependent upon them. Where rain is abundant, forests have slowly evolved and become dominant. Where there has not been enough precipitation to build trees, vegetation has reached its climax in grasslands. In areas of still lower precipitation, as on the coast of northern Chile, vegetation may be completely absent; or in the Gobi or our own Southwest, drought-resistant plants, whose density is proportionate to the water available, have somehow contrived to invade and survive.

As plants depend on soil to anchor them, to feed water to their roots, and to provide them with mineral foods, so does the soil depend on plants and on associated animals. Some of the basic materials of soils are raw minerals. The carbon dioxide of the air, combined with water, etches away the surface of rocks. Rain erodes them, and the wind sweeps along tiny bits of sand that cut at their surface. Water seeps into cracks in the rocks, freezes, and breaks them. Primitive plants such as lichens feed on their surfaces and help to eat them away. Seeds of trees falling into cracks, sprout, grow, and despite their being made of soft materials, often split rocks apart. Those who write of "the unchanging earth" or of the "timeless mountains" are not geologists; the earth is constantly changing, mountains are constantly being worn down, and from this parent material, soil begins to form.

This, however, is only the beginning. A much more accurate phrase than "the unchanging earth" is "the living earth," for soil is truly alive. Primitive plants help to disintegrate it, and with their own rotting bodies fertilize it. As it becomes thicker and richer, the higher plants are able to take over. They continue the transmutation of the inorganic material—including carbon dioxide from the air—into rich organic matter. With the plants in every cubic foot of soil are associated millions of bacteria, microscopic animals, worms, crustaceans, etc. At rates that vary with temperature, rainfall, slope, and the parent material, a humus-rich layer of topsoil—the A-horizon—is built up.

There is a large number of soil types, each of which has developed in response to specific environmental influences, and which must be cultivated in a highly specialized manner to be of maximum use to man. On cool forest areas, leached of soluble matter by water that falls from the skies, acid soils form and are given the general name of *podsols;* laterite soils are built by forests of the humid tropics. In the grasslands that have slowly developed under a lower rate of precipitation, basic minerals are not leached out, and the earth has the granular structure that is in the opinion of specialists the indicator of the finest type of soil. Typical grassland soils are called *chernozems.* "Podsol" and "chernozem" are, of course, from the Russian, pioneer work on soils having been done by Russian scientists. Another widely distributed soil is *loess*, an extremely fine, powdery soil deposited by the wind. It is highly vulnerable to wind erosion and some of the most extreme examples of this type of destruction can be seen on the great loess beds of northwestern China.

The combination and occurrence of these soil materials, living as well as dead, depend on their geographic distribution, slope, fauna, flora, climate, etc.

THE LIVING WEB

As the varied soils depend on many interacting factors, so does the form that the life upon them takes. The interrelationships of these factors are dynamic, not static. A system of stresses and strains is set up, and an ecological equilibrium is reached over long periods of time. In any area, plants and animals themselves influence the total environment and thus the equilibrium. Large numbers of ruminants, such as the American bison or the big game herds of Africa, may function in holding back the forest in the transition zone between areas of high and lower humidity.

One of the most interesting examples of these relationships is reported from Scotland.[2] About 1892 a few black-headed gulls began to nest on a typical grouse moor and within fifteen years increased to some fifteen hundred pairs. Their droppings and trampling changed the environment of the heather until it was replaced by rushes and sorrel. Pools of water formed in the puddled vegetation, European teal joined the colony—and there were no more grouse. For this reason, protection of the moor was stopped, the gulls began to decrease, and twenty-five years after formation of the colony, only about thirty of the birds remained. Heather and associated plants again invaded the area, which once more became a good grouse habitat.

Within any environment genetic changes in plants and animals are constantly taking place. Variations well adapted to the total environment survive; those not well adapted, perish. The stable vegetation that results is known as a climax. The grassland climax of the central United States evolved twenty or thirty million years ago when the uplift of the Rocky Mountains changed the climate of the region.[3]

In the Northern Hemisphere, other climaxes are the tundra, forest, woodland, and scrub. These have existed during millions of years and may be expected to persist until a major climatic change takes place. Man may disturb them by burning, cutting, lowering the water table, etc., but once these influences are suspended, as through the establishment of protected areas or the disappearance of human populations, climaxes redevelop. Large-scale bacterial warfare would be an effective, if drastic, means of bringing back the earth's forests and grasslands.

The time required for return of the climax will depend on the severity and extent of disturbance, in relation to local conditions. The development of the climax will pass through a number of rather orderly transitions or successions. For example, logging and burning may be followed by an invasion of fireweed, blackberry and bracken, which will come to be dominated by birch, poplar and aspen, which will, in turn, give way to climax or subclimax trees. The valuable Douglas fir represents the subclimax, and may be maintained by fire or logging; undisturbed, it will eventually be succeeded by cedar and hemlock.

Within the climaxes occur associations of plants named for their dominant species, such as the pine-hemlock, beech-maple, and oak-hickory forests. Successions may be seen, even in undisturbed climaxes, where varying topography alters local conditions. The succession in dry land may begin with soil-building lichens on large rocks. In the transition from water to dry land the changes will be more obvious—from submerged waterweeds, such as coontail, through floating forms (water lilies), to cattails and bulrushes of the water's edge; sedges, rushes, grasses, mints, etc., of the land's edge; water-loving trees such as willows; and finally the climax forest. Since ponds tend to fill with eroded soil and rotting vegetation, they progressively become drier and prepare the way for the plant associations nearer to the climax. Just as human beings pass from infancy through adolescence to maturity, so does the landscape.

The tendency for disturbed vegetation to return to the climax condition is so strong that it will often defeat the efforts of man to substitute different plants. An example of considerable economic importance may be seen in southern Chile, where the blackberry is an introduced and undesirable alien, has got out of hand, and tends to overrun pastures and cultivated land. For decades the Chileans have tried to control it by burning, not knowing that in its northern home the blackberry may normally be expected to occur after a forest fire. Burning creates favorable conditions for it. This is merely one of thousands of examples that could be given of the value of understanding plant ecology.

In the tropics, pure stands or nearly pure stands of trees, such as are characteristic of temperate climates, are uncommon. In the Amazon forests, for example, several hundred species of trees may be found in a single square mile. The reason for this seems not to be known.

EARTH'S GOLDEN MEAN

As in a democratic society, the climax survives through a system of checks and balances. If the number of any native species tends to increase disproportionately, some force will arise to control it. This may be disease, starvation, competition for light, an increase in the number of species that prey on it, etc.

Where man introduces a new species into an environment without its normal checks, it often flourishes excessively. The starling in the United States is a too-familiar example. It has taken over the nesting places of our native birds, and in roving flocks has wiped out, in a few hours, what otherwise would be adequate winter food resources for native bird populations. The starling, when introduced into New Zealand, not only developed into a plague of itself, but became a most effective agent in spreading the blackberry, one of the worst pests to which that abused island has been subjected. The skylark, so eloquently hymned by Shelley, became a nuisance of the first magnitude when introduced into New Zealand. Another example is the prickly pear that thrived so well after it had been introduced into Australia that at one time it was reported to be spreading at the rate of three acres an hour. The rabbit that game commissions spend thousands of dollars to propagate in the United States is a major plague in Australia because there is no effective check on its rate of reproduction; there it is without its normal predators. New Zealand actually pays a bounty on introduced deer, and has thus disposed of hundreds of thousands.

A comparable problem is found in the United States, where the increase in second-growth forests following the destruction of the climax and abandonment of farm land has, in combination with the extermination of such predators as the mountain lion, built up such excessive populations of deer in many states that they are destroying the range upon which they depend for survival. It is reported that Wisconsin's excellent laws, designed to restore her forest wealth, are being nullified by too many deer; their numbers are maintained by a sentimental objection to killing does—and by the desire of tourist interests to maintain large amounts of meat-on-the-hoof, for well-heeled visitors. In the Kaibab forest on the north rim of the Grand Canyon, thoroughgoing government predator control was followed by an increase in the mule deer population from four thousand to one hundred thousand in *fourteen years*. Consumption of all browse within reach was followed, in two years, by a 60 per cent reduction in the herd through starvation. In 1943, when I visited the area with Dr. H. L. Shantz, the range had not completely recovered, and its carrying capacity is probably still below what it was in 1910. This is, perhaps, the most violent outbreak and adjustment known, but it has been repeated less dramatically in many parts of the country.[4] It is a phenomenon the human animal should ponder well.

These, however, are abnormal cases, and under natural conditions numbers do not get out of hand—for long. The maximum productive capacity of the land in equilibrium is reached, for the conditions in any given locality, and this is used in one form or another. Limiting factors operate to hold numbers in check. In nature, death is as important as birth. This is a fact man tends to forget as he develops the transitory illusion of independence of nature.

The Society of Plants

Below the level of the climax is a series of subclimaxes. Under primitive conditions the way may have been prepared for these by such natural catastrophes as the ice ages, tidal waves, volcanic eruptions, fires caused by lightning, or land slips resulting from earthquakes. One of the most dramatic opportunities ever given man to study the succession of subclimaxes occurred when the volcano Krakatoa erupted in 1883 and wiped out all life on the island. Within three years algae had begun to prepare the soil for the growth of higher plants. Six years after the eruption a lizard had become established, and was feeding on a considerable variety of insects. Less than forty years after the catastrophe, the island had been repopulated with nearly six hundred kinds of animals.[5] A similar phenomenon may be seen on scores of lava flows through the volcano belt of the Americas.

Animals are not so limited in distribution as plants, because of their mobility and the fact that most of them are able to survive through eating a variety of foods. Many insects, however, are found on only one species of plant. The Kirtland's warbler, nesting only in the lower peninsula of Michigan, is a curious and interesting example of what might be called a subclimactic species. It is found only in a certain stage of jack pine forests that are recovering from fire. Were all forest fires excluded from Michigan, it is possible that the bird would disappear.

Within the various plant associations animals maintain food chains. These, of course, must begin with vegetation since animals (aside from a few microscopic forms) are not able to synthesize their own food; many of the chains are familiar. A chickadee, for example, will eat plant lice, be eaten in turn by a screech owl, and the screech owl may fall prey to a great horned owl. The antelope eats grass, and is preyed upon by the coyote. A complex food chain of the sea off Peru is partially shown in Figure No. 6.

The food chain concept has led to another that has been important in ecological thinking—the idea of the pyramid of numbers. Every animal feeding on another species that is lower in the food chain must select a species that is much more numerous, and usually one that is smaller. Enormous numbers of field mice must exist to feed the much smaller population of hawks and owls. Large populations of deer are necessary to support the small population of mountain lions. A tremendous store of plants is necessary to sustain the herbivores.

In keeping animal numbers in check four factors are important. The first of these is predation, which may be intraspecific as well as one species preying on another. The common lizard, Tropidurus, on the Peruvian islands, actually eats its own young. This is probably one of the oldest forms of infanticide. A second factor is parasitism, which is in a sense predation in another form, and with the pyramid of numbers reversed.

A third is competition. When numbers of animals become excessive they tend to destroy their food supplies and compete sharply for breeding areas and shelter. This results either in a direct mortality or in a reduced breeding rate. An example of this is the enormous numbers of guano birds on the coast of Peru. Their population varies in cycles of about seven years; as their number approaches the peak there is literally not enough suitable space on the islands for them. Competition breaks up nests, and hundreds of thousands of eggs are abandoned.

Finally, numbers are limited by what might be called the psychological factor. The instinctive pattern of the lower animals—though in this they show a far higher type of survival behavior than does man—has given many species a sense of space ownership that prevents overcrowding. Most male songbirds will, when they reach the breeding grounds in spring, immediately take over a territory, which they advertise by singing and display, and defend by fighting. The power of this psychological drive was dramatically shown in studies of two song sparrows with adjacent territories. When bird *A* wandered into the territory of bird *B*, he was invariably driven off, and vice versa. When, however, he was trapped, caged, and placed in the territory of *B*, unable to escape, he apparently died of fright when the territory's owner threatened him. Some years ago I experimented with mounted birds in defended territories; stuffed willets and yellowthroats were literally torn to pieces by their living "rivals."

Within the plant and animal associations, numbers are further kept in check by a great many limiting factors. They have been discussed to some extent in relation to man and it will be sufficient to mention here a couple to show their control of plants and lower animals. The copihue, Chile's national flower, drapes its exquisite blossoms in the southern rain forests, from south central Chile to the Strait of Magellan. The soils on which it lives are acid and strongly leached by the heavy precipitation. It was probably no surprise to Dr. D. S. Bullock of Angol, who possesses the finest collection of copihues in existence, to discover that they will not tolerate a trace of lime in the soil. A reverse condition has been found in attempts to plant crayfish artificially in certain rivers; these were a complete failure because the water contained insufficient calcium for the crustaceans to develop a "shell." The tiny elf owl of our West depends on the presence not only of a large cactus in which it nests but upon two kinds of woodpeckers that excavate nest-holes for it! Where these woodpeckers do not exist, the owl cannot survive.

THE IMPORTANCE OF DYING

The productivity of the land—the biotic potential in relation to the multitude of environmental resistances throughout the entire plant and animal kingdoms—results in widely varying carrying capacities. These are different not only for every region—and a region may be, in this context, as small as a square foot—but for every species.

Primitive man's ability to survive was little different from that of the lower animals. He adapted himself in various ways. In most of North America he pursued a hunting culture that altered the environment but little, except where he used fire to drive game and perhaps to improve conditions for hunting it. Ohio's Indian population probably did not exceed one person for each four square miles.[6] In Malayan Semang, each wandering band requires fifteen or twenty square miles of forest; "the territory of a group of Australian aborigines may include 8,000 or 10,000 square miles of arid country." [7] In some parts of the world, notably the tropics, ancient man resorted to shifting agriculture that profoundly changed the environment. However, the area of forest he would cut down and burn at one time was limited. From the point of view of racial survival, he possessed the inestimable advantage of a high death rate that kept down his population. This permitted long periods of land-fallowing that extended up to thirty or forty years. Except in a very few areas where primitive man achieved a high degree of socialization, the plant cover on the land was little disturbed.

As a result, the relationship of water to the land was stabilized under primitive conditions. The soil produced the maximum amount of cover permitted by its own structure, chemical composition, etc., and by the climate. Steep slopes, such as those formed by volcanoes, were worn down by slow degrees through geological erosion. The rate of this erosion was much slower on the older, less precipitous slopes, like those found in the North American Laurentians. Vegetation built soil, and its formation more than compensated for geological erosion, unless slopes exceeded the angle of repose.

Every substance has its own angle. A fine face powder will have a steeper angle of repose than granulated sugar, which will, in turn, have a steeper angle than a handful of marbles. On the land this angle is greatly influenced by the tangle of roots binding the soil, and by biotic influences such as burrowing animals.

Before man became "civilized," his environment maintained itself in relatively stable equilibrium over extremely long periods. In the stabilized landscape the ecologist and geographer see a beautiful harmony that has much in common with the symphonies. There are dominant and repeated themes, movements that pass naturally from one to another, brilliant or subtle contrasts of phrase and tone. The Peruvian Andes, high above the timberline, where the vast and ancient movement of the earth's crust lies recorded before the eyes of any observer who will stop to look, are so majestic, so awe-inspiring, that it has long seemed to me they could be described only in terms

of Beethoven's Ninth Symphony. Even the awful words of
Paradise Lost are puny symbols to apply to a might that is so
incomprehensible.

The relationships, balancing one another and growing so
naturally out of one another, give every landscape its own character and write their history upon it. The understanding of such
content in the landscape is one of the satisfactions of the ecologist, amateur or professional. Whereas many people will look at
or travel through a countryside with as little understanding as
have the oxen in the fields, the student of environment finds
meaning and stimulation for his mind wherever he looks. He
appreciates the richness and perfection, as does an artist that of
a painting; he resents the destruction of an element of the landscape—the ivory-billed woodpecker, or the Sitka spruce—as a
Frenchman would resent a slashed Mona Lisa.

THE REWARDS OF UNDERSTANDING

The sheer intellectual and emotional satisfaction to be had
from understanding—really seeing—the countryside is a privi-
lege within reach of anyone. By failing to show us the way
to it, our schools deprive us not only of a great and lifelong
gratification but of the comprehension that should guide all
our relations to our environment. The fortunate people who
have been afield with such a teacher as Homer L. Shantz, Aldo
Leopold, or Isaiah Bowman not only are going to find excitement and satisfaction in living; they are going to be much more
useful citizens in a world that desperately needs them. Unless
we rapidly adjust our demands and uses to the complex of land
limitations and potentialities, the human race is going to suffer
such travail as it has never known.

Man is the only organism known that lives by destroying the
environment indispensable to his survival. Parasites tend to do
this, but their destructive effectiveness is limited by the absence
of intelligence. Man uses his brain to tear down. It is only rarely,
geographically or historically, that he has learned to stabilize

or to rebuild; and the more "advanced" he is, the more destructive he is likely to become.

THE BROKEN CYCLE

The most damaging impact of civilized man on his environment is the shattering of the hydrologic cycle. It is possible that this reduces the amount of water that falls. It is certain that, to a critical extent, it reduces the amount of water available to man.

The first step in breaking the hydrologic cycle is destruction of the plant cover. This may be done with the ax, with fire, with grazing animals, with the plow, etc. With the trees or grasses gone, the mulch or mass of vegetative accumulation at the surface of the soil begins to disappear. This may result from excessive oxidation, from high temperatures, and from exposure to the sun in the tropics. It may come through the unbroken force of desiccating winds. It may come through unchecked fires, once the mulch has been thoroughly dried. Most often the mulch is washed away by concentrated rainfall.

The next step is the washing or blowing of the complex topsoil. Where water is the agency, this loss will, of course, be most rapid on the steepest slopes. Erosion may be all but imperceptible as great sheets of the soil are washed away. Sheet erosion usually precedes rill erosion, which deepens into dramatic and easily visible gullies.

An important factor in erosion, a factor considered by some students the most important, is change in soil structure. The ideal soil, such as is found on prairies, is granular. This permits maximum aeration, easy passage of roots, ideal conditions for the soil fauna, and optimum infiltration of rain water. When the granules are broken down, as through improper methods of cultivation and destruction of organic matter, the soil packs and becomes denser, losing its granular qualities. When the interstices in the soil grow smaller, hard rains rapidly fill them with water and solid matter. Infiltration of rain water into the soil is reduced, and the rain that falls begins to move down the surface of the slopes, carrying fine particles with it. Subsoils, which lack humus, plants, and animals, are more nearly impervious to water, and the choking of their pores takes place rapidly. It is for this reason, in part, that control becomes more difficult as erosion becomes more advanced. The erosion-control technician has a much more difficult medium upon which to work his art.

One of the most powerful forces influencing infiltration, runoff, and therefore, soil erosion is the substitution of agricultural crops for natural plants. Row crops, such as soybeans, uncontoured cotton, corn—including hybrid corn!— and tobacco will lose 100 or more times as much soil as will woodlands, forests, and undisturbed prairies; and such small grains as wheat, oats, barley, and rye will lose 16 to 40 times as much. The relationship between erosion and cropping practices is shown by Table 1.[8]

TABLE I

Relative Amount of Erosion under Different Vegetal Covers;
Values Selected to Apply to the Pacific Northwest

Crop or Cropping Practices	*Relative Erosion*
Forest duff	.001–1.0
Pastures, humid region or irrigated, excellent	.001–1.0
Range or seeded pasture	1–5
Range or seeded pasture (poor)	5–10
Orchards (*a*) perennial cover, (*b*) contoured, with winter cover crops	5
Legumes—grass hayland	5
Crested wheat properly managed	5
Alfalfa	10
Small grain (standing or stubble)	10
Wheat fallow (stubble mulch)	10
Orchards—vineyards (clean tilled, irrigated and contoured, not terraced)	15
Orchards—vineyards (non-irrigated; with cover crops)	20

Crop or Cropping Practices	Relative Erosion
Wheat—peas (stubble not burned)	20
Small grain (adverse rain at or after seeding)	40
Wheat fallow (stubble not burned)	60
Wheat fallow (stubble burned)	75
Orchards—vineyards (non-irrigated, clean tilled, no cover crop)	90
Row crops and fallow	100

In reading this table one should constantly bear in mind that along with erosion goes a diminishing capacity to absorb water.

It is because corn increases soil erosion at least a hundred times that I believe it has probably contributed more to the world's misery than that other great gift of the Americas, syphilis. Corn has now ringed the earth, and wherever it has gone it has torn down the land even as it has built human hunger by building populations. From Capetown to Korea, especially on the hillsides of backward and unfortunate peoples, it has channeled the water of the rains in their swift march to the sea. Syphilis is visited upon the children unto the third and fourth generation; corn erosion, unto the tenth—and even to all time.

As the capacity of the soil to receive rain water diminishes, the normal ground water that supplies nourishment to plant roots shrinks rapidly. There is less infiltration of rain to underground levels, from which it may reappear in springs and artesian wells. Water tables are not replenished over great areas where the soil has been badly eroded or its structure changed; cornfields in one part of a state may rob wells fifty miles away. Since the water cannot get into the ground, it must run off the surface. It carries soil with it. This soil or silt flows into lakes, reservoirs, and rivers.

VANISHING WATERS

When water cannot find its way downward through the soil to be stored for future use, it must take the way of least resistance—over the surface. When the forest floor is covered with a thick duff underlaid by a thick A-horizon, these function as sponges. The water they hold is released in part by a slow gravity movement downward, in part through the roots of plants and in part by evaporation. Ground cover of this sort is of the highest value in flood control; indeed, so much water may be held back that this type of cover will reduce the effectiveness of reservoirs. In some areas, recent studies have shown that these reservoirs are best protected by grass-covered hills, which will deliver rain water without loss of soil. Here again we encounter the uniqueness of each piece of landscape; if rainfall is copious throughout the year, and the storage capacity of the reservoir is unlikely to be strained, forest cover may be preferable. When, however, the reservoir is large enough to store all needed water—and the difference in water loss between forest and grass may be critical—the grass cover may be preferred.

As soon as the bare ground becomes waterlogged, the rain flows down gullies, brooks, and rivers. When a large unprotected watershed is combined with light rain or a small watershed with extremely heavy rain, so much water piles up in rivers that they cannot contain it and the people downstream climb onto their roofs—or drown. When heavy rains fall over a large, unprotected watershed, the downstream effects may be catastrophic. Such a situation may be seen frequently in the Yellow River Valley of China, and less commonly in our own Missouri-Mississippi Basin.

Erosion tends to increase at a geometric rate; it has often been called the cancer of the land. When it is treated early, control is usually fairly simple, but when sheet erosion has been allowed to degenerate into gully erosion, heroic and costly measures may be required to stop it. An even more violent form of erosion, called gravity erosion, may be seen in many parts of the American tropics. Here, on geologically young land, forests build soil and hold it in place. When, however, a farmer clears an area in which to plant corn, the change in the angle of repose will at times cause steep mountainsides to lose all their soil in earthy avalanches. This soil is gone for good.

The erosion that we see is, as Dr. Shantz points out, merely one stage in a process that began much earlier. In discussing our western range lands, he says:

"The term 'soil erosion' has captured the imagination of the American people. If accelerated erosion, that produced by over-use or abuse, is evident, something must be done. But erosion is years behind the cause. The cause should be treated, and the effect forestalled. The detection of its cause, long before erosion actually begins, is the duty of those who manage wild land, and is imperative if land is to be properly maintained.

"Plants, by their presence or absence, and by their conditions and the density or sparseness of the whole vegetation cover, indicate the beginning of causal conditions which will lead inevitably, with months or years of continued abuse, to the final soil destruction stage which we recognize as erosion. Therefore, in the management of wild land the ecology and vegetation development must be so well understood that the diagnosis will detect the predisposing causes long before the disease arrives in that virile form which we recognize as induced erosion. . . .

"Induced erosion is years behind its cause and scores of years ahead of its cure. Wild land, forest and range should be so managed that plant cover is maintained and soil erosion avoided. The horse is already stolen when erosion has begun. Of course, more damage can be done, and it should be stopped. But the barn door should be locked before the first horse is stolen. Erosion should be avoided entirely by maintaining the plant cover intact. Induced erosion should not be induced.

"Take as an example the fescue bunchgrass on one of the western mountains. It appears in several stages: (1) as a dense stand catching and holding rainfall and developing a rich, dark soil; (2) with moderate grazing the bunches are eaten back, but as long as use is not too heavy they are healthy and vigorous;

(3) too heavy use leads to partial death of the bunches; (4) continued heavy use leads to their death, but the dead clumps remain and many plants find on the old clumps a favorable habitat; (5) continued grazing cleans out the intermediate plants and surface soil moves away from the bunches; (6) the bunches of dead stems finally wear away and surface soil or A-horizon disappears with them. Recovery from the erosion phase (6) may require centuries. Recovery from the partly destroyed stage (5) may be far more rapid. The recovery from the stage (3) showing only partial death of the bunches may be effected in a year or two. It seems evident that to await actual erosion is the height of folly, when one considers the great loss in productivity and time involved if the grass cover (the patient) is allowed to die before remedies are applied. The use of indicators and especially of the vegetation cover in its entirety to detect this deterioration is a most fertile field of study and management. Such studies . . . should revolutionize range management whether for domestic livestock or wildlife.

"Those who manage wild land should have a thorough knowledge of the natural trends of plant succession, and work with nature to bring about desired results. Without this knowledge the management of vegetation for the support of domestic herds or for wildlife may lead unknowingly to serious results. Artificial destruction of vegetation to improve food and cover, artificial reseeding or planting for soil protection and to improve grazing or timber production, for increasing the conditions favorable to man, domestic herds, or wildlife should not be undertaken on wild land without a clear perception of the natural plant succession on the area. To attempt to revise or change the natural succession means continued expense and in all probability ultimate failure. Often the reestablishment of the natural grass, brush or forest cover is delayed in proportion as a temporary success is secured by the use of the introduced species. . . .

"Proper management of wild lands must be based on our best knowledge of the soils, and the climatic, physiographic, biological, social and economic factors for each management area." [9]

VANISHING LANDS

It has repeatedly been shown that the productive capacity of the land varies, of course within reasonable limits, as the thickness of the A-horizon. In other words, the farmer with three feet of topsoil will produce twenty or thirty times as much from his land as the farmer with three inches of topsoil. As the rain and the wind carry away the A-horizon they carry away the productive capacity of the land. In many parts of the world the topsoil is completely gone and the subsoil has followed it, leaving nothing behind but bare rock; this may be seen, in our hemisphere, from the Adirondacks to the Chilean Andes. Where this has happened, centuries may be required to build one inch of fertile topsoil, such as could be swept away in a single rainstorm. The re-establishment of an A-horizon on the subsoil is, of course, a much more rapid process and the time needed varies with local conditions; however, decades will be required in many parts of the world to build an inch of fertile topsoil, even from subsoil. A single inch is of precious little use to the farmer. The villain in this human tragedy is primarily the uncontrolled raindrop—which is why I maintain that it is probably the most important single factor influencing man.

When it is uncontrolled, the environmental resistance rises so high that it almost cancels out the biotic potential, and the carrying capacity approaches the vanishing point, if it does not reach it.

This has happened over and over again, through many centuries in many parts of the world, and it is still happening. It has wiped out earlier civilizations from Mesopotamia to Honduras. *But never before has the hydrologic cycle been badly dislocated in the presence of so many hundreds of millions of people.* These themselves have become an integral part of the environmental resistance.

It is obvious to students of the land sciences that natural laws impose limitations on use. Whether it is convenient or not, whether it is politically expedient or not, whether it is in accord with religious creeds or not, water is going to run downhill and its erosive force is going to increase with the rate of runoff. Where large and hungry populations exist, the politician may find it more than inconvenient to say to them, "No—you may not put your cornfields, and your excessively large herds, on the slopes; we must protect them with forest." The clergyman, watching hunger and deficiency diseases mount among his parishioners as they are forced onto overcrowded, eroding lands—the only lands there are—may find a sharp conflict between traditional morals and his knowledge of the land, or even his common sense. The farmer, meeting the dilemma of washing soil and certain hunger a decade hence, may come to question the position of both the politician and the clergyman. And this is not a problem that concerns merely the people on the land; those who buy products from it, though they may be thousands of miles away, must share the responsibility and the consequences. Amsterdam bankers, opposing freedom of the Indonesians who have so long contributed to Holland's wealth, should look beyond the high hopes of freedom-loving men to the overcrowded, eroded slopes on which these men must try to survive.

The angle of repose with vegetation is one thing; without vegetation it is a very different thing. It varies from field to field and man must accept it and adapt himself to it. This adaptation must be made in its widest sense, for this flow of water across the land, through its effect on the carrying capacity, has a profound meaning in terms of human populations, standards of living, and therefore government policies—and peace. The rain will continue to flow and man cannot stop it. It will continue to run downhill at a rate governed by the slope. Unless there is vegetation to protect it, soil will go with the water.

RUNOFF AND LIVING STANDARDS

This is a relatively simple state of affairs but the remedy is complicated. The rate of runoff can be reduced on even the steepest land. The Incas, for example, grew corn on the flanks of the Andes by building terraces that would now cost $18,000 an acre. Obviously it is cheaper today for Peru to buy corn from the eroding hillsides of Iowa than to protect its own slopes. In the Vosges Mountains, soil that has been washed down to the valley during the growing season is carefully shoveled into baskets during fall and winter and carried on the backs of men to be replaced on the ground. This, of course, is costly in terms of labor and must necessarily result in a low living standard.

One of the principal aims of the U.S. Soil Conservation Service has been to discover methods of keeping soil on hillsides and water in the soil—except where excessive amounts require drainage—at a low enough cost to bring it within reach of the farmer who must sell in a competitive market. Actually they have not been able to do this and have depended on so-called benefit payments, which shift the burden to the taxpayer. Nevertheless, the methods developed have brought such generally higher yields that the initial investment is certainly justifiable. Some of the farmers who have been converted to soil conservation do not backslide—but when prices are high, many again plow marginal land that is excessively vulnerable to erosion.

One of the commonest erosion-control methods used in the United States is contour plowing, which is to say, making the furrows level or nearly so around a hill, instead of leading the furrows from top to bottom. The contours act as miniature dams, hold water back long enough for it to sink into the soil, break its flow, and reduce its velocity and therefore its erosive power.

Another device in wide use is strip cropping, where, between belts plowed on the contour, grass or grain-covered strips are interspersed to catch soil that may wash down the slope despite the contouring. Strip cropping can be made part of the normal rotation and thus help to restore fertility as well as keeping soil on the land. Some nine thousand farmers, when queried by the USDA, reported an average increased yield of nearly 36 per cent from land cultivated according to sound conservation practices. These, of course, represent an attempt to adapt use of the land to its innate capabilities as we now understand them. It represents an obeisance to nature's laws. Certain lands will be destroyed if they are placed under cultivation and on others, with low productive capacity, it will be economically impossible to utilize the methods devised by the SCS. This organization recommends the retirement from cultivation of some forty million acres in the United States.

An Idea to Live by

One of the major contributions of the Soil Conservation Service, a contribution that may have a profound effect on human civilizations for centuries to come, is classification of land according to the uses it is capable of sustaining. Its eight classes are as follows:

Land Suited for Cultivation

Class I: Very good land that can be cultivated safely with ordinary good farming methods. It is nearly level and easily worked. Some areas need clearing, water management, or fertilizing. Usually there is little or no erosion.

Class II: Good land that can be cultivated safely with easily applied practices, such as contouring, protective cover crops, and simple water-management operations. Common requirements are rotations and fertilizing. Moderate erosion is common.

Class III: Moderately good land that can be cultivated safely with such intensive treatments as terracing and strip cropping. Water management is often required on flat areas. Common requirements are crop rotations, cover crops, and fertilizing. Usually there is moderate to severe erosion.

Land Suited for Limited Cultivation

Class IV: Fairly good land that is best suited to pasture and hay but can be cultivated occasionally—usually not more than one year in six. In some areas, especially those of low rainfall, selected land may be cultivated more than one year if adequately protected. When plowed, careful erosion-control practices must be used.

Land Not Suited for Cultivation

Class V: Suited for grazing or forestry with slight or no limitations; needs only ordinary good management.

Class VI: Suited for grazing or forestry with minor limitations; needs protective measures.

Class VII: Suited for grazing or forestry with major limitations; needs extreme care to prevent erosion or destructive burning, or to overcome other hazards.

Class VIII: Suited only for wildlife or recreation. This land usually is steep, rough, stony, sandy, wet, or highly erodible.[10]

In introducing this classification to Latin America I have added a ninth class of land—desert, whether natural or man-induced. So many million acres of land south of the Rio Grande have virtually lost their productive capacity and so many more millions of acres are being reduced to a nonproductive status that recognition of Class IX land has been extremely helpful in making people understand the dynamic trend.

In areas of excessive population, such as El Salvador, Haiti, Greece, the Punjab, and the island of Luzon, it is difficult for man to adjust his use to the capability of the land. There is simply not enough land surface. Grain *must* be grown on Class

VI or VII land—or man will starve. Thus, the worse the human dilemma the more difficult its solution; the more the land is being abused the more likelihood of its being subjected to worse treatment. Man can die quickly, as he does in frequent Asiatic famines. He can die somewhat less quickly, as he is doing in some parts of the Caribbean and Central America. He can compromise with unsuitable land by elaborate irrigated terracing, as in Java and the Philippines, and postpone famine until he has once more outbred the land's productive capacity. This final choice unavoidably condemns him to a low standard of living.

He has no hope of maintaining a high living standard unless he adjusts his use to the capability of the land—and restores the land to something approximating its normal capability. And implicit in this rational use of the land is a limitation of population, a control of man's demand for fruits of the earth.

Millions of DPs

The people—scores of millions of people—who are using the land in disregard of its capabilities are Displaced Persons in a much more serious sense than the few hundred thousands in European refugee camps. They are displaced in the ecological sense. They can feed and clothe themselves, and supply food, fibers, charcoal, and wood to cities only by destroying the land on which they live and the resources associated with it. It is they who wreck forests, start soil erosion, exterminate wildlife, set the flood crests rolling. It is they who are every year piling the environmental resistance higher.

Scores of millions of them must be moved—down the eroding slopes, out of the degenerating forests, off the overgrazed ranges—if they are not to drag ever lower the living standards of their respective countries—and the world. The solution of the problem of European DPs is simple in comparison with that of the ecological DPs.

While the nine classifications recognize productive capacity of the land, they also recognize the limitations that natural conditions impose. They are designed primarily for crop or grazing land, and do not give full recognition to the concept of multiple use. This is the notion that came into being among foresters, that an area might at one time produce many kinds of benefits to mankind. National forests, for example, may be used for controlled grazing and lumber production and at the same time protect watersheds, provide hunting and camping facilities, etc. Watershed land will tend to fall in Classes IV-VIII, but there may be some instances in which good agricultural land will have its greatest value as watershed protection, as, for example, in supplying facilities to large cities.

Certain areas that are potentially useful for agriculture may be more valuable if dedicated to wildlife. Waterfowl sanctuaries through the Middle West are an example of such type of land use. All of them could undoubtedly produce some crops—many of them do produce crops along with ducks—but their importance as way stations for migrants is so great as to justify their retirement from intensive agriculture.

Our national parks undoubtedly have a slight potential agricultural value and a somewhat higher potential grazing value. However, because of their extraordinary beauty, scientific interest, and importance as wildlife and human refuges, they have been wisely set aside to perpetuate these values.

THAT WE MAY UNDERSTAND

Quite apart from possible commercial uses to which they might be put, it would be of enormous advantage to mankind to set aside primitive areas typical of *all* major plant and animal associations. The world has been extremely remiss in recognizing the importance of such areas; many types have been destroyed and, of course, can never be restored. One of the principal values of such primitive areas is as an outdoor laboratory. Scientific investigations of them can teach us so much about the sort of life to which the land is adapted that such studies have considerable practical value to agriculture, forestry, wildlife management, etc. A partial explanation of the Russians' superb scientific work on soils is that they could begin their investigations with undisturbed, virgin tracts of land. This made possible studies of plant climaxes, normal successions, primitive soil structures, and soil fauna. With an understanding of the environment as it had developed over hundreds of centuries under natural climatic and other conditions, they are much better prepared to adjust human management of the land to natural limitations than are soil scientists who, in other parts of the world, may have to guess at normal, natural conditions. The cultural value of primitive tracts, with their rich complex of species and relationships that expresses the culmination of natural forces over millions of years of evolution, will undoubtedly be widely recognized one day. Some universities are now beginning to maintain research stations in such areas. The danger is that the recognition will come too late to save most primitive areas from destruction.

Ecologists in the United States have for years been trying to have established a grasslands preserve in which the environment under natural conditions might be available for study. Thus far their efforts have been fruitless. Recognition of the importance of such areas was given by the Convention on Nature Protection and Wild Life Preservation in the Western Hemisphere, which has been ratified by eleven American governments. One of the expressed purposes of the treaty is to give permanent preservation, where possible, to primitive areas. Unfortunately, relatively little has been done to implement it.

It should be obvious that the use man makes of any piece of land must be adapted to the natural laws operating upon it, and that the first of these is that the relationship between any land-area and water must be respected.

There are many others, such as conforming to imperatives of plant successions, maintaining a balance—even in altered associations—among competing species, not introducing species that might become pests, not permitting excess numbers of any species, such as the overprotected white-tailed deer, etc. During millions of years, nature has maintained by a beneficent circle its marvelous richness on the surface of the earth; it has constantly returned to the earth by slow soil building and natural fertilization whatever has sprung from it.

No Wealth without Limits

Except in a very few areas, man has maintained an extractive economy. He has taken the bounty of the earth and made little or no return. Where he has not actually lost soil and water he has overgrazed and overcropped, and by the removal of animals and plants has carried away important soil minerals, broken down the all-important soil structure, and generally exhausted his environment. The Chinese, by liberal use of animal manures and night soil, have closed the circle in some areas. Since World War I, Western man has made extraordinary progress in extracting atmospheric nitrogen and restoring it to the soil. But after only fifty-five years of cultivation of the virgin soils of Ohio, Illinois, and Wisconsin, Van Hise estimated that 36 per cent of the natural phosphate had been lost.[11]

Small wonder that students give Wisconsin less than four hundred years of anything like its present productive level, using the best agricultural techniques now known. One of the greatest obstacles to the survival of modern man is his highly developed system of sanitation, which every year sends millions of tons of mineral wealth and organic matter, taken from his farms, forests, and grasslands, to be lost in the sea.

In countries with a sound ecological development man achieves a balanced agriculture through fertilization, crop rotation, green manuring, etc. He manages his forests, his wildlife, his fisheries, and his grasslands on a sustained-yield basis. Backward, overpopulated countries are unable to achieve this biological balance by themselves, and if we want to live in a world of peace we should make certain that technological resources are extended to the more retarded areas.

We return once more to the formula—$C = B:E$. *We cannot force land into the pattern we wish to impose upon it, but must fit the use to the land*, its capabilities, and its limitations. All management of land should be designed to maintain as favorable a ratio as possible on the right-hand side of the formula, improving it where possible, and at the very least maintaining the status quo. Where the relationship is deteriorating we must inevitably reduce the demand on the carrying capacity—either by a lower living standard or by a reduced population.

Chapter 6

The Long Knives

Aɴʏᴏɴᴇ ᴡʜᴏ ᴛᴇɴᴅꜱ ᴛᴏ ꜰᴇᴇʟ ᴄᴏᴍᴘʟᴀᴄᴇɴᴛ ᴀʙᴏᴜᴛ the American land should look long and thoughtfully at our muddy rivers, from the Potomac to the Los Angeles. And anyone who is complacent about our complacency should look long and hard at Congress, at our pressure groups, at big business, at our farmers, stock raisers, and lumbermen, at federal and state bureaus charged with resource management, at our schools and colleges, at our folkways and social patterns, and at our population dynamics. Our natural resources, the basis of our national strength, are being poured into that modern limbo, the rathole. We are engaged in a complicated process of autophagy—self-cannibalism. Every year, what we boast of as the greatest nation on earth is significantly weaker.

What was the United States like three hundred years ago? What was there in the colonial pantry?

Aꜱ Wᴇ Wᴇʀᴇ

Approximately half our total area was covered with forests. These protected watersheds and kept the hydrologic cycle turning smoothly. Most of our rivers ran clear. There were floods, at times, but these were far less violent than today. Our streams teemed with fishes. Salmon were so abundant in eastern rivers that indentured servants included in their articles a limitation on the number of times a week they should have to eat this fish.

Beaver colonies were the El Dorado of the United States.

Where the Spaniards sought for gold, our own trappers and those of Canada pushed back the known frontiers primarily in search of beaver pelts.

Game was so common across much of the United States that living off the country was no problem. The heath hen, an eastern variety of the prairie chicken, was so easily shot along the Atlantic seaboard that it was one of the cheapest of foods, and also discriminated against in articles of indenture. Passenger pigeons moved from north to south in flocks estimated by several trustworthy observers in *thousands of billions*. The wild turkey was shot for the pot from New England to Texas and became a symbol, at Thanksgiving, of New World abundance.

The forests of the United States were the finest and most accessible source of timber in the eighteenth-century world. Stout ships of Britain, as well as the Yankee clipper, were built of them and carried their superior woods to hundreds of ports around the world. Our forests existed in pure or nearly pure stands that made cutting profitable and easy. Someone has said that a squirrel could have traveled from the Atlantic to the Mississippi without ever touching the ground. In the far West existed a belt of great trees that for decades were almost untouched.

Between the forested zones lay the mighty domains of the grasses. In the more humid East these grew to saddle height. As precipitation diminished toward the west, they were succeeded by short grasses. Some seventy-five million bison drifted north and south with the changing seasons, between Mexico and Canada and east to Pennsylvania, without damage to the range. Antelope were so common that the mountain men shot them as carelessly as the modern hunter kills cottontails. The prairie chicken abounded and was ignored by hunters as not worth a charge of shot. The song of the Eskimo curlew poured down on the grasslands of a dozen states, and when it became profitable to ship this bird to market it could be, and was, slaughtered literally by the wagonload.

Throughout much of this interior region soils were rich and

stabilized, as was evidenced by the vegetation that grew upon them. The Middle West, especially the area now occupied by the corn belt, was a region of some of the most productive earth to be found anywhere on our globe. Perhaps richer soils exist farther west in the wheatlands of Kansas and Nebraska, but these are less susceptible to man's control because of undependable rainfall.

The vast area between the Rio Grande and Lake Winnipeg and the Atlantic and Pacific oceans might, if rationally used, have been developed into a human paradise. It could have supported a hundred million people at a *permanent* high standard of living. It was a prodigally rich continent. And each year the slow, biological processes took more wealth from the air, and with it enriched the land.

Then the European arrived.

THE SPOILERS

Unfortunately, our forefathers—whom some of us still pay homage to in D.A.R. meetings and on the Fourth of July—were one of the most destructive groups of human beings that have ever raped the earth. They moved into one of the richest treasure houses ever opened to man, and in a few decades turned millions of acres of it into a shambles. We, their descendants to the fifth or sixth generation, are still trying to cut their losses —and paying heavily for them in working hours and lowered living standards.

In the museum and old church at Jamestown there are tablets in memory of John Rolfe, and a tribute to his skill in making possible the drying and commercial exploitation of tobacco. A National Park Service sign states that his technique affected the economy of Virginia for a hundred and fifty years. This is a major piece of understatement. Virginia has not yet recovered from the effects of John Rolfe's brainstorm, nor is it likely to for many years to come.

Avery O. Craven of the University of Chicago summarized

the relationship between this pioneer economy and the land, probably as well as it has ever been done. He says:

"An early period of pioneer simplicity and even lack of comforts may develop a new standard of living, but there will also be a decided effort to create a surplus and find a staple of some kind for that exchange which will widen the field of supply and lift the standard of living set by the available materials. Such exchange, when developed, can seldom be on equal terms and the surplus produced must come from an extravagant spending of the material resources of the new community. Seeming abundance of raw materials encourages waste; the lack of capital forbids the economies of production and the heavier burdens of carriage and marketing fall upon the producer of raw materials and exchange . . .

". . . the abundance of land, combined with the scarcity of capital and labor—a condition which characterizes all frontiers throws the burden of intensified production upon the soil as the cheapest factor of production. Only the most fertile soils will be used and only those methods employed which give the greatest immediate returns regardless of future consequences. The problem is one of rapid spending, not of conservation. The speed with which the privations of the frontier may be passed depends upon the rapidity with which the riches of the soil may be exploited. The section is most fortunate whose fertility may be most easily spent, and its progress toward a complex life will be most rapid.

"This process of exploitation has gone on from one end of our land to the other, and from the earliest times down to the days of the last American frontier. What sugar production was to the West Indies, tobacco to Virginia and Maryland, cotton to the lower South, corn to the Mississippi Valley, wheat and flax have been to the Northwest of our own day.

"The length of natural fertility under cultivation will vary, of course, with the type of soil, crops produced, methods used, etc.; but experience furnishes some data for certain sections. In the long-leaf pine uplands of the cotton states where corn is raised continually, the yields range from twenty-five bushels per acre the first year to ten or less the third year; where short-leafed pine is intermingled with the long, production of goodly crops holds out for some five to seven years; and if oak and hickory are added, crops may be counted on for a period of as high as 13 years. . . .

"In the tobacco region of the South . . . the planters seldom counted on a paying fertility lasting more than 3 or 4 years." [1]

Land was abandoned on the eastern seaboard nearly as rapidly as it could be cleared. Thomas Jefferson was concerned about this destruction and wrote, "We can buy an acre of new land cheaper than we can manure an old one." On April 5, 1798, in order to save soil, George Washington "decided to give up the cultivation of corn entirely and purchase his supply from the outside."

Craven describes the countryside between Port Tobacco and Hoe's Ferry, Maryland, in 1796, as seen by a traveler of that day. "The country is flat and sandy, wearing a most dreary aspect. Nothing is to be seen for miles together but extensive plains that have been worn out by the culture of tobacco, overgrown with yellow sedge and interspersed with groves of pine and cedar trees . . . in the midst of these plains are several good homes which shows that the country was once very different from what it is now. These houses . . . have been suffered to go to decay as the land around them has worn out and the people find it more to their advantage to remove to another part of the country and clear a piece of rich land than to attempt to reclaim these exhausted plains." This, we should remember, was only twenty years after our revolution.

In 1799, Albemarle County, Virginia, was called a "scene of desolation that baffles description—farm after farm . . . worn out, washed and gullied, so that scarcely an acre could be found in a place fit for cultivation." This was nearly two hundred years after John Rolfe discovered how to dry tobacco and today, another hundred and fifty years later, much of this region is still fit only for low-grade, second-growth forest.

CARRYING CAPACITY AND WAR

The shattering effects of this land destruction were visualized almost with clairvoyance by that extraordinary leader of the Confederacy, Edmund Ruffin. He, as is pointed out by Craven, "insisted that the proportional political and economic decline of the South was purely a matter of the exhaustion of the soils. Had the original productivity of the lands remained, southern population would have been held at home and the increase would have been equal to that in other parts of the nation. Southern representatives in Congress would have thus been large enough (*sic*) to have checked injurious legislation, such as tariffs, prohibition of slave extension, etc.; and the South would have continued to prosper and hold her own in national affairs. A declining fertility of soil had produced a declining population and its attendant ills." Whether or not Ruffin overemphasized the power of this factor could be argued at some length; that it was important can scarcely be denied. Considerable support is given Ruffin's contention by the intelligence and effectiveness with which, in the years before the Civil War, he set about reviving southern agriculture through fertilization and erosion control. His methods produced a notable success in limited areas and might well have swept the South had the War Between the States not terminated them. With the bitter defeat of the Confederacy, Ruffin, one of its most constructive leaders, committed suicide.

The march of destruction, which our ancestors undoubtedly hailed as progress, was only the start of a macabre procession that advanced across a continent. As man chopped, burned, drained, plowed, and shot his way westward, he rolled up a nation-long windrow of environmental resistances that he is trying to reduce and to wish out of existence, while he still keeps the rolling process going! The procedure has certain burlesque-stage aspects, like the troubles of the clown who involves himself in the strip of carpet he is trying to remove; but what it is doing to the American people is far from funny.

The total area now classified as forest land in the United States is approximately 630,000,000 acres. On this we have left the following:

Mature forests	100,822,000 acres
Second growth, bearing saw timber	112,030,000 acres
Second growth, cordwood size	100,971,000 acres
Second growth, fair to good replacement	71,336,000 acres
Stripped, with little or no replacement	76,738,000 acres
	461,897,000 acres

The situation is even blacker than the statistics show because the cutting of mature forests has been accompanied by disproportionate destruction of high-quality woods. In 1909 the total stand of saw timber in the United States was estimated at 2,826 thousand million board feet. The reappraisal estimate of 1945 was 1,601 thousand million—a drop of 44 per cent in thirty-six years.[2] Many mills are cutting ten-inch logs as saw timber! At the present time, our mature forest resources consist principally of soft woods, and these reserves are mostly in the West. As the Joint Committee on Forestry points out, "The old growth forests represent the production of centuries. The second growth is the result of nature's pressure to reclothe cutover or denuded land. Often these forests are composed of a transition species of an inferior quality or inadequately stocked, or injured by fire or abuses through prevailing cutting practices."[3]

The need for forest products is increasing—not decreasing. The 1946 saw-timber requirement for the nation was estimated at 53,900 million board feet and the annual growth at only 35,300 million board feet, or a deficit of more than 50 per cent! The very freedom of our press is threatened by shrinking supplies of wood pulp. The great gap that has formed between what used to be one of the most richly forested nations in the world and the United States of today should be uncomfortably clear to millions of Americans now looking for a place to live. A major factor in the national housing shortage is the lack of lumber used in building and in additional wood products that go into construction at every step. And even as we supply our current needs we further mortgage our future.

Over thousands of square miles of the United States, watersheds have been deforested and overgrazed. Thousands of silted stock-ponds, power and drinking water reservoirs, and miles of muddy, flooding rivers show the effects of this devegetation. Our National Forests had as one of their primary purposes the protection of watersheds. The Act of 1897 said, "No public forest reserve shall be established, except to improve and protect the forest within the reserve, or for the purpose of securing favorable conditions of water flows, and to furnish a continuous supply of timber for the uses and necessities of the citizens of the United States." Much of the land in National Forests consists of areas that had been cut over, largely ruined by commercial groups, and then turned back to the government. It is probable that only 10 per cent of the timber-growing capacity of the United States is in public lands "because most of the land in public forests is poor land which private owners did not want."[4]

Our grasslands, from the juniper-dotted pastures of New England to the mesquite of the Southwest, have been badly hurt. Range lands cover nearly one billion acres, of which some 65 per cent are privately owned. The western range lands, comprising nearly 800,000,000 acres, support almost 75 per cent of the nation's sheep and more than 50 per cent of its cattle. Originally the grazing capacity of western lands was able to carry about 25,000,000 head but the vegetation has been so seriously damaged by overgrazing that by 1935 the capacity had fallen by half. Since then, largely because of an increase in precipitation, the range has made a partial comeback, but as a result of rising prices during and after World War II, numbers of livestock have again become dangerously high.

"Not quite 100 million acres, or less than one-seventh of the western range area, are in satisfactory condition. No less than 589 million acres are eroding—more or less seriously. Most spectacular among the maladjustments of rangeland uses has been the attempt to use more than 50 million acres for dry-land farming." [5]

In 1935 range managers calculated that more than fifty years would be needed to restore the range enough to carry even the 17,300,000 head of stock then being grazed—and probably an additional fifty years to regain its original capacity of 25,000,000 livestock units. Range livestock production was once almost wholly pastoral; in 1935, 35 per cent of the feed for western livestock came from crop lands or irrigated pastures—a tripling in forty-five years! [6] In Texas, the use of commercial feed increased about 400 per cent between 1906 and 1940. Hay acreage has been sharply expanded since 1920 on some western range areas, and the average winter feeding period has been extended as much as six weeks in some localities.[7] These are expensive measures, which help to explain dollar-a-pound steak, but they are unavoidable because of range deterioration. The stockmen have not only pushed up environmental resistance on the grasslands; their destructive influence has seeped eastward as they draw on the eroding cornfields of Iowa and Illinois.

Overgrazed range land is highly susceptible to wind erosion, and the decrease or absence of vegetation increases the rate of runoff. No little part of the floods that rush down the Missouri and Colorado rivers and their tributaries has its origin in the excessive numbers of sheep and cattle about the headwaters. We may well say, with Sir Thomas More, "Your sheep that were wont to be so meek and tame and so small eaters, now as I hear say become so great devourers and so wild that they eat up and swallow the very men themselves. They consume, destroy and devour whole fields, houses and cities."

THE LAND RUNS TO THE SEA

The most obvious result of deforestation, overgrazing, and bad farming methods is soil erosion. American civilization, founded on nine inches of topsoil, has now lost one-third of this soil. Dr. Hugh H. Bennett, testifying before a Congressional committee in 1939 said, "In the short life of this country we have essentially destroyed 282,000,000 acres of land, crop and rangeland. Erosion is destructively active on 775,000,000 additional acres. About 100,000,000 acres of cropland, much of it representing the best cropland we have is finished in this country. We cannot restore it.

"It takes nature from 300 to 1000 years or more to bring back a single inch of topsoil and we sometimes lose that much topsoil as the result of a single rain, if it is an especially heavy torrential type of rain . . .

"We have some land left that has not been used; but it is scattered. We have no large aggregates of land to which we may turn. We are losing every day as the result of erosion the equivalent of two hundred forty-acre farms. We have lost that much since we were here yesterday. It is gone, gone, forever. . . .

"The evil effects of erosion do not stop with the removal of topsoil and the further gouging of the land by the gulleying process, but the products of such processes of land impoverishment and outright destruction travel on downslope to fill reservoirs, streams, channels, drain ditches, and irrigation ditches . . . In the southeastern part of the United States thirteen costly, major reservoirs have been filled to the top of the dam with the products of erosion over an average period of less than thirty years . . . Engineers have not found an economical method for cleaning a reservoir once it is filled with sand and mud." The Sweetwater Reservoir in California lost 48 per cent of its storage capacity in less than seven years. Near Stillwater, Oklahoma, a flood-control reservoir covered a thousand acres in 1937, and in 1944 nearly three thousand acres; silt had backed up the waters, and of course cut down the flood-control usefulness by that amount.

During the past hundred years the Potomac River has carried more than half a billion tons of soil past Washington, or about seventy-five tons of soil from each of the 7,400,000 acres that make up the drainage basin above Washington. Some of the land is in woods and some is so steep or stony that it has never been cultivated. Accordingly, the actual per acre loss on the cultivated land is much greater than indicated.[8]

Since early colonial days, erosion has removed from one-fourth to three-fourths of the best part of the crop-producing topsoil from more than five million acres of the complete Potomac River drainage basin. In addition, from three-fourths to *all* of the topsoil has been eroded from another 221,000 acres. Small wonder that the deep harbor into which came oceangoing ships from the seven seas has filled with silt and is now the site of the Lincoln Memorial.[9]

It was estimated by the Soil Conservation Service that approximately 5,500,000 tons of sediment would flow by Washington in 1947. This, in spite of the fact that twenty soil conservation districts have been organized on the Potomac watershed. These districts embrace almost 87 per cent of the basin's land. With the help of Soil Conservation Service technicians, supervisors, and farmers, there have already been worked out almost 55,000 complete conservation farm plans, which provide for the acre-by-acre treatment of almost 1,000,000 acres. Yet five and a half million tons of earth a year go down the river. And this is merely one rather small stream.

At the head of Chesapeake Bay, 85,000,000 cubic yards of sediment were deposited between 1846 and 1938; the average depth of water over an area of 32 square miles was reduced 2½ feet! At the site of two Maryland ports, once open to overseas trade, the mooring posts are more than two miles from navigable water. In the seventeenth century oceangoing vessels sailed up the creek to Piscataway, Maryland; the depth of the water at the creek's entrance is now about two feet. The decadence of the countryside about Port Tobacco, reported by Craven's traveler, also contributed to the silting and abandonment of many ports on Chesapeake Bay. Port Tobacco is, itself, now a mile from tidewater.

Though during the past hundred years the federal government has spent about $17,000,000 digging out the port of Baltimore, the depth of water under its Hanover Street Bridge fell from seventeen feet to six inches by 1924.[10]

CRYPTIC COSTS

The effect of this siltation on business, shipping, fishing, oyster culture, etc., has of course been extremely costly; yet it is unquestionably only a minute fraction of the hidden expenses paid by the American people for the unproductive luxury of unsound land use. It is possible that in our national history more billions of dollars have been spent in an effort to compensate for the abuse of resources than have gone into all our battle budgets, including those of World War II. Adjustment to land abuse accounts for a large share of the cost of our agricultural colleges, Agricultural Experiment Stations, Agricultural Extension Service, Soil Conservation Service, Forest Service, Fish and Wildlife Service, Geological Survey, State Conservation Commissions, and Army Engineers. Land abuse has inflated our taxes to pay for flood relief, for dredging of rivers and harbors, and for building of levees and flood-control dams. Repair of railroads and canals, loss of hydroelectric power, damage by insects and rodents, augmented fertilizer needs, and the results of bad and inadequate food, poor education, etc., all add something—often a very considerable something—to the expense of American living. We do not see these concealed costs; careful and prolonged research would be required to gain even an approximate understanding of them. Yet if the burden they impose on tax rates and the cost of food, clothing, and services were suddenly to be lifted, we should unquestionably feel a significant improvement in our living standard.

Through the nation-wide program of soil conservation, much has been accomplished in controlling erosion and conserving soil, but in the thirteen years in which the Soil Conservation Service has existed only about 10 per cent of the job of applying conservation measures has been accomplished. This is scarcely enough progress to justify a sense of security. And the Eightieth Congress cut the appropriations of the service!

In July, 1947, during the Missouri floods, it was estimated that more than 115,000,000 tons of the topsoil that has made the state of Iowa one of the greatest agricultural regions in the world had been carried off by the rain. At least a portion of the topsoil from *25 per cent of Iowa's total cropland* has been washed away. Federal soil conservation workers estimated that the 115,000,000 tons came from about 6,000,000 acres of rich loam that had been planted, or prepared to be planted, either to corn or to soybeans; these row-tilled crops, as pointed out earlier, may increase the erosion hazard more than a hundred times above that on forest and grassland. The *Washington Post* headlined its story, "Iowa Paying in Soil for Nourishing World," as though this were news and as though Iowa had not been doing it for decades.

It was estimated that 1947's erosion loss for Iowa alone was $134,000,000. This is, of course, a fallacious concept, since the soil of the nation is literally above price. To place a real estate dealer's evaluation upon it is a particularly dangerous form of semantic confusion. It is identification of the symbol and reality, with a vengeance.

And to think of "soil erosion" simply as "soil erosion" is dangerously elementalistic. Not only is soil washing into the seas but, as Jay Darling points out, bread and pork chops and potatoes. The Gulf of Mexico, off the mouth of the Mississippi, is stained with the substance from which our children build bone and muscle and blood. Those tawny waves are drowning the future of America.

Not only soil erosion, but loss in fertility is a problem. Virgin soils in Ohio, with unimproved seeds and no insect control, yielded a hundred bushels of corn per acre, and sixty bushels of wheat. Crops now average forty-two bushels of corn and twenty of wheat. And even this yield per acre in one of the most advanced agricultural states in the Union, where there is greatly increased knowledge of disease and pest control, fertilizers and plant breeding, is being maintained with difficulty and at great expense.[11] Here is a measure of the degree to which we Americans have raised our land's environmental resistance.

Resource losses do not add up to the simple facts of destruction of timber, grasses, soils, and wildlife, but to an extremely complicated increase in the total environmental resistance that every year lowers the carrying capacity of the American nation's land. What has probably never been adequately assayed is the lowered living standard as mirrored in health and education. In terms of democracy and social values, the South, with its high crime and illiteracy rate, its Ku Klux Klan, its intolerance and its lynchings, is certainly one of the most depressed regions of the country. How much of this can be attributed to the attempts of human beings to eke out a living on exhausted land no one can say, but the influence must be considerable.

Canada, too, has an erosion problem that, augmented by the pressure of world demands for food, has injured her land far more than would the needs of her own happily small population. There was heavy drifting of soils in Saskatchewan in 1887, which apparently began soon after the prairie lands were plowed and planted with grain. Control has been successful but so sporadic that the total effect has been slight. In 1934 some 8,500,000 acres of cropped land were affected by drought and blowing, and the yield averaged less than five bushels per acre. Water erosion, though less severe than in the United States, has been reported from both eastern and Pacific provinces; it is relatively more dangerous than farther south, because of Canada's limited areas of good land.[12]

The floods of our Middle West and the almost hysterical demands for flood control through engineering methods are a by-product of misuse of the land. People who have settled on the flood plains of the Missouri, Mississippi, and their tributaries, and then wail that the rest of the country must bail them out, remind one of the man who jumped off the Empire State Building—and changed his mind. The land on which they have built and the fields they till have obviously been deposited by past floods. Simply because human beings occupy the flood plain is no reason why there should not be further floods.

To reduce temporary floods by building a series of dams that would permanently submerge some of the richest land in the world—the project of the U.S. Army Engineers—would seem to compound the foolishness. Yet an inquiry addressed to the Army Engineers on July 7, 1947, brought forth the information that they had no idea how many acres their reservoirs would cover. How much good land would be forever removed from use by the American people under a Missouri Valley Authority has never been calculated. Unless this is done, and any MVA development adjusted to this factor, the MVA plan may well be a national liability. We no longer can afford to waste fertile fields beneath hydroelectric reservoirs. Nor can we afford to sacrifice many of them to protect downstream urban areas against floods. *We do not have enough good land to meet current needs*, as recent events—including high prices—have clearly shown. We are far from ending the erosion loss of the good land we have left; and both world and domestic drains on it are increasing.

The concept of resource management on the basis of watersheds is one of the most promising and soundest of modern times. But, like many human activities, it is plagued by Aristotelian identifications. Unless we start with the premise that every watershed is unique, the Valley Authority concept may lead to destructive and costly mistakes. The Missouri Valley is *not* the Tennessee Valley; even were the TVA an unqualified success, it should be profoundly modified before it is transferred to other regions. Mistakes made in the Tennessee Valley, such as flooding productive land and neglecting the watershed, might be far graver elsewhere; the Missouri Valley is, to a considerable extent, a region of light, extremely erodible soils that are extensively and intensively cultivated.

An especial danger is that the engineers will be turned loose before adequate studies have been made. Some of our foremost scientists gave a brilliant exposition, in MVA hearings, of the complexity of the problem of sound land-use development, and especially of irrigation, in the Missouri Valley; this testimony made it clear that there are vast gaps in our understanding of the region. Satisfactory studies cannot be made overnight, and to locate dams without them—as the U.S. Army Engineers and Bureau of Reclamation have been doing—seems like irresponsible abuse of both the land and the taxpayer.

The hundreds of millions of dollars that we are asked to spend to prevent destruction of cities and avert loss of life are an enormous burden on the taxpayer. At a time when our school system threatens to break down because we cannot pay teachers a decent wage, or support hospitals to care for the sick, we are urged to spend billions on people too stupid to stay off flood plains, and on damming rivers that have got out of hand largely because of destruction of forests and grasslands. The Okies who flocked into California in 1936 and 1937 were products of ignorance and abuse of nature's laws and resources. A period of favorable rainfall has brought many of these people back to the danger zone; it is certain that within a few years drifts of topsoil will once more be overwhelming farmhouses— and the Okies will be on the move again. People who overgraze and deforest watersheds and plant themselves in the path of the floods are as much of a national liability as the Okies. So, one is tempted to say, are western senators who, while they advocate enormously expensive Valley Authorities, continue to foster overgrazing and erosion of valley watersheds by voting for sheepmen's subsidies!

A resource that should worry a good many Americans, but does so very little, is our underground waters. Throughout much of the United States the water table is falling. About

Baltimore, presumably as a correlative of the erosion and siltation just described, it has dropped 146 feet in thirty-two years.[13]
In other words, a well must be dug 146 feet deeper in 1948
than would have been necessary in 1916. This, of course, increases the cost of making water available, and brings nearer
the time when there will not be a large enough supply for the
city's requirements. Baltimore, in a situation like that of
Mexico City, without water for fire protection and for industrial and sanitary needs would be a dismal spectacle that
might teach the rest of the country a needed lesson in elementary biophysics.

One of the most asinine wastes in history was in California's
Santa Clara Valley. A couple of years after this came under the
"progressive" administration of the North Americans, the valley's artesian resources were discovered and tapped for irrigation. By 1910 there were a thousand flowing wells; in the 1890's
pumped wells were sunk above the artesian belt.

Replenishment of the underground supply is largely dependent on storm-fed streams rising in adjacent mountains;
nothing was done to foster this supply and as late as 1932, when
hydrologists and engineers had been protesting for decades, 71
per cent of the runoff water was wasted in San Francisco Bay.

After 1915 the situation became serious. Still nothing was
done to increase the supply. On the contrary, pumping expanded rapidly. It jumped from 25,000 acre-feet in 1915 to
134,000 in 1933. The water table fell about five feet a year until
1933—when it dropped twenty-one feet!

As the water level fell, artesian wells stopped flowing; the
last one was closed in 1930. In 1934 the average pumping lift
was 165 feet, and irrigation had become both precarious and
costly.

With the supporting water gone, the valley floor itself sank
five feet in twenty years. Costly damage, totaling millions,
was inflicted on buildings, pipelines, orchards, and streets; set-
tling *permanently* reduced underground storage capacity by
500,000 acre-feet.

Through all this, the Californians could not see what was happening. In 1922 a $4,000,000 conservation plan was voted down 7 to 1; yet in twenty ensuing years, valley farmers spent over $16,000,000 for new wells, more powerful pumping equipment, etc. They undoubtedly prayed, too. When salt water, seeping in from San Francisco Bay, began to come through their pumps in 1934, they started to do something about it—to get rain water back into the ground.[14]

Between Baltimore and Santa Clara Valley this story has been repeated with variations hundreds of times. The situation is worst in the arid and semiarid West; but it is also bad, and growing worse, in many parts of the humid East, where the large supply of potentially available water is offset by destruction of vegetation and by excessive use for municipal and industrial purposes. In Ohio the water table has been falling "at an alarming rate." In numerous counties *farmers must buy and haul water* at great expense—which is, of course, passed on to the consumer.[15] Man, through stupidity, raises the environmental resistance; he may, with afterthought, get back part of his water, but we all pay for it in increased prices of Santa Clara fruits and vegetables.

THE BEASTS OF THE FIELD

A national resource which, to quote Jay Darling's famous phrase, we treat like the bow-legged girl at the picnic, is our wildlife and its habitat. We nearly always place wildlife last in listing our natural wealth, and our justifications of its defense often seem like apologies. There are a number of reasons for this. One is our national propensity, which has caused even the money-minded French and Latin Americans to stigmatize us as moneygrubbers, to use the dollar sign as one of our principal standards of measurement. How can one assign a cash value to the heart's lift at the flash of a scarlet tanager, the outpoured song of the solitaire, the towering of white ibises over the Everglades, or even the homely chattering of the dooryard wren? What of the blue sweep of crow's-foot violets across the prairie, the indescribable scarlet of the cardinal flower, the dainty perfection of Dutchman's-breeches and moccasin flower, the spring tocsin of the humble skunk cabbage? The whistle of greenwings over the tules, the pitch of canvasback as they come to stool? Can any Old World architecture equal the living arches of our southern swamps, where prothonotary warblers dart like living jewels? Could the sewage-choked canals of Venice be anything but an anticlimax to one who had paddled quietly through nature's canals in the Delta Marshes? We do not value Chartres or the Louvre for what they might bring at auction, nor should we try to ring up the value of our wildlife on the cash register.

We are also a practical people and prone to demand that if a thing does not have a cash value it should at least be "good" for something. How many times have people asked me what a wildflower or salamander or bird is good for. What is a sunset good for? Or the salt tang of wind off the sea? Or the deep velvet of hoarfrost on a weeping willow? Or the ringing of tiny bells beneath the ice of a January brook? The quiet of a remote forest, when even the insects are still? Is it not sufficient good that they delight man's eye, and nose and ear, quiet his spirit, and stretch his mind?

A love of the outdoors and its creatures has been an important part of our heritage from the time when Catesby made the first paintings of American wildlife, down to 1947, when over twenty-five million people visited our National Parks. Thoreau, Emerson, Whitman, Melville, Cooper, Jeffers, Beebe, and a host of other writers have been profoundly influenced by our forests, our birds, our surrounding seas. Painters from Audubon to Benson, Rungius, and Jaques have sought the beauty of our wildlife. A consciousness of nature has influenced our culture more than that of any other people except, possibly, the British. Today, as we are caught in the grinding mesh of a mechanized civilization and the monotony of unrewarding tasks, we need as never before to turn to the healing hills and forests, with their rich company of plants and animals.

Yet we have neglected and abused and destroyed that company. The last of the innumerable hosts of passenger pigeons died in a cage in 1914. The heath hen has not been seen since 1932. The Eskimo curlew that heaped the wagons of market gunners was last taken in Argentina during its winter migration in 1924. The eastern puma, which controlled deer populations as an escapement keeps a watch from running away, was destroyed over fifty years ago. The grizzly bear, leading character in much of our folklore, survives in pathetic and precarious remnants. The magnificent bighorn sheep clings on in only a few isolated outposts.

The list of species whose existence hangs by a thread is a long one; it includes the glacier bear, fisher, marten, wolverine, kit fox, timber wolf, Florida cougar, several seals, key deer, woodland caribou, Florida manatee, several whales, great white heron, trumpeter swan, California condor, the magnificent whooping crane, and the ivory-billed woodpecker—largest and most spectacular of its family in North America.[16] Whether our wild ducks can survive the hammering they get from two million hunters is far from certain.

During thousands of years, nature evolved a reproduction rate, among these birds and mammals, that would provide enough replacements to ensure perpetuation of the species, despite normal, natural losses that evolved along with the animals. These included predation, disease, parasitism, the hazards of weather and migration. Most of these checks are still effective. But to them man has added his own destruction of the animals—and vast desolation of the swamps, forests, rivers, and fields that are the only places in which these creatures can live. Small wonder their survival depends on eternal human vigilance in their behalf!

That we have not lost more of them we may attribute to the size and richness of our country, and—compared to the Old World—the relatively low human pressures on the environment. But now, with the stockmen seeking the ultimate blade of grass, the sawyer the last great tree, and the engineer sites for enormous reservoirs, protection for our wildlife requires constantly increasing thought and effort.

Because we have not lost more of them, because we still are possessed of a considerable wealth of wildlife, many of us have remained unconcerned. This is a good deal like the attitude of the small boy who didn't want to earn a quarter because he had a quarter. Or, on a higher plane, like melting down Cellini vessels with the justification that those of Leonardo remained.

Indeed, the vandalism that wipes out the last whooping crane, the last ivory-bill, seems far worse. Vessels are dead things, contrived by man in a few weeks or months. The condor that rides the winds over the California hills, the curlew that spanned two continents with its crying, were millions of years in the making. The very forces that shaped the earth molded their form, determined their destiny. Through thousands and tens of thousands of generations, the wind and the cold, the march of the seasons, the changes on the land, the failure and success of plants, and the craftiness of enemies hammered at the malleable substance of these creatures. Endless sorting, endless discarding, endless change brought them to ultimate perfection for the world in which they live. Can man, like some blundering sorcerer's apprentice, afford to smash the crucible in which they have been refined, reduce them to a mere memory, a bunch of stuffed feathers in a museum? Not, it seems to me, without pitifully impoverishing himself!

Fortunately, for those who are unimpressed by any value not backed up by a gold reserve, it is possible to show that the worth of our birds and mammals and reptiles and even many insects can be measured in terms of cash-on-the-barrelhead. Our game birds, mammals, and fishes support a two-billion-dollar a year industry—hunting, fishing, and associated activities. Our fur bearers are worth probably a quarter as much. The value of wild creatures in maintaining a balanced, healthy ecology in which man can thrive is unquestionably far greater than any figure that has been assigned to their direct exploitation. They add incalculably to the health—psychosomatic health—of those who turn to them for outdoor enjoyment, with or without gun and rod. The basic training their pursuit gave our young men contributed significantly to the speed with which we were able to turn a group of nonmilitaristic citizens into a superb corps of jungle fighters. The appreciation and defense of our wildlife need no apology. But they do require a constant renewing; we must keep on reminding ourselves that this treasure is unequaled, and that only positive actions can preserve it for our enjoyment.

This brief survey of our renewable resources brings into sharp focus a cherished part of our national life: free enterprise. We have heard it discussed with increasing frequency over the past decade and a half. Its elementalistic-minded champions cry, over and over again, "Free enterprise has made our country what it is!"

To this an ecologist might sardonically assent, "Exactly." For free enterprise must bear a large share of the responsibility for devastated forests, vanishing wildlife, crippled ranges, a gullied continent, and roaring flood crests. Free enterprise—divorced from biophysical understanding and social responsibility.

Those who would preserve what is left of free enterprise should sit down by themselves and thoroughly ponder the answers to two questions: Could free enterprise have made this country powerful and prosperous and democratically free if it had not been endowed with perhaps the world's greatest store of natural treasure? And can enterprise remain even partially free if we continue to waste our birthright like a sailor on a bender?

Abuse of the ranges resulted in the Taylor Grazing Act, a minimum scientific control over the stockmen. They have sandbagged it by political manipulation. Unless they adjust cropping of the grasses to their reproductive ability—and there is no present indication the stockmen will do this—the nation

U. S. EXPORTS OF WHEAT
and Wheat Flour 1790-1929
TEN YEAR MOVING AVERAGE

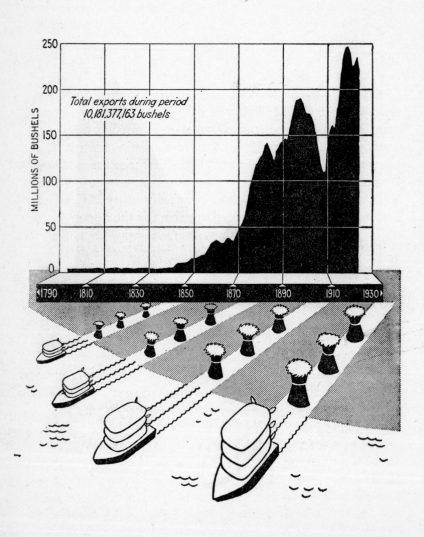

Total exports during period
10,181,377,163 bushels

U. S. EXPORTS OF COTTON
1789-1932
TEN YEAR MOVING AVERAGE

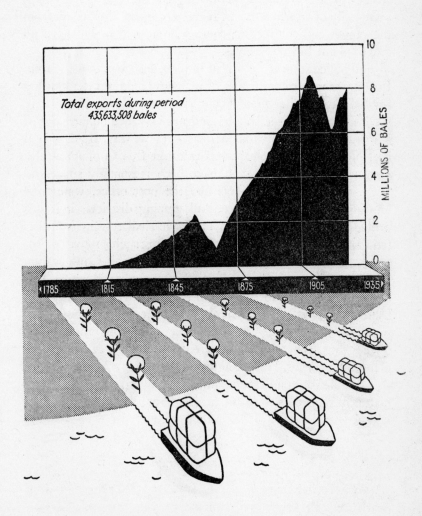

Total exports during period
435,633,508 bales

MILLIONS OF BALES

1785   1815   1845   1875   1905   1935

must in self-defense adopt control measures at once more sweeping and more stringent—an SEC of the ranges. The U.S. Forest Service is courageously advocating a system of controlled lumbering. Sustained-yield forestry by private owners would certainly be desirable. If, however, this cannot be achieved (and there is no present evidence it can), most Americans would prefer a control of cutting to outright government ownership of all forest lands. If free enterprise disappears from the ranges and the forests, those who abused it will have no one to blame but themselves.

The police state is abhorrent to most men who have known freedom; there are very few of us who would not die fighting for the latter rather than accept the former. And, if one may reconstruct the crime by the scraps of evidence coming out of Russia, the police state has not yet found the way to sound land use. Neither has the near socialistic but free Commonwealth of Australia. We, however, have been reasonably successful with state-managed projects like the post office, waterfowl hunting, the Forest Service, and grazing districts; it is improbable that, in the face of need, we shall refrain from extending this management. We are avoiding such a move to protect our soil, by the democratic device of Soil Conservation Districts. These, however, their efficacy unproved, are still on trial; and they are not hampered by the power concentration found among stock- and lumbermen. Members of Soil Conservation Districts deliberately place limitations upon themselves; thus, they maintain an enterprise of free choice by democratic means. How long other exploiters of our resources will be able to retain comparable freedom would seem to be a matter of their own decision. Unless I am badly mistaken, they will not have long to make up their minds.

THE ROAD BACK

We have begun to heal our land—but we have not done nearly enough. Our Forest Service, Fish and Wildlife Service,

National Park Service, and Soil Conservation Service are admirable but inadequate. Universities and land-grant colleges have carried out much of the research that has been the basis of improvement of land use, but they never have had sufficient funds or personnel. Some State Conservation Commissions have made important contributions, but many of them are staffed with political hacks, timeservers, and incompetents. Citizens' organizations such as the Izaak Walton League, National Parks Association, Emergency Conservation Committee, National Audubon Society, Wildlife Management Institute, and National Wildlife Federation have done constructive work, but both their funds and their memberships are pitifully limited, in a nation of 145,000,000 where at least one-third to one-half seek outdoor recreation. Most of these groups of people, governmental and nongovernmental, are hampered by an insufficiently critical evaluation of their own work.

According to Carl W. Shoemaker of the National Wildlife Federation, total expenditures for conservation research, education, and operations in the United States in 1945 were approximately $1,000,000,000. This, in a nation with an annual income approaching $200,000,000,000! Our wealth and our survival depend on our natural resources and the land; yet in preserving and restoring them we spent only about ½ of 1 per cent of our national income. We spend tens of billions on our Army, Navy, and Air Force to protect our national boundaries against a possible attack. Yet we are willing to invest only a small fraction of this amount in protecting ourselves against *the multiplicity of attacks now going on*, within our borders, on the very means of national survival.

The stupidity of such parsimony is even more obvious when we recognize that sound land management actually augments our national income. When the range is in good condition, more meat per acre can be produced by less animals. A Texas rancher, when he began management of his land in 1937, produced 21,000 pounds of wool, an average of 8.6 per sheep;

69,000 pounds of lamb; and 39,000 pounds of calves. "This looked so easy," he reported to the Soil Conservation Service, "that I decided to increase my wool clip to 25,000 pounds by raising the number of sheep.

"This worked fine for several years. In 1939 I added goats and by 1942 had ninety animals on every section. This was the year I noticed a big change—I sheared only 16,000 pounds of wool, an average of 6.7 per sheep, and produced only 36,000 pounds of lamb—an average of 51 pounds. It was then I decided a ranch has a limit to its production.

"I have cut my units about one-fourth and have my sheep shearing 8.5 pounds, the lambs weighing 61 pounds, and the calves 460. My calf and lamb crops are higher, I buy feed only for bucks and bulls, and my death loss and breeding cost are less. Before 1946 I used about fifty tons of feed; this year it was only ten tons." [17]

It has been stated that "if all the corn and soybeans planted in Iowa in 1944 had been planted on the contour, then the farmers in the state would have had $37,000,000 more money to spend in 1945 than they actually did have." The estimate was based on minimum expected increases, in bushels per acre, of two and a half bushels for beans and five bushels for corn.[18] That year, it should be remembered, had favorable weather; prices were relatively low; there were neither floods nor droughts of serious proportions; had there been, the potential return to the farmers, per bushel, would have been even greater.

A Human Resource

One resource, the value of which has never been adequately appreciated, is the men and women engaged in conservation activities in federal service, universities and colleges, and in some of the state governments and private organizations. Through the years I have known scores of them. Their intelligence and dedication to their work are one of our mightiest national assets. A high proportion of them are shamefully underpaid, in terms of what their intelligence and personality could earn in the business world.

Two of them, Gifford Pinchot and Hugh H. Bennett, have probably done more for their country than any except our greatest presidents. Pinchot, with the support of Theodore Roosevelt, fought and won the first major conservation battles in behalf of our forests. He was responsible for the establishment of the U.S. Forest Service and, probably more than any other man, made conservation a familiar word in our vocabulary. Hugh Bennett campaigned nearly twenty years in defense of the soil before he received an adequate hearing. A combination of scientist, administrator, and evangelical preacher, he held virtual revival meetings in behalf of the land from one end of the country to the other. Under his leadership, the U.S. Soil Conservation Service was built; it is recognized throughout the world as the finest organization of its kind. In some parts of the country it has been incredibly successful; indeed, when one considers what it has achieved in thirteen years, its record stands as one of our proudest national accomplishments. The people of America, a thousand years from now—provided they have not been wiped out through wars or other catastrophes—will continue to enjoy the benefits that came into being through the great faith, selflessness, and ability of these two men and their fellow workers.

Despite the impressive conservation record of the United States, we are still losing ground, figuratively as well as literally. We continue to go into our land capital; and demands—both national and international—on our land and associated resources are steadily increasing. At a time when we are faced with the greatest shortage of timber in our history, industry is developing a multiplicity of new uses for wood. Some of this increased demand will be taken care of by more efficient use of wood waste but, despite this, the trend is steadily toward greater reduction of our forest reserves. Incredible though it seems, there are still in the United States 136,000,000 acres of forest land without organized fire protection! One of the worst forest fires in history occurred in Alaska in 1947, where Congress had crippled the Interior Department fire fighters by an appropriation cut.

The world demands for food, and correlated high prices, have sent our agriculture sprawling back into that ecological half-world where all is well—*if* it rains. It is estimated that twelve million acres that should not be cultivated have once again been placed under the plow, and government officials state that the only thing that saved us from a reappearance of the Dust Bowl in 1947 was unusually heavy precipitation.

With world populations as well as our own climbing, there is no likelihood of a decreased need for food for many decades to come; food—which means our land—has become a major political weapon in a world struggle. Higher living standards among low-income groups during the war have increased the national appetite for meat, which can be supplied at home only through overstocking—and destruction—of our ranges. Argentine mutton, superior to most of the meat produced in the United States, could be imported, but the sheep raisers will not permit it.

Cultivation of unsuitable land, bad agricultural methods, deforestation, and overgrazing played their usual part in increasing the rate of runoff and contributed to the serious floods of the spring of 1947; the cycle goes round and round, and comes out in the Gulf of Mexico. Enormous hurdles must be cleared if our nation is to be placed on a sustained-yield basis. Ever higher bars are added by the need to alleviate distress and thus diminish political tensions in the rest of the world.

THE INADEQUACY OF CONGRESS

One of the loftiest hurdles to be cleared is the Congress. Its shortcomings merely mirror some of the shortcomings of our way of life. The Congress represents the people, and is of the people. It almost certainly possesses a higher average of intelligence and education than the electorate as a whole. With rare exceptions, it is composed of sincere, honest men who work extremely hard at one of the most important jobs in the world.

But this, unfortunately, is not enough in an overpopulated world whose complexity is almost beyond human understanding; most members of Congress are unaware of man's impact on his environment and its impact on him. The Aristotelian cast of our education tends to exaggerate emphasis on the things they know best. The great majority of them are unacquainted with the ecological field, or even methods of scientific research. Many of them pride themselves on being "practical" men, ignorant of the definition of a practical man as "one who follows the theories of forty years ago." They have not brought to their evaluation of land-use research the understanding of our eminently practical industrial leaders, who spend hundreds of millions of dollars on scientific investigations, many of which cannot have immediate "practical" applications. Few congressmen have any comprehension of the necessity of understanding climates, soils, plant successions, plant and animal competition, plant and animal numbers, limiting factors, and the host of complex interrelationships. Our lawmakers are trained for the most part as lawyers, and know as little of biophysical law as the average biologist does of corporation law. Because of lack of appreciation of the problems of people who work on the land, they are intolerant of these problems; they have still not learned that *we need to know what we are doing*. They are often suspicious of government advisers—unfortunately, at times, with some justification—and they have not provided themselves competent advisers outside of government bureaus. By and large, their methods of evaluating scientific work done by the government they control have advanced little, if any, in a hundred years.

They spend hundreds of millions of dollars and influence millions of lives in fields of which they are profoundly ignorant. A comparable situation would exist in having five hundred members of the American Association for the Advancement of Science reorganize the country's tax structure, or in appointing an eminent pomologist to the Supreme Court. Scientists will dedicate twenty or thirty years to learning about a subject and finding out what needs to be done—and then they must take orders from Congress as to what they may do. Management of our country's resources is not likely to be put on a sustained-yield basis until Congress learns that there is a great deal about which it is ignorant, and gets competent, objective advisers.

Congress must learn that, in the long run, it is more economical to lose a hundred million dollars a year on land-use research than to save a hundred million dollars at the expense of our land and resources. Most members of Congress seem not to realize that a research project that fails is often as valuable as, and at times more valuable than, one that succeeds; we need to know what we cannot do, as well as what we can. The Congress, in respect to research, has too often been like an oil company executive who insists that all drilling must bring in wells.

As a result, government research has long been hobbled. Scientific investigations can rarely be brought to successful conclusion within one year, yet budgetary limitations reduce the planning of long-range research to the level of mere hopefulness. The results of much costly research lie buried in bureau files because funds are not available for publication. The history of government is littered with the wrecks of other potentially valuable scientific investigations that had to be abandoned because Congress would not continue to finance them.

COUNTRY OF THE BLIND

Again, the damage this does results from our elementalistic, Aristotelian heritage. We think in compartments and, finding limited solutions that ignore the major part of highly complicated problems, we assume we have "all" the knowledge we need. If we are religious, we pray when we should be building dams and setting up birth-control clinics. If we are liberals, our creed begins, "I believe in God and economic reform." If we belong to the Union League, we are convinced that the world will be saved by cutting loose all controls except those that protect our own dividends. If we are Communists, we have faith that the police state will coerce us all into righteousness. It is rare, indeed, that our education has shown us the dynamic, ever-changing relationships between the actions of man and his total environment. Neither the Congress nor the electorate understands this.

Even our topflight scientists display unhappy ignorance in these matters. A president of the American Association for the Advancement of Science recently pleaded for commercial exploitation of the brush and second-growth forests of New England hillsides, apparently with a total unconsciousness of their role in bringing back timber, controlling erosion, protecting wildlife, and stabilizing the hydrologic cycle. Discussions of a National Science Foundation, beginning with the "Bush Plan," have emphasized medical, industrial, and military research and almost totally neglected the relationship of biology and physics to the land—a field in which we are appallingly retarded. Many "natural scientists" oppose including "social scientists" under the National Science Foundation, despite the fact that we must depend on the social scientists to have reasonable use made of the fruits of natural science. Until a realization of the relationship between man and his environment has become part of our education and a principal basis of its orientation, a long-range improvement of land use is improbable. We must understand this relationship, sense it so deeply that it colors our feeling about children, country, laws, survival, foreign relations, and nearly every other thought and emotion we have. We need a revolution, in Kropotkin's sense of a profound change of fundamental ideas.

Meanwhile, in large part because we have only begun to comprehend our relationship to the land, we are undermined by an ecological Fifth Column that is selling out our country whenever and wherever it can find a buyer. It is composed of pressure groups—lumbermen operating both in the United

States and abroad, farmers, stock raisers, Chambers of Commerce, labor unions, etc. Not all of these pressure groups are bad, by any means, but enough of them have tripped the process of sound resource management often enough to represent a national danger. An egregious example is the electric power monopoly that has fought, by fair means and foul, the orderly development of our watersheds. *The good of the individual, and even of groups, must often be sacrificed for the general good.* Until we understand this and accept it as a basis of resource-management policy, we are not likely to progress far toward a harmonious relationship with the land.

One of the major obstacles in the way of a rational forestry program is our landownership pattern. Ninety per cent of the timber-growing capacity of the United States is on private lands, held by four or five million private owners. Many of these have tracts so small that they cannot afford to maintain a sustained-yield program. Timber ownership is often in isolated, inaccessible blocks, and surrounded or obstructed by lands of the big operators. Also, the owners of small tracts usually lack the technical knowledge requisite to sound management.

Whatever the answer, sustained yield must be achieved, in the national interest. Some European countries have found a solution in public ownership, as in our system of national and state forests, and by controlled cutting that requires official permission before a tree may be felled. This last system would be, to put it mildly, odious to many American timber owners, whose ideas have survived from the days when we thought we had no timber problem. A compromise between forest control and the free-ownership system was proposed in a bill introduced into the 79th Congress, which would have extended to private timber owners benefits comparable to those paid to farmers. In other words, the taxpayer would have been saddled with an additional load to bolster up a timber-ownership system that has been out of date fifty years. Perhaps, in view of the emotions involved, some such approach is unavoidable.

KALLIKAKS OF THE LAND

The question of how to solve our forest problem opens up the wide, grim vista of ecological incompetence. The Jukeses and the Kallikaks—at least those who are obtrusively incompetent—we support as public charges. We do the same with the senile, the incurables, the insane, the paupers, and those who might be called ecological incompetents, such as the subsidized stockmen and sheepherders. These last, in so far as they deteriorate and destroy the grasses, expedite erosion, and contribute to flood peaks, are worse than paupers. They exist by destroying the means of national survival; were we really intelligent about our future, we should recognize such people as ecological Typhoid Marys—the source of environmental sickness with which they are infecting us all. The same is true of the cutout-and-get-out lumberman, the wheatgrower who recklessly sets the trigger for a new dust-bowl explosion, the hunter or trapper who takes more than his share of *surplus* animals, and the farmer who exhausts his soil and fails to utilize soil-stabilization methods.

These individuals are comparable to the patent medicine manufacturers of three decades ago. The nostrums poisoning Americans were finally wiped out or controlled. It is obviously more important to control the destruction of the grasses, forests, and soils on which our national survival depends. The stockraising business, lumber business, hunting and fishing, even much farming, have overextended themselves like other businesses. But here, except through slow-moving processes, there is no way of increasing capital. In relation to existing resources, these industries—or at least substantial sections of them—are essentially bankrupt. They have not only emptied the bank vaults; they are trying to keep alive by peddling the desks, chairs, and cuspidors. In our national interest they must be liquidated, at least in part. In the process, a good many people are certain to be hurt, as in any liquidation. But the longer it is postponed the more people will suffer.

One of the chief causes of our ecologic imbalance is our economic thinking. We identify the symbolic dollar with real wealth, which is very like talking of yards of heat. We discuss national income as though it were somehow different from national outgo. We write books to discuss whether or not we can "afford" to conserve soil.[19] We extract oil, and iron ore, and fine timber, and canvasbacks, and call it *production*. By a distortion of the Prometheus myth, we gobble our own liver and congratulate ourselves on a good meal. The money evaluation of the exploitative lumberman, farmer, stockman, trapper, and industrialist—of our growing population—must be subordinated to a biophysical evaluation; our place in international affairs must be measured by the same yardstick. Our ancestors were known, by the people they displaced, as the Long Knives. It is about time we stopped scalping our continent. We are tangled in a monstrous web of semantic confusion and until we abandon such identification, discriminate among the levels of abstraction, we are not likely to break our bonds.

Too Many Americans

It has been asserted that, at Asiatic standards, North America could support a population of 577,000,000.[20] In terms of what we like to think of as American standards, especially since in self-defense we must help feed the rest of the world, we are now probably overpopulated. In the opinion of one of our foremost population students, our optimum would be 100,-000,000. He says, "The larger the population the larger the amount of farm land, mineral deposits, and other natural resources which must be used, or the more intensively a given amount must be worked to provide the basic necessities of life. Since our farm lands and mineral deposits vary in quality and accessibility, working a larger quantity of them will necessitate working poorer grades. Both this expansion and intensification of methods tend to reduce the average production per worker, which in turn tends to lower wages in industries or raise the prices of their products. Either will lower the living levels of the population.

". . . a population of 100,000,000, as compared with 150,-000,000, in the United States should have a higher output per worker in agriculture, forestry, and mining, about the same output in manufacturing and trade, and a lower output in communication and transportation. Considering the fact that in 1930 agriculture and mining employed about three times as many workers as transportation and communication and supported a still larger proportion of persons, the net advantage lies clearly on the side of a smaller population than the present, rather than a larger population. The United States is *now* over-populated from the standpoint of per capita economic welfare . . ." [21]

It might be objected that mechanization of agriculture in the years since the 1930 census has increased the output per worker. This, if true, is far from an unmixed blessing. The drift away from family farms to the city labor pool reduces the effectiveness of the self-contained rural population as an economic shock absorber. In the next depression there will be several million unemployed on the relief rolls who, if our farms had not been mechanized, would be able to take care of themselves and their families on at least a subsistence basis. Mechanization is of dubious value to the land, as it is more purely extractive than older methods; one does not find a manure pile outside the tractor shed. Furthermore, it tends to put under cultivation Class IV to VI land which, before the advent of the tractor, would have been kept in pasture. Were it not for mechanization, the Great Plains wheatlands would not be in such great danger.

What is going to happen to our increasingly mechanized agriculture as the petroleum famine overtakes us, or as the necessity of importing gasoline or refining it from coal or shale boosts its price? No one seems to have determined this.

Another high hurdle in the way of progress toward sound land use is the problem of farm tenantry. For many years agricultural economists have been concerned over the increase of absentee ownership of farm lands. More and more these have become the property of banks, insurance companies, and other nonoperators. Because sharecroppers and other farm tenants do not have a long-range stake in the land, their tendency—a reflection of our industrial philosophy—is to make as large a profit as possible and to spend on the land as little as possible. The high costs of tiling, drainage, fallowing, long-range rotations, wood-lot management, etc., are not likely to be undertaken by a man who next year may have to move to another farm. A promising if quite inadequate attack on this problem has been made in the shape of government loans to tenants, which permit them to buy their land, but there is no certainty of continuation of the program. This problem is a knotty one, especially on run-down, relatively unproductive farms that need to be restored to their full capacity.

Too Many Cities

A political influence militating against an improvement in land use is the trend from rural to urban concentrations. Sixty per cent of our people now live in towns of 2,500 or over; 30 per cent live in cities of 100,000 or more. These people, with a disproportionate influence in electing congressmen and state legislators—disproportionate from the point of view of land management—tend not to think beyond the butchershop, the can of spinach, and the milk bottle. They have little realization of their dependence on the soil, grasslands, forests, wildlife, and underground waters.

It is no exaggeration to say that in educating our urban voters to understand the land our school system has been a miserable failure. This might have been offset, to some extent, had such government agencies as the Soil Conservation Service, National Park Service, and U.S. Forest Service been permitted to carry on adequate educational activities. There is probably less likelihood of this today than there might have been twenty-five years ago, because of the attitude of Congress that almost any educational effort carried on by government departments is *ipso facto* an attempt to build prestige and secure greater appropriations. The majority of school children in the United States have probably never seen the vivid publications of the Soil Conservation Service. Ten million dollars a year spent on the bulletins and films of this service, and more millions on those of the Forest Service, Fish and Wildlife Service, National Park Service, etc., to teach the nation's school children the concept of sound land use, would be about as effective national insurance as one could conceive. The Departments of Agriculture and Interior work on the land and with the people who work on the land. It is high time they also began to work with the scores of millions to whom the land is merely a place where one spends vacations.

Excessive exploitation by ten or twenty million people, when the continent was opening up, may have been defensible, as Craven suggests. For a long period after the settlement of Virginia, North America was producing more than man was extracting. But with the destruction of the environment and with increasing population, that day has long since passed. The present living standard for 145,000,000 people is being maintained only by living on our resource capital. Within about a hundred and fifty years we have lost one-third of our topsoil, more than half of our high-grade timber, an unknown proportion of reserve waters, and a large but unmeasured part of our wild-life. As we reduce our capital, our income from interest naturally falls; so we use still more capital.

Obviously, this cannot continue indefinitely. In terms of lost productive capacity and the cost of patching up the damage we have already inflicted on the continent, we have heavily mortgaged the welfare of our children and grandchildren—as our ancestors put ours in pawn. The railroad barons wrote tragedy across the Great Plains, the lumbermen crippled at birth a thousand rivers; John Jacob Astor and the Gentlemen-Adventurers squeezed the lifeblood out of our landscape when their trappers destroyed the beaver whose dams had held back the little waters. The Great Plains are still being sold out to the highest bidder—as wheat and livestock; lumbermen think that thirty pieces of silver paid for land entitles them to destroy for all time the catch basin of our rivers; and if the beaver are no longer here to control the floods, we shall do it—say the ecologically ignorant—with concrete and billions of dollars. Our ancestors skimmed the continent's cream; we are rapidly separating out the butterfat that is left.

The destruction of our land and associated resources is not going to affect only our material standard of living. If we had to look forward merely to less automobiles, less ornate plumbing, less of the trash the radio dins into our homes, less of the meretriciousness in which Hollywood specializes, less gadgets of all kinds, a greater divergence from the living standards set for us by movie stars, we should have little to worry about. One of the great weaknesses of our civilization is the value we place upon *things*, and the abuse we feel as we are deprived of them. If destruction of land resources could return us to cultivation of inner resources, as during the period of New England's flowering, we should be a happier, serener, and more stable people.

But our growing national poverty will not stop with this. As our wealth goes down the rivers with the runoff it must inevitably carry with it a fall in purchasing power, and a consequent industrial dislocation. The sense of security known to most Americans a hundred years ago, when it was possible to put by enough for one's old age, has been largely replaced by a social "security" system that offers little more than an old-fashioned almshouse. What is it going to be worth forty or fifty years from now, when millions really need it, if our soil and water, forests and grasslands, the basis of our national wealth, have been destroyed at the same rate as during the past fifty years?

WAKE UP, AMERICA!

Democracy can survive, in our widely integrated world, only if it is guided by an adult, educated electorate. Insecurity breeds immaturity, and as we struggle to adjust to an ever-poorer, more uncertain world, we shall find the attainment of adulthood more and more elusive. As the means of producing wealth—again our natural resources—shrinks, as our living standard washes down our rivers, the fast we have imposed on our schools and libraries may develop into a famine; our entire educational system may sink to the level of Alabama's or Mississippi's. Even the possibility of this is an evil portent for a free people.

Without an abundant and balanced diet, without resources of water, timber, minerals, without dependable supplies of food from good soils, freedom from floods, dust storms, clogging reservoirs, our nation can remain neither strong, great—nor, in this overpeopled world, safe from aggression.

I am not suggesting that such decadence lies in store for the United States. It need not. We, more than any other people on earth, are aware of this problem, and intellectually (if not emotionally) prepared to cope with it. The future of our country is within our control. But a few more decades of such abuse as we have subjected it to will wrest the control out of our hands. We shall be slipping toward the oblivion of Ur, of Timgad, of Angkor Wat, of the North Chinese, the ancient Mayans, and at a speed too great to check.

The greatest danger may lie in lack of time to apply the brakes.

Chapter 7

The Land on Edge

Aʟʟ Lᴀᴛɪɴ Aᴍᴇʀɪᴄᴀɴ ᴄᴏᴜɴᴛʀɪᴇꜱ ᴇxᴄᴇᴘᴛ ᴛʜʀᴇᴇ ᴏʀ four are overpopulated. They are able to feed and shelter their citizens, and supply water for their many needs, only by a progressive and accelerating destruction of natural resources; biological bankruptcy hangs over their heads like a shaking avalanche. It has already fallen on Haiti and El Salvador, where hundreds of thousands of people are slowly starving to death. Unless there is a profound modification in its treatment of the land, the greater part of Mexico will be a desert within one hundred years, unable to supply even the fifteen hundred daily calories on which the average Salvadorian (and thousands of Mexicans) must now subsist.[1] The same fate is in store for Chile, in perhaps fewer years.

Were it possible to eliminate the time factor, the future of this important area—52 per cent of the Western Hemisphere's land surface—could be regarded much more optimistically. Unhappily, one of the most critical factors is time, and the Latin Americans are losing this along with their other resources.

The Latin American equation, like that of everyone in the modern world, is limitlessly complex; our twenty neighbor nations to the south are the resultant of many forces. The leaders in many of the countries are still hampered by a cultural lag that had its origins in sixteenth-century Spain and nineteenth-century France. Their people have been exploited by foreign countries for many years, and some of their gravest difficulties incubated in this exploitation. The lotus-dream of North American living standards is wafting many Latin Americans into a Never-Never Land, whose golden light casts an impossible sheen over reality. Some of their hungry and discontented masses are reaching for a Soviet-Lydia Pinkham compound that, quite without reference to their own basic pathology, they are certain will bring a cure.

In this tangled skein there are three strands that stand out with dominating color. One is dyed by geography, and the other two by European and primitive New World folkways.

THE HOSTILE LAND

Latin America's geography is the harshest and most inescapable factor limiting its human betterment. If the reader does not have a clear memory of the relief that characterizes the Western Hemisphere from the Rio Grande to Cape Horn, he will do well to read this chapter with a good map in front of him—preferably such a map as that published by the American Geographical Society. Even a cursory glance at this will show what an extremely small proportion of level or near-level land is to be found in the Latin American republics. Russia has her Ukraine, the United States and Canada their Corn and Wheat Belts, and Latin America has only the pampas.

Chilean and Argentine Patagonia is a semisteppe, with but thirteen inches of rain per year. It produces coarse grass, of low carrying capacity, and is fit only for grazing. It is already overgrazed in some areas, with a resultant degeneration of the range through the invasion of plants of low palatability; and it is reported to be suffering from wind erosion. The high and relatively level plateau northwest of Rio de Janeiro has poor soils and deficient rainfall, and can be used, again, only for light grazing. It is comparable to our own Southwest. Northeastern Brazil is plagued by frequent, killing droughts. In its level areas, the enormous Amazon Basin is covered with a heavy rain forest. Its soils are poor, and when the forest is removed, indispensable chemicals are rapidly leached out by rainfall that exceeds seven feet per year in places. The organic matter at the surface of the soil is oxidized, under the excessively high temperatures of the tropical sun, "like burning magnesium powder," as one geographer has put it.

The coastal plains, greatly extended during the past eight hundred years by soil eroded down from the uplands, also suffer from excessive heat and rain. Banana culture on the coasts of Central America often runs within seven or eight years from virgin forest to abandoned brush land. The *llanos* of Venezuela, the only additional level area of any extent, are poor in soil for the most part and receive a very unfavorable rainfall—excessive for part of the year and inadequate for the rest.[2]

Except for the Argentine pampas, these lands have such low carrying capacity that farmers are largely restricted to small intermont basins or forced up the slopes. The intermont basins, for reasons that will presently be explained, do not begin to support the populations they should. On the slopes, the land is being washed out from beneath the farmers' feet.

In the United States it is generally true that any grade of more than 5 per cent requires special treatment by the farmer, in the nature of strip cropping, contour plowing, or terracing. Population pressures and landholding systems have forced the Latin-American farmer to cultivate slopes of 100 per cent or more. On some soils, tree crops like coffee can safely be grown, especially where such terracing is used as El Salvador's. But, even though many Latin-American soils are far less erodible than those in our own country, they are being lost at an appalling rate. Over most of the southern continent, *soil erosion is all but universal on cultivated lands.*

AN OLD SPANISH CUSTOM

A second dominating force throughout Latin America is the Spanish tradition of centralized government, imposed on the New World; this goes back at least to the time of Julius Caesar. It has been kept alive by ruling groups, including government officials, and many and powerful unfavorable influences stem from it. Almost without exception, capital cities and provinces receive a disproportionate share of both national income and government service. The country dweller is the forgotten man and his environment is neglected—except for exploitation. It has been said with painful truthfulness, of the United States, that "local government here at home is a reeking shambles of corruption, incompetence, waste and misrule." [3] Where local government is weak or inconsequential, as in most of Latin America, the corruption and incompetence are likely to be characteristic of national governments. For this reason there is, at present, little possibility of responsible and intelligent management of natural resources in relation to population needs.

Politicians feather their own nests and those of their friends. They sell out to the highest bidder on the national scale, as our "bosses" do on the local. Business is able to maintain the living standard it desires only by corrupting government, as in the pattern described by Lincoln Steffens forty-five years ago. So much money is stolen and payrolls are so thoroughly padded that many governments cannot pay living wages to responsible, able employees or carry on such activities as are necessary to resource management. One government actually set up a $250,000 fund for erosion control under direction of an American specialist; of this sum he received $1,300, a mule valued at $300, and a typewriter—without ribbon.

In some countries technical training is a distinct liability. The politicos who run the ministries cannot afford to have under them men who really know what is going on. A civil service is nonexistent, with a few conspicuous exceptions such as the Guano Administration of Peru. The personnel of many government departments change not only with administrations but often with kaleidoscopic shifts in ministers that in some countries take place every five or six months. Over much of the hemisphere, as a Latin-American scientist observed, the number one problem is moral erosion; until it is controlled, the problem of soil erosion, certainly next in importance, cannot possibly be resolved.

THE INDIAN MOVES MOUNTAINS

Probably the third most important element in this factorial tangle throughout most of Latin America is the progressive, or milpa, system of agriculture, handed down by indigenous populations. In primitive times, when the aborigines possessed only crude tools, they would hack down some trees, burn others to make a clearing, and then use fire to burn off the remainder of the vegetation. They would till a patch of land for three or four or more years, depending on local conditions, until its fertility had been exhausted, and then move on to a new tract and repeat the process. Meanwhile, the first tract would be allowed to lie fallow for perhaps as much as twenty or thirty years, until some of its fertility had been restored. In areas where rainfall was not excessive, populations were small, and slopes not highly erodible, this system of agriculture worked reasonably well. In other areas, such as highland Honduras, Guatemala, and Mexico, it brought about a progressive destruction of the land, and archaeologists attribute the fall of highland Mayan and early Mexican civilizations to the milpa.

Ephraim is wedded to his idols, and over hundreds of thousands of square miles of Latin America milpa agriculture is still the dominant system. But whereas under primitive conditions it could be defended in many areas as perhaps the only feasible method, there are few parts of the New World where it is not disastrous today. Populations have grown several hundred per cent, and the need for cultivable land is increasingly pressing. It is no longer possible to fallow as it was in pre-Conquest times. The steel ax and the machete have made the destructive activities of the small farmer far more vicious.

Under primitive conditions, scratching sticks and drills were used in planting corn, the principal crop required by native American populations. These are still used in many areas, and they cause a minimum destruction of the land. Cheap plows, however, drawn by oxen—another European innovation—strip the land of its vegetative cover and open it to the full erosive impact of torrential tropical rains that sometimes exceed 112 inches a month!

Lesley Byrd Simpson called a brilliant chapter in his *Many Mexicos*, "The Tyrant." By "the tyrant" he means corn. The dependence of the Latin American masses on corn, coupled with increased population and modern methods of agriculture, has played a far more influential part in the history of most of this area than have all other factors combined.

The Spanish tradition, imposed upon the Indian tradition and reinforced by the modern competitive economic system, has resulted in one of the most vampirish, extractive economies existing anywhere in the world today. The United States, still going into the red in terms of its natural resources, is spending in the neighborhood of a billion dollars a year on conservation. Latin America, with a larger population and after hundreds of years of destruction, is spending less than 1 per cent of this amount.

THE WATERS ARE UNCHAINED

One of the gravest problems throughout the entire region is the lack of fuel. It is probable that at least seventy-five million people depend on charcoal and cordwood for cooking, heating, and even for industrial purposes. British-owned railroads in El Salvador run wood-burning locomotives in a country that is almost without forests. Railroads depend on the same fuel in Peru, Brazil, Mexico, and many other countries. In Brazil, cordwood for the locomotives is transported as much as ninety miles, by truck and cart.[4] In Brazil and Chile, wood is still used for smelting minerals, as it was by the Spaniards in the sixteenth century. Wood for fuel is undoubtedly the most important single crop in all of Latin America, yet not one of the twenty republics has a forestry department that even approaches adequacy; and there is not one of them that is not exhausting its capital in terms of available and useful woods. It is estimated by various technicians in Chile that the quantity of forest destroyed by fire is from six to thirteen times as great as that destroyed by lumbering. In 1944, forest fires spread over a quarter of a million acres of Chile's forests—and the Chilean government did not have a single fire warden or forester in its employ.

As a result of the irresponsible destruction of forests, the entire hydrologic regime of Latin America is being dislocated. Waters, freed of the leash imposed on them by the plant cover of the uplands, are ripping away the surface of the soil, carrying heavy loads of silt, flooding towns and cities, blocking navigation, destroying hundreds of people. In 1947 the Grace Line canceled all sailings to Barranquilla, Colombia's second largest port, because of silt deposited by the Magdalena River. This stream, only 950 miles long, according to Colombian engineers carries more soil than the 4,000-mile Mississippi-Missouri. Water tables are falling even in countries like El Salvador and Chile, where there is a rainfall of some six feet a year.

Adjusting human needs to resources so as to maintain a reasonable living standard on a permanent basis is an extremely complex and delicate problem. Soil-conservation methods applicable in Georgia are useless in Costa Rica. The work of plant breeders to improve crops in the Northern Hemisphere is largely lost when these crops are transferred to environments where day length, temperature, rainfall, plant diseases, and insect pests weave entirely different biological patterns. In countries of such highly pronounced relief, a distance of ten miles will produce as much difference in climate as would require 500 miles in the United States. Just as no two human beings are exactly alike, and just as every cow pasture in the United States has its own physical and biotic pattern, so do the regions of Latin America vary.

THE SCIENTIFIC VACUUM

But the variation is far more exaggerated. To cope intelligently with the problems that stem from the extreme variations requires reliable climatic data over long periods. Biological surveys, covering both plant and animal life, are indispensable before land managers can even know what species they are talking about. The limiting factors that hold down the numbers of desirable species, from nitrogen-fixing bacteria in the soil to rodent-controlling hawks, must be known if useful elements of the environment are to be increased. The normal relationships among the climates, soils, fauna, and flora that produced the environment invaded by modern man have scarcely begun to be studied—as they must be if man is not to boggle land management. The factors limiting fungus plant diseases, and destructive insects such as the locust hordes that ravage Central and South America, also need to be known in order that these numbers may be held as low as is desirable. Statistical data and the training to interpret them are a *sine qua non* in the world of modern biology, whether this biology is concerned with plants, man, or the so-called lower animals. Soil surveys and analyses are basic to the improvement of agriculture. If human beings are to receive the greatest benefit from products of the land, we need to know something of their nutritional needs and the ability of the soil to satisfy them. Without the results of research, it is impossible to evaluate the effect of unintelligent or venal exploitation of the land.

In Latin America, even such elementary data as resource inventories are nonexistent. No business could hope to survive without inventories. How much more difficult is it to manage the complex of natural resources without knowing what they are, where they are, and in what quantities they exist! The complacency with which most Latin Americans accept their resource destruction is undoubtedly due to this absence of inventories. There is no way for them to see what is happening.

As this book is written, only the Argentine among the Latin-

American republics can be said to have an adequate meteorological service, as the means of securing climatological data. In only Argentina and Mexico is significant climatological research being done, and in the latter country the brilliance of the investigations is considerably dimmed by the lack of information. Not more than two or three countries are carrying on any sort of forest research, and these programs are picayune. Not more than two or three countries have even initiated respectable soils research. The same is true of biological surveys. The situation is even worse in regard to hydrological surveys.

A few valiant and high-minded research men are carrying on useful investigations, but their poverty frequently walls them off from the discoveries of the rest of the world. In countries where the cost of living is at higher levels than in the United States, government and university scientists often receive salaries of less than $100 a month. Most scientific workers must hold two or three jobs to make ends meet. A brilliant research biologist will have to teach high school in order to feed his children. Government interference and the spoils system in many countries require that a scientist be primarily a politician; sharp elbows may have a greater survival value than brains. In no more than one or two countries does there exist even the degree of co-ordination that the United States has, through its Department of Agriculture, Department of the Interior, agricultural colleges, universities, and scientific societies.

Nor is there much prospect (in 1948) that this situation will improve. Many Latin American universities are still medieval in their didactic methods of teaching. Others follow the pattern of France of seventy-five years ago. So-called botanists will reel off hundreds of scientific names and not be able to identify a score of plants in the field. They have never heard of Louis Agassiz's cry: "If you study nature in books, when you go out of doors you cannot find her!" Despite the millions of dollars that are spent on highways, armies, and graft, the povery of most Latin American institutions of higher learning is so stringent that biologists must work without laboratories or libraries. An entire biology class will often have only one poor microscope. The unavailability of scientific journals and reference books makes it impossible for a man to stay au courant of his field, even if he has secured good initial training. In many Latin American universities, scientific teaching is below the level of that of good high schools in Scandinavian countries, Great Britain, or the United States. This is not, it should be emphasized, for lack of intelligence or ability. Latin Americans are aggressively proud of their culture, and prone to regard Anglo-Saxons as little better than barbarians. Latin American poets and philosophers are nearly as common as salesmen are here; but physicists, zoologists, botanists, physiologists, geographers, and ecologists are rarities, and when they are turned up they are usually found to be suffering from malnutrition.

No Thought for the Morrow

As a corollary to the absence of research, there is an almost complete void in the field of resource management. El Salvador, with more than six hundred people per square mile of arable land, has only now established a Department of Agriculture. Mexico, which was once a heavily forested country, has slipped into a state of forest famine. Modern concepts of selective cutting and silviculture are all but unheard of; the country is depending on an old law that requires the planting of the somehow magical number of three trees for every one that is cut down. Needless to say, a mordida—payment of graft—costs the lumber exploiters less than a reforestation program, and forest production in Mexico is sixty to eighty years behind destruction. The same is true of Chile, except that in Chile one does not even have to pay a mordida.

In the tropical countries, accessible timber, the only timber that has actual economic value, is being rapidly wiped out. Even were there a desire for sound management of the tropical forests, the requisite scientific knowledge is nonexistent. No country, with the possible exception of Argentina, has a soil-conservation service that even approaches the adequate. Not a single country south of the Rio Grande is conserving its wild-life resources. As fast as man is able to get at game—including such birds as robins—and fur bearers he exterminates them. The only defense of the creatures is the inaccessibility of the lands in which they live, the poverty of the people, which makes the purchase of firearms difficult. But there is enough hunting with slingshots and traps so that many species have been ex-tirpated from large areas. Nor can we fairly censure the people for this killing. There is consternation when we are asked to give up meat one day a week; millions of Latin Americans eat meat one day a week—or less.

The possibilities of conservation in Latin America are dimin-ished by the patterns of landownership. In the majority of countries large tracts of land, and in virtually all countries the best land, is in the hands of large landowners. These frequently know little or nothing about agriculture or land management, and they judge the condition of their lands by this year's re-turns. In Central America, the finest lands are generally held in large coffee fincas and ranches or by foreign corporations. The mass of the population is forced up the hillsides, onto slopes and soils that can only be destroyed by current methods of subsistence agriculture. In most countries, it is no uncom-mon sight to see fine herds grazing on intermont valley lands that have been washed down from Indian milpas above. Any rational system of land use would, of course, put the corn on the bottom lands and the cattle on the slopes.

The purely exploitative attitude of the majority of the large landowners, plus their frequent ignorance of agriculture, re-sults in every possible abuse. To bring quick profits, forests are burned, rather than selectively cut or maintained as wood-lots, in order to get new and fertile land. The need for fertiliz-ers is almost universally ignored; many landholders would rather spend money on a trip to New York than on the main-tenance of farm fertility.

On most of these areas nothing is done to check erosion. In Chile, for example, where I have traveled some 10,000 miles, I saw soil erosion on well over 90 per cent of the cultivated slopes and in the central part of the country on *all* the slopes where cattle were grazed. In this entire distance I saw only one field plowed on the contour!

Mexico has attempted to break the old pattern of the latifundio by reverting to an approximation of early Indian communities, the ejido. This well-meant attempt, which grew out of the undoubted idealism of men like Juárez, Zapata, and Madero, and was largely brought to maturity by President Lázaro Cárdenas, has very generally backfired. The ejidos were established on a communal pattern, in which the farmer was often given a totally inadequate tract of land. With perhaps ten acres for a family, rotations, fallowing, grazing, and fertilizing are impossible. The ultimate tribute must be wrenched out of every square yard. Soil erosion is ripping down the ejidos. Many farmers are so uneducated that they do not know how to manage their land. Land hunger has spilled the ejidos over onto many tracts totally unfit for agriculture. Political corruption has entered, even here, and the ejidatario may cut trees and plant potatoes in national parks in disregard of the laws. He can usually find some politician to "tear up his ticket." (These comments on Mexico, it should be pointed out, were written before President Alemán had had time to prove the effectiveness of his effort to exorcise the mordida. He is working against heavy odds of custom, poverty, and apathy. If he succeeds, it will be one of the outstanding accomplishments of Latin American history. One may, perhaps, be pardoned for wondering whether his reform administration will not meet the usual fate of such attempts in Los Estados Unidos del Norte.)

THE MENACE OF MEDICINE

Upon all these factors there has been imposed a series of phenomena from the North, and from across the Atlantic, and the tangled skeins have been twisted until they form almost a Gordian knot. Well-meaning public health authorities, completely ignoring the problem of how millions of Latin Americans are to be fed, have helped to reduce the death rate. Yellow fever has been banished from most of Latin America. Malaria has been significantly reduced over wide areas. Smallpox is disappearing. Despite the growing difficulties occasioned by shrinking supplies, drinking water has been improved in many cities to such an extent that intestinal diseases, the most effective factor limiting populations, have dropped sharply. Like most of the rest of the world, most Latin American countries are facing the very pressing question of how to feed more young, hungry mouths.

Foreign markets for the raw materials of Latin America have expanded, and this again has tended to speed the soils down the slopes. Quebracho bark, for tanning, has been at a premium. The tree has been wiped out over large areas in Paraguay and the Argentine; little or nothing has been done to replace it. Chilean timber is finding an increasing market abroad, and an American forestry mission that visited Chile showed both the possibilities and the methods of forest exploitation and injected a large dose of adrenalin into the lumber industry. Up to the present time little or nothing has been done to replace trees that are being destroyed.

In this destruction of a continent, American lumbermen and American capital have played an important and disgraceful role. The sort of irresponsibility that destroyed much of the United States has been turned loose in the far more vulnerable environment of Latin America. Here there is neither organized public opinion nor sufficient technical knowledge to protect these basically poor countries against the despoilers. It will be to our eternal shame if we permit the destruction to continue.

If only in our own national self-interest, we should control American vandals abroad. We have spent many millions of dollars trying to prove that we mean what we say about the

Good Neighbor Policy—and at the same time we permit, even encourage, American businessmen to destroy the very means of subsistence of millions of people. This is an especially dangerous form of dollar diplomacy that can scarcely fail to have violent repercussions when the people of Latin America awake to what is being done to them. The fact that Latin Americans themselves are selling out their countries will be forgotten; the dead cats will be heaved at the Colossus of the North.

The development of oil fields in Venezuela has created an autophagous economy. Oil, a nonrenewable resource, is rapidly and surely being exhausted. For years the country has been content to float along on this golden tide, and has not even bothered to produce the crops, meat, and dairy products of which it is capable. The mass of the people, receiving little benefit from the oil, have carried on subsistence agriculture, with the result that Venezuela is one of the most eroded countries in the hemisphere. In 1948 it is budgeting $82,000,000 for public works, $35,000,000 for national defense—and $25,000,000 for agriculture.[5]

Partly as a military measure, the United States has been driving the Inter-American Highway south toward the Panama Canal, with some small help from the Central American countries. Local politics dictated to some extent the route followed by this road, and those who planned it explain its vagaries by saying they also wanted to make it as useful as possible to the countries through which it passes. They have been all too successful in speeding up communications, an end that might have been desirable were it not that the highway has become an instrument of destruction. The countries through which it passes are totally without the technical skills or the financial resources to manage the new lands it taps. This has made a holiday for such lumbermen as the Jim Hanrahan described in Chapter 1. Already, the result is devastation.

Not the least destructive force in Latin America today is what is thought of as the "American standard of living." This has sent all classes awhoring after strange gods, and may well prove one of the most troublesome influences loose in the Southern Hemisphere. The automobile, radio, and flush toilet, with which men from Omsk to Magallanes have decorated their altars, have been accepted by dictators and democrats alike as the norm by which life should be measured. American motion pictures are taken seriously south of the Rio Grande, and millions of people would like to live as they have come to think Americans live. American business has not been slow to take advantage of this desire, and the American government has pumped millions of the American taxpayer's dollars—or, one might say, of his working days—into Latin America in efforts to "raise the standard of living." That this has been done with a sometimes incredible degree of ignorance and lack of intelligence is more or less beside the point. For by no economic alchemy can the dross of the Latin American land be turned into the fine gold of the Northern Hemisphere's.

THE *Ignis Fatuus* OF INDUSTRIALIZATION

With the possible exception of Argentina and Brazil, the countries to the south of us are fundamentally and inescapably so poor that a living standard approaching that of the United States is unattainable. Thousands of Latin Americans are bemused by the word "industrialization" and assume that what this has meant to other parts of the world it can also mean to them. They ignore the fact that the coal that made possible the development of the European continent, Great Britain, and the United States is nonexistent south of the Rio Grande except for small deposits that are mostly of low grade. Some countries have high hopes of harnessing enough hydroelectric power to permit the development of industrial centers, but they overlook the remoteness of the sources of this power; in most cases they are beyond reach. Where waterfalls are accessible, watersheds are usually being denuded recklessly, without any apparent consideration of the relationship between plant cover and hydroelectric power. A most significant commentary on the possibility of industrializing Latin America is the fact that so few European and North American companies have attempted to establish branches in the Southern Hemisphere.

Latin America is Balkanized, in the political sense. Only Brazil, and possibly Mexico and Argentina, have large enough populations to offer sufficiently large internal markets to permit any degree of industrialization. And the masses of people in Brazil and Mexico, like the masses in most of their neighbor countries, are scarcely able to buy shoes. Latin American governments have traditionally depended on import taxes as a principal source of revenue, and they are now elevating these high taxes to protect the industries they are trying to establish. Were it possible to make visible the tariff barriers, Latin America would have the appearance of a series of walled nations. "For world prosperity we must have free markets," the economists tell us. And "to raise the standard of living we must industrialize." How a country like Chile or Mexico can industrialize without strong tariff protection the economists do not say.

Chile borrowed $21,000,000 from the United States to build a steel smelter. The great majority of its own population of five million rarely buys anything made of steel that is larger than a knife or a hatchet. Peru, with a population of seven million whose purchasing power per capita is lower than the Chilean (see Table 2), is also building a steel plant that will, of course, compete with Chilean and Brazilian steel.

The ideal of the Latin American businessman, unlike that of the North American, is high profits and small sales. In Chile, in 1942, a hand towel such as could have been bought in a ten-cent store in the United States cost 60 cents. It was made of Peruvian cotton on which there was a heavy import duty. Other Peruvian products going into Chile, products not in any way competitive, pay taxes as high as 135 per cent ad valorem. Despite the low costs of labor in Chile, domestic products there in 1945 frequently cost ten times as much as comparable objects in the United States.

A fact that cannot be escaped is that *the land of Latin America has such a low carrying capacity and is able to produce so little wealth per thousand acres* that the purchasing power of the people cannot be increased to a degree even comparable with that of European and North American countries. With internal markets limited, Latin America can only sell the products of its industrialization abroad—and it can scarcely hope to compete with the United States, Great Britain, Belgium, Switzerland, Czechoslovakia, and eventually Russia.

Perhaps the situation in Latin America will become clear with a more detailed consideration of a few of the countries. Actually, one is not justified in writing about "Latin America," because it is such an extremely varied region. Despite its being unified by the Iberian cultural tradition (excluding, of course, Haiti) and by a consistently difficult geography, it would nevertheless be a grave error to identify one Latin American country with another.

Land of "The Tyrant"

As the republic nearest the United States, Mexico is best known to the American people and has most felt the impact of our culture. English, or what passes for it among many Americans, has corrupted Mexican Spanish, to the dismay of purists. Mexico City has largely lost its Spanish character (except for the plumbing) and reminds one of Winnipeg or Minneapolis with a Spanish accent. A favorite rendezvous for Mexicans and Americans alike is an American drugstore, with tearoom attached. Newspapers are filled with AP and UP stories, and Walter Lippmann and Louella Parsons are read as avidly as in Los Angeles. It is small wonder that American businessmen, tourists, or diplomats are likely to regard Mexico through glasses tinted in Chicago or Dubuque, and that Mexicans tend to accept our evaluation. According to a Mexican acquaintance, one of his fellow countrymen visiting Fort Worth or San Antonio will glance about him at the fine streets and buildings, and exclaim, "Look what the gringos took away from us!" A longer, less superficial look—reaching to California—would justify a more choleric indignation. For Mexico, today, has her back to the wall.

The most recent available information showed 17,000,000 Mexican acres under cultivation and it is estimated, probably with undue optimism, that 24,000,000 additional acres at the outside might be placed under the plow and digging stick. Most of the 17,000,000 acres are suffering, in greater or less degree, from erosion. Thus Mexico, with 22,000,000 people and growing fast, must count on less than two acres of *potential* arable land per capita—with good fortune. "The conclusion could not be more discouraging. The Mexican land, alone, cannot adequately feed the mass of its population which, at the present time, does not possess more than a third of the land it requires for a reasonable diet." [6] Most of the land now cultivated, or likely to be brought under cultivation, does not fall in Class I—and erosion-control measures are quite inadequate, despite a technically excellent soil-conservation service. Mexico's arable land is being rapidly washed into the sea.

This is not a new problem for our southern neighbors. According to the late George Vaillant, one of the greatest authorities on the Aztecs, "Ixtlixochitl has related that religious conflict, revolt and crop failure contributed to the downfall of Teotihuacán. . . . Crop failure could have resulted from deforestation and the consequent drying up of streams. At Teotihuacán lime cement covered all the buildings and formed the entire paving. The modern Maya Indians burn ten times as much wood as the quantity of limestone to be reduced and they have the advantage of steel axes. It is not too fanciful, therefore, to assume that the Toltec masons, lacking metals of any kind, found it easier to use hearths of charcoal obtained by burning over the forest, than to try to obtain the requisite fuel by chopping out their logs with stone axes. If this interpretation is correct, the hills must have been widely denuded of timber with a consequent drying up of streams and erosion of fields. Furthermore, the barren aspects of the hills of Teotihuacán today must be due to something more than the requirements for fuel and timber of the post-Conquest population. The Toltecs and their successors, Chichimécs, Acolhuas, and Aztecs, undoubtedly contributed their fair share to this wastage of the forests." [7]

The same process of land destruction has operated over thousands of square miles of Mexican territory. Where once mighty forests built and protected rich soil, their denudation left behind only sterile hardpan, hardpan that will scarcely grow the maguey cactus. Between Mexico City and Morelia, a distance of approximately two hundred miles, I counted kilometer posts from which it was possible to see erosion. There was active gullying visible about every two miles!

Between 1930 and 1945, the population of Mexico increased some 30 per cent. Accompanying the increase in mouths to feed, there was of course a correlative increase in demand for the land. Cornfields have been driven ever higher, from the bottom to the top of the slopes. The casual traveler in Mexico, with only the most rudimentary understanding of soil erosion, is likely to be impressed by the land destruction. It is common along the Laredo Highway by which motorists reach Mexico City. In 1944 I flew at a low altitude over much of the part of Mexico lying west and north of the capital. More than 90 per cent of the cultivated land I saw was gutted by erosion. Many of the cornfields were perched precariously between deep gullies that were surely devouring them. Meanwhile, the Mexican government, instead of attempting to check this trend, has done much to encourage it, even offering prizes for increased production of corn.

One of the North American values that has been uncritically accepted by the Mexicans is the benefit of good roads. Enormous sums, in Mexican terms—in one year, eighty million dollars—have been spent on highways. These have made forests and marginal agricultural land increasingly accessible to markets. Nothing *effective* has been done either to educate the

Mexican people in the use of lands opened up by these highways, or to control their depredations. As a result, destruction has raced in all directions, alongside and ahead of the roads, as disease spreads from a polluted well.

Not that roads were needed to destroy Mexico's land! The state of Oaxaca, through most of which travelers must go by foot or on muleback, will, in the judgment of one of the Mexican authorities who knows it best, be a desert within fifty years. Nearly all of its land, falling in Classes VI, VII, and VIII, is totally unfit for agriculture, and it is being intensively cultivated. Peasants accept as the normal order of things a walk of five or six miles from their huts to the fields where they grow their corn. The story of the little Indian woman who had to carry all her drinking water five miles is not fantasy. Probably thousands are in the same situation.

The destruction of the forests has resulted in the desiccation of numberless wells and springs. I have seen and photographed illegal lumbering and grazing in numbers of Mexican national parks. A trip to a co-operative sawmill in the Cofre de Perote National Park was like a visit to moonshiners in the United States; *contrabandistas*, armed with the "thirty-thirty" of Mexican song and story, watched from behind trees until they identified our guides as friends. Lakes and stock ponds, as well as modern hydroelectric reservoirs, have been filled with good soil. The state of Michoacán is a red sea of mud in the rainy season; mud which if it had been kept in place on the land could have produced the raw materials that would build the wealth of Mexico.[8]

In the fall of 1944 a tropical hurricane roared inland over the Mexican tableland and dumped millions of tons of water within twenty-four hours. Rivers flowing into the Caribbean and Pacific from deforested watersheds went wild, and more than three hundred persons were drowned. Communications to the capital were interrupted; the pipeline carrying gasoline and fuel oil was broken. The absence of charcoal and kerosene for cooking caused a near-panic. The government, which had been futilely trying to protect forests against the ravages of charcoal burners, now disregarded the fact that deforestation to provide charcoal had been one of the principal causes of the high flood peaks and removed all restrictions on its production. A few weeks later I flew into Mexico City from Guatemala and counted seventeen forest fires, most of which were allowed to burn themselves out.

Informed Mexican friends have told me that half their compatriots do not get enough to eat.

TABLE 2

Food and Income in Latin America [9]

| | Calories per Capita, Prewar | | Annual Income |
	Number	Per Cent from Cereal	Per Capita, 1938-40
Mexico	1,909	52.6	$ 50
Colombia	1,934	39.7	68
El Salvador	1,944	47.9	25
Costa Rica	2,014	34.6	84
Honduras	2,079	51.6	34
Peru	2,090	49.4	32
Dominican Rep.	2,130	31.0	40
Chile	2,481	44.6	133
Brazil	2,552	33.6	49
Paraguay	2,813	19.4	33
Uruguay	2,902	33.5	82
Cuba	2,918	29.9	105
United States	3,249	27.3	555
Argentina	3,275	37.9	171
Haiti	....	....	15
Ecuador	....	....	22
Guatemala	....	....	28
Nicaragua	....	....	38
Bolivia	....	....	67
Venezuela	....	....	105
Panama	....	....	135

This is not a new story for Mexico. Food hunger and land hunger were two of the mainsprings of the Mexican Revolution. An attempt to solve this land hunger broke up many of the large estates and turned them over to Indian communities. But soil erosion was rampant before the Mexican Revolution; one may often see stone walls balanced four or five feet in the air, on narrow plinths of earth from which the adjacent soil was washed away many years ago. The new system of landholding has probably not improved this situation. The few thousand landholders of the Porfirio Diaz dictatorship have now been multiplied several hundred times, and there is the difficulty of convincing many more people of the necessity of changing their farming methods—and showing them how to do it. In view of the rapidly growing population and the constant need for more production, this is not going to be an easy task. The cry of the great agrarian leader, Emiliano Zapata, was: "The land belongs to him who works it!" Apparently it never occurred to Zapata that ownership of anything as indispensable as land imposes unavoidable responsibility, along with "rights."

Another modern nostrum swallowed by the Mexicans, with full confidence that it has miraculous curative powers, is industrialization. Industrial development has been largely a hit-or-miss affair, with little relationship to national and world factors that might be influenced by it or determine its success or failure. An "artificial silk" plant was built to utilize the forests protecting the watershed of the city of Colima. To make this timber available, the boundaries of Colima National Park—in part established to protect the city's watershed—were changed to exclude all forests. What Colima is going to do for water twenty-five years from now no one seems to have considered.

The enormous demands modern industry makes on water resources have been given little thought by the Mexican people or their government. One of the largest American corporations, exploring the possibility of establishing branch factories in Mexico City, abandoned the idea after its engineers discovered that water supplies were inadequate. Mexico City is built on an old lake bed and for well over a hundred years has been actively attempting to lower the ground water level. This has changed Lake Texcoco, which formerly surrounded the city, from an invaluable catch basin into an arid plain, whose alkaline dust is whirled through Mexico City all during the dry season and alleged to be largely responsible for the high incidence of respiratory and pulmonary diseases. As the water level falls, buildings settle and crack. Even the magnificent cypress trees, more highly esteemed by Quetzalcoatl than by his modern descendants, are dying.

Mexico City's water supply is, in many sections, completely cut off from late afternoon to about sunrise. Only buildings with private storage tanks have water during the night, and when a fire breaks out it is permitted to burn—because there is no water with which to fight it.

Hydroelectric reservoirs built at Necaxa, it was optimistically reported, would solve Mexico City's electricity problem. But the watershed has not been protected, and precipitous slopes are generally planted to corn. No figures are available but it is obvious, from photographs, that the rate of runoff has been sharply augmented, and siltation started. These conditions were widely commented on in Mexican newspapers when, *during the rainy season* of 1947, a shortage of water forced the authorities to decree a 40 per cent cut in power. Factories had to close, some parts of the capital were without light for more than a few hours a night—and the cornfields continued to eat away the slopes.

In part, the scarcity of water results from the rapid growth of the city, and there are ambitious and costly plans to tap the distant Lerma River. Meanwhile, the headwaters of the Lerma are being as rapidly denuded of forests as hungry markets and modern techniques permit, and probably less than 50 per cent of the watershed remains in forest.

Where upland forests are not being lumbered on a cut-out-get-out basis, they are usually being overgrazed. Instead of having a normal understory of young trees and associated plants, underlaid with a rich, moisture-holding humus, they are more like the open parks of European estates. Their carpet of grass is often of low palatability for cattle, and it is regularly burned to clear away tough, inedible blades. The fire, of course, destroys not only the organic matter in the soil, but young seedlings and the food and cover required by wildlife.*

This kind of resource destruction generally characterizes the country, except for the forests of Yucatán and Tehuantepec. These have been more or less immune to destruction because of the difficulty of access and their mixed composition. However, with so much of the world now facing a shortage of timber, lumbermen are clean-cutting these tropical forests. No one has investigated the ecology of such areas enough to be able to say with certainty what the result of this deforestation will be. Because of the intense heat, high winds, extremely heavy seasonal rainfall, and in the case of Yucatán porous, limestone soils, it seems probable that such deforestation of Mexico's tropical lowlands will turn them into a sterile desert.

The rapid growth in the Mexican population is in part attributable to a relatively long period without revolution, and in part to improved sanitary and public health measures. The few statistics available show that the life expectancy of the Mexican is still only about half that of his North American neighbor, but considerable progress is being made in reducing infant mortality. The rise in the population curve may be expected to continue for some decades. Mexico may well have twenty-eight million people by 1955.

Meanwhile the curve of land productivity is rapidly falling. If half the Mexicans are hungry at the present time, considerably more than half of them are going to be underfed by the

---

* One of the first acts of President Alemán was the issuance of a decree forbidding further lumbering on government forest land, primarily to protect watersheds. Mexico's first forestry law was promulgated in 1550. The degree of its observance reminds one of the exclamation of Manuel Antonio Meléndez: "God forbid that we should think these and other admirable laws were obeyed in the Spanish dominions!"

end of this century—assuming that they continue down the path they have been following. Every year the Mexican peasant, who makes up the great bulk of the Mexican population, suffers more hunger pains as his little patch of land shrinks. He becomes thinner, and his children, with ever poorer diets, are less well prepared to cope with the struggle for existence. The falling curve of infant mortality, resulting largely from a reduction in intestinal diseases, is not so significant as it seems. It merely means that the Mexican of the future, instead of dying after a few months of life, is going to die a few years later, after an increasingly miserable existence. His national source of food is drying up.

Even if he finds a place in industry he will not be much better off, since the areas of the world that have food surpluses, like Argentina and the United States, also have markedly higher standards of living. He produces in terms of pesos and buys in terms of dollars at a ratio (in 1948) of five to one. Furthermore, as has been pointed out, nationalistic economies have already raised walls against the movement of low-priced goods.

Few Mexicans in any period of the country's history have recognized that theirs is a poor country. Even today, when mankind has become conscious as never before of its dependence on the land, Mexicans exult in their national wealth. But they cannot turn on an empty water faucet without evidence of national impoverishment. They cannot travel any considerable distance in any direction without seeing eroded lands, destroyed forests, shrinking cornfields. They cannot walk the streets of Mexico City, early in the morning, without seeing hundreds of people "queued up" for charcoal, every year scarcer and more expensive. When they look at their sidewalks, they see blood-streaked sputum, coughed up by underfed consumptives. In the dry season they cannot see across their valleys, for smoke from uncontrolled forest fires. Mexico is an impoverished country. Under the pressure of a rapidly growing population, it is steadily becoming poorer. Until these facts are given proper weight, Mexico's brave struggles toward social, economic, and industrial progress can only result in increasingly bitter frustration.

The Parabola of Misery

There is an old saying, relished with patriotic fervor by the Salvadorians, that in their country "no one dies of hunger." They have accepted this national boast for so many decades that they do not realize it is fundamentally hunger from which most of them do die, that their only abundance is on the verbal level. Into a tiny country the size of Vermont are crowded two million people. For each of them there is only about one acre of cultivable land—a patch two hundred feet square—to produce the food they eat, the cotton that clothes them, and the crops they export. Within the cultivable area is included a high proportion of Class II and III land and this can safely be farmed only by agricultural techniques far beyond the grasp (in 1948) of 90 per cent of Salvadorians. In country districts, their illiteracy rate often approaches 100 per cent.

They have neither coal nor petroleum. Their hydroelectric developments are not adequate, even for the few towns having electricity. "At maximum output during the rainy season, the available plant is sufficient to supply only minimum requirements, allowing no room for industrial expansion. At the restricted level of dry season capacity, maximum output is sufficient to meet only 60 per cent of even minimum needs." [10] For cooking and industrial processes, Salvadorians are forced to depend almost entirely on firewood. They are rapidly approaching the point, reached years ago by the Indians in some parts of Guatemala, of having so little fuel they will not be able to eat tortillas (corn cakes) for lack of means to cook them. Their forests have been all but extirpated, and they have not taken even the first step toward any sort of forestry program. The country suffers a long dry season and the level of ground water is steadily falling. Because of deforestation and excessive cultivation of land, the rivers carry such heavy silt loads that any sort of storage, such as the United States has developed under the TVA, would be impossible.

The average diet of the Salvadorian is estimated at fifteen hundred calories a day. Since a small group of prosperous people have far more than this, many of the poorer people do not have even fifteen hundred calories. Most of them eat tortillas and black beans; a meal that includes animal protein is an event. Tuberculosis, hookworm, dysenteries, venereal disease, and malaria are rampant. The situation of these people is worse than that of the Puerto Ricans, who at least have a couple of fingers in the pockets of their Uncle Sam. In all the Western Hemisphere, only Haiti is in a more miserable situation than El Salvador.* Like all countries or regions shackled to a monoculture, El Salvador often finds herself in a highly precarious condition. She has little but coffee, which is her only considerable export. The coffee lands are of such a character that they would be ruined if used for growing row crops such as corn and beans. Many coffee fincas are now eroding so rapidly that their productivity is dropping fast.

Because the Salvadorians are forced by downright scarcity of land to depend on areas they are (1948) incompetent to protect, the carrying capacity of their country is falling significantly every year. Were the population a quarter of what it is today, El Salvador could maintain its people at a decent standard of living—although there would be no possibility that it could equal that of a well-endowed country like the United States. With the excessive population—which has been excessive since 1890—an improvement in conditions must be, at best, painfully slow.[11] An agricultural experiment station, largely staffed by technicians from the United States, may well increase agricultural production per cubic foot of such topsoil as remains. How far-reaching the effects of this work can be,

---

* This calorie intake, lower than that reported in *Population Index*, is an estimate given me by a distinguished Salvadorian physician, Dr. Ranulfo Castro, his country's Minister of Education.

until illiteracy rates have been sharply reduced, is dubious. At best, such work can only slow the rate of land degradation, in view of rapidly mounting population pressure. The population of El Salvador has doubled since 1910.

The graph of this increase (Fig. 8) is well worth studying, because it is applicable to so many parts of the world. One of Europe's leading crop ecologists calls it "the parabola of misery." Unfortunately there are no data to show the decrease in natural resources. And while the United States, through its agricultural technicians and an educational mission, is taking all too inadequate steps to help El Salvador better its condition, it is also co-operating in a health campaign designed to reduce the death rate even further. Nothing is being done to reduce the birth rate. As in India and Puerto Rico, this is brutally misguided well-doing.

There is this one factor strongly in El Salvador's favor: the tough-mindedness of its people, especially of its leaders. They are now giving inspiring indications of facing their situation honestly and courageously. One of the poorest countries in the hemisphere, it is one of the few that is not whining about being too poor to help itself. It is rolling up its sleeves to go to work—and the Salvadorian is famous as a worker.

If El Salvador were not panting through perhaps its final lap against time, its people would give one considerable cause for optimism. Had it a wide enough margin of wealth to give it a breathing spell of fifty years, it might well show the remainder of Latin America the way out. But, as might be expected where the great bulk of the population is both hungry and ignorant, it is socially unstable. It has suffered a number of both Communist and Fascist attempts to take over the government. The starving man will grasp at any crust. And only through long-term, intelligently directed government activities, with far greater stability than the country has recently enjoyed, can El Salvador's problems be solved.

RICHES—AND TIME!

Going to Costa Rica from El Salvador gives one the stimulating sense of leaving a region of exhausted hard-scrabble for the rich farm of a vigorous young man. Here are some of the finest soils in the world, and at the same time some of the most erosion-resistant, in local areas. Costa Rica, with its population of 800,000 and its area of 23,000 square miles, is in terms of potential living standards—even of *actual* living standards—one of the most favorably situated countries in the hemisphere. It still possesses some good, unsettled agricultural land. It has considerable areas of forest. It has undeveloped hydroelectric power. Were its general understanding of land-use problems not approximately at the level of the sixteenth-century Spaniard, it might look toward such a future as that of Switzerland, which it resembles in so many ways. Unhappily, however, the healthy young farmer is—in his attitude toward the land—an extremely ignorant and provincial man. He takes it for granted, as have people across the entire earth, that his riches are unlimited. He is exploiting them recklessly, and his point of view is that he cannot afford to spend anything to protect his wealth.

Costa Rica has been saved by its small population. Wherever the density of people has increased to any extent, as on the Meseta Central, natural resources have been destroyed. Over much of the country the volcanic soils are deep, rich, and so permeable that the twelve or fourteen feet of annual rainfall sinks into the substrata without the great gashes of gully erosion familiar to us in the United States. Nevertheless, the organic matter has been washed off even the best of soils and the minerals needed to produce plants leach rapidly away. Coffee production has fallen, over wide areas, as much as 80 per cent. For this, erosion must bear much of the blame.

Erosion-resistant soils are limited in extent. In many parts of the country an incline as low as 2 per cent will let the rains carry away the rich earth. On the Pacific slope of the country, which must endure burning suns and a dehydrating dry season, clearing the forests immediately sets off the erosion chain reaction. The land passes from virgin forest to low-grade range, or useless second growth, within twenty-five years. Here, the most effective limiting factor is the burning months without rain. The variation in rivers is one hundred to one, a matter of grave concern to those interested in hydroelectric developments. Rivers carry silt loads as high as 20 per cent.

In the canton of Guanacaste, where most of Costa Rica's range land is found, floods are a serious problem and are rapidly growing worse because of deforestation. Thousands of cattle must be driven off the lowlands to escape drowning. During the torrid summer, the parched grass cannot support the animals nor can they find water to drink, a problem that is yearly becoming more serious. Much of Guanacaste was formerly forested, and ranchers who protect their scrubby second growth, which helps to maintain the level of ground water, have far more success in bringing their cattle through the dry season. Most ranchers, however, are substituting grass for forest and it seems probable that Guanacaste will within a few years be facing a serious problem of wind erosion.

Nowhere in the country is protection given to headwaters of streams and rivers. In the normal course of events, this exaggerates flood hazards that may make uninhabitable large sections, such as the El General Valley into which the Costa Rican people are hoping to expand. With the decrease in upstream water control, malarial regions are extended by flooding and by silt-extended swamps.

The forest lands of Costa Rica are largely in mixed and inaccessible stands that cannot be economically exploited at the present time. Most of the remaining forested uplands would fall into the Class VII and VIII groups, and to cut them over, unless sound forestry practices are used, will result in complete destruction of the land. Exploitation of Costa Rican forests is on a purely extractive basis. No management practices are used, the government does not have a forest service; and even were lumbermen inclined to manage their forests on a sustained-yield basis they could not do it efficiently because of an almost complete absence of information about forest ecology and because so much of the land is held in small parcels. On forest lands open to homesteading, the farmer is *required* to get rid of his trees without any consideration being given to land-use classification, to the economy of the country, or to the effects on the land itself and on the hydrologic regime.

Costa Rica has such low taxes as to make the country seem a paradise to Americans and the British. Its income taxes are nominal and it is generally reported that, with a good tax lawyer, it is not necessary to pay these. Costa Rica is spending considerable sums of money on highways (it is one of the principal victims of the Inter-American Highway) and on an extraordinary variety of health and social services. Many large landowners are wealthy people, and in automobiles, the country club, and fine homes one sees much evidence of great prosperity. Costa Rica has borrowed heavily from the United States and is trying (1946) to extend its borrowing to develop a public works program. Theoretically, these loans must be repaid. The annual budget (1946) is over $11,000,000—not one of which is spent on conservation.[12]

On every side in Costa Rica one hears how poor the country is. Few of its citizens have awakened to the fact that it is rapidly becoming poorer, nor is there any evidence of a willingness to curtail present incomes in order to protect those of tomorrow.

Costa Rica is one of the very few small countries in the world that has the possibility of escaping the exhausted poverty of nations like Haiti and El Salvador. In her relatively high literacy rate, her well-distributed school system, and the reported willingness of her farmers to mend their agricultural ways, she possesses advantages shared by few of her sister republics. But obviously a know-nothing, do-nothing policy is not going to save her.

PERU LEADS THE WAY

One of Peru's presidents eloquently, if inaccurately, described his country as "a beggar sitting on a bench of gold." This phrase so fired the imagination of Peruvians that most of them have remained under its semantic spell ever since. They rarely see their country as it is.

The coastal third of Peru is desert, most of which is too dry to support even cactus. The only sign of life in it is the shadow of vultures' and condors' wings as the great birds soar toward the sea to hunt for carrion on the shore. At intervals it is crossed by short rivers originating in Andean snows. These have been used since days long lost in paleolithic times, for local irrigation. Intensively farmed for at least three thousand years, the lands they water maintain their fertility only by the use of guano, which a happy accident of nature has made available on islands off the coast.

The central third of Peru consists of mountains and small intermont basins, many of them at an altitude of twelve thousand feet or more, where scarce and badly distributed rains combine with the high-altitude cold to keep production low. So broken is this country that towns now receiving Lima newspapers by airplane have never been reached by automobile. Much of the upland can produce no plants more nourishing than bunch grass fit only for small numbers of llamas and sheep. The Indians who live on this beautiful roof of the world eke out an existence that is surpassed in harshness only in such areas as Patagonia and Tibet.

Peru's third region, on the east side of the Andes, receives the full impact of the southeast trades and has not only an abundance but a superabundance of water. This is notably a land of the tropical rain forest. When trees are cleared from lowland sandy soils, the downpours leach out minerals from the upper levels and the equatorial sun rapidly burns out organic matter. Because this is a region in which the jungle finds ideal conditions for existence, attempt after attempt to colonize eastern Peru has been drowned in the backwash of modified tropical forests.

Wherever man lives in Peru the soil is washing away. Irrigation ditches are carrying it off along the coast; hillside farms as steep as are to be found anywhere in the world are losing it in the uplands; wood-burning railroads, such as the line that runs north from Cuzco, are taking off the trees and tearing the land down behind them, flood waters are uncontrolled, and entire farms have been washed into the Vilcanota River. Within gunshot of the Agricultural School, near Cuzco, one may see as shocking gully erosion as existed in the state of Georgia a few years ago.

Peru is an inhospitable land. Acre for acre, it has one of the lowest carrying capacities to be found anywhere in the American continents. Until two or three years ago, when a road was driven over the Andes, it was cheaper in Lima to buy pine from Oregon than the hardwoods growing in Peru's forests less than two hundred miles away. This may still be so, but if it is not it will almost certainly be true again, because Peru is destroying her forests and is, as yet, little concerned with sustained yields.

The problem of conservation in Peru is especially interesting because of her outstanding accomplishment in restoring her flocks of guano birds. In the soundness and integrity of this project she set an example not only for the Americas but for the entire world. Were natural resources generally managed as intelligently as the Peruvians have—in this century—managed their guano, the future of the human race could be regarded with considerably more optimism.

Without guano, the productive capacity of the coastal lands rapidly falls away to almost nothing. With guano, they have few equals.

The guano exists on the coast of Peru through an unusual and extremely interesting complex of circumstances. Most important is the offshore drift of her waters, caused in part by the influence of the trade winds as they reach the surface after having crossed the Andes and in part by the spinning of the earth. As on the coast of California, this results in upwelling of cold waters from the depths, waters rich in the chemicals needed by marine plants. The Andes, desiccating the trade winds by adiabatic cooling, protect the guano deposits against the washing they would suffer were it not for the Andean dam. The cold Humboldt Current has made possible an invasion of Peru's tropical-zone waters by the white-breasted cormorant, the chief guano producer, from subantarctic regions. These birds live on Peruvian islands, literally by the millions, and form one of the densest concentrations of vertebrates known anywhere in the world.

Guano was used by the pre-Columbian Peruvian Indians, much as menhaden were used to fertilize corn in early New England. The Incas protected the guano islands and the trespasser on them was subject to the death penalty.

With the advent of the Spaniards, whose primary aim was to steal all the gold and silver they could lay their hands on, both the native population and Peruvian agriculture went into a nose dive. The guano islands were largely neglected and the excrement of the birds was permitted to accumulate, with only small cargoes being removed, until the middle of the nineteenth century. Then, stimulated by the geographer Humboldt, interest in guano rapidly mounted until sailing vessels came from all over the world and Peru had a guano boom comparable to California's Gold Rush. Like most men in most of the world, the "developers" of the guano resource assumed that it was limitless. Von Tschudi, a nineteenth-century naturalist, estimated Peru's guano supplies at over 23,000,000 tons. During a period of years, known among the Peruvians as the "Saturnalia," the guano accumulation founded many fortunes and paid the entire cost of operation of the Peruvian government. The birds that produced the guano were regarded as nuisances, and small boys were paid to drive them away from their nests because they interfered with guano collection! By the latter part of the nineteenth century, the guano exploiters were scratching bottom on most islands, and in 1911 the entire coast of Peru was able to produce only 30,000 tons of the fertilizer.

After much discussion, pro and con, there was established in 1909 an entirely novel conservation organization, the Peruvian Guano Administration, or Compañía Administradora del Guano. This was a limited stock company, the shares of which still pay a guaranteed 10 per cent, in which the Peruvian government held a 51 per cent interest. Operation of the company was left entirely in the hands of the business organization, which was given a complete monopoly over the guano islands. For more than thirty years the guano administration was under the direction of Don Francisco Ballén, to whom most of the credit for its success is due. Rigid control was established over all the islands, full-time wardens were employed to protect the birds, and the slow climb toward a full avian population was once more begun. The success of this Peruvian venture is best shown by the increase from 30,000 tons of guano in 1911 to 168,000 tons in 1938. Peru has thus assured herself of a means of completing the cycle that, in most countries, is carrying the riches of the land down to be lost in the sea. In Peru the current is reversed, and through the medium of the birds the all but inexhaustible riches of the sea are being restored to the cultivated fields.[13]

Were it not for its guano, Peru would indeed be in a sorry state. There is, unhappily, more than a little truth in the cynical statement of a North American mining engineer, after some twenty-five years near Trujillo: "The chief wealth of this country lies in its cheap labor supply."

THE UNSTABLE LAND

One of the greatest national assets of Chile, perhaps the greatest asset, is its high death rate. This is a shocking statement. Nevertheless, if one does not believe there is a virtue in having more people live ever more miserably, destroying their country with increasing rapidity, the conclusion is inescapable.

The northern third of Chile is occupied by one of the most sterile deserts to be found anywhere in the world. It is rich in nitrates desperately needed by many countries, but for the most part by countries that cannot pay for them—or think they cannot. It does not have the advantage, enjoyed by the Peruvians, of scattered river valleys where crops can be grown on irrigated land.

Parts of central Chile are, acre for acre, one of the richest regions anywhere on earth. Irrigation water, flowing from Andean snows, is abundant and dependable. The carrying capacity of this land would be far higher were it not for the systems of landownership.

Enormous tracts of land, visited only occasionally by their wealthy owners, are undercultivated; it is no uncommon thing, south of Santiago, to see rich, irrigated fields of Class I used as pasture. In the central provinces, 5,396 haciendas of more than 500 acres contain 80 per cent of all farm land; 69,761 small holdings add up to less than 5 per cent of the total rural area—and average 16 acres each. Some 400,000 people are eking out a living on farms of less than 4 acres. With these plots we may contrast 375 farms of more than 12,250 acres! [14] Various gestures have been made toward redistribution of land but so powerful are the hacendados that little progress has been made. The government (1946) takes orders from them, rather than control being exercised in the reverse direction.

The Andes of central Chile are forest land. The central valley is further locked in by the coastal range whose semiarid pastures are heavily overgrazed and everywhere eroded. On a train trip from Llo-Lleo to Santiago, I made a random count of gullies on such land, and found one every 1,300 feet. South-central Chile possesses some excellent pasture, but much of it is so sloping that it cannot withstand the heavy rainfall, once it has been cultivated. There are many areas here that have passed from virgin timber to abandoned land within twenty years. In the provinces of Arauco, Bío-Bío, Malleco and Cautín

—formerly the breadbasket of Chile—erosion has injured about one-third of the land, as it has in the eight provinces to the north. The fall of wheat yields, in quintals per hectare, in eight central departments tells the story: [15]

1911–1917	10.4
1918–1924	9.9
1925–1931	8.4
1932–1939	7.1

South Chile, so brilliantly described in Darwin's *Voyage of the Beagle*, is covered with a dense, temperate rain forest, except for the small segment of Patagonia that is semiarid grazing land. When Darwin's shipmates went ashore on the island of Chiloé, they were forced to scramble over the lush recumbent vegetation—and they took soundings through the tree branches to determine how far beneath them lay the ground. Much of Chiloé's sour soil has now been cleared of its forest, and in the hundred years since Darwin traveled along the coast a substantial percentage of this topsoil has been washed into the sea.

Most of southern Chile must be written off the agricultural books. It is predominantly an area of low temperatures that retard soil development; in many places, on the ubiquitous slopes, the cutting of a single tree will initiate disastrous erosion.

Chile, despite her relatively stable population, shares the land hunger of most American countries. She is turning toward interior valleys in the south, much as the United States turned toward the wild West a hundred years ago. Along the Simpson River, in the province of Aysén, she is attempting to develop grazing and agricultural areas, and on a small scale she is repeating many of the errors made in the United States.

Towns and farmhouses are being established on flood plains where, like the towns and farmhouses of the Mississippi and Missouri bottom lands, they are as vulnerable as possible to floods. She is logging and burning off precipitous hillsides, and losing not only topsoil but *all* the soil in the process. Along the inland waterway approaching Aysén, one may see farms that have been settled and abandoned within two decades. The entrance to the Simpson River is already so full of silt that the small steamers connecting Aysén with metropolitan Chile can pass only at high tide. The United States, neglecting upstream engineering, has spent hundreds of millions of dollars on "pork" for its Rivers and Harbors Committee, but there is no possibility that Chile can produce enough wealth to dredge out her rivers and build levees. Osorno, one of the chief towns of the south, was formerly reached by a navigable river; soil from the uplands now makes it impassable. The principal southern port of Corral is rapidly being cut off by siltation. Chile is, in the most literal sense of the world, by mismanagement of her difficult lands, committing national suicide.

One of Chile's greatest riches is the unequaled beauty of her countryside. Hundreds of miles of snow-capped peaks stretch from the Peruvian border to Cape Horn. In south-central Chile, many of these peaks have their own lovely mirrors, in such lakes as we of the United States have preserved in our national parks. This beauty has drawn visitors from all the world. Were it protected, it might well give Chile a tourist business that would rank with that of Switzerland. Instead of guarding its natural beauties, Chile is wrecking them as fast as they can be sold for a few pesos. Most of the forests surrounding the lakes lie in Class VII and Class VIII land. This is all being treated as though it were Class I land. Forests are being burned and witlessly cut. Farms are set up on slopes that need only a few years to become sterile wastes. When I was in southern Chile in 1945, smoke from forest fires was so thick that it was impossible to open the windows of my bedroom at night. Visitors who had gone into the country from Argentina, and from Santiago, left by the first available train. Fires swept the fringes of the lakes, to the very doors of tourist hotels. Unless Chile takes prompt and intelligently calculated steps to preserve the exquisite loveliness of her southlands,

HUMBOLDT CURRENT
FOOD CHAIN
(PARTLY SUPPOSITITIOUS)

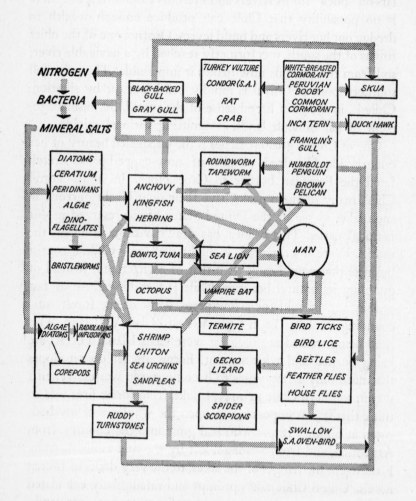

they will soon attract no one except the naturalist interested in the slow march of destroyed land back to productiveness.

THE NEW ATLANTIS

Not all of Latin America has been caught off ecological balance, and in many countries a change in land-use practices promises a favorable prognosis. Eastern Bolivia still possesses rich, unimpaired lands. Some of the finest, unoccupied soil in the world is to be found in Paraguay. The Dominican Republic, partly because it has protected itself against the Haitian hordes, has room for more people. Vast Brazil, with scientific management of its resources, could absorb several millions of people —though only a tiny fraction of the vast numbers suggested by many advocates of immigration; for Brazil, more important than immigration is the necessity of resettling millions of her citizens and stabilizing the slopes they are tearing down. And there always remains Argentina, with the deep, rich soil of her pampas, which are less vulnerable to abuse than perhaps any soils in the world. Most of the rest of the earth can well envy this bountiful environment.

Latin America's dilemma is inextricably ecological. Because of her climate, many millions of people have concentrated between two and eight thousand feet altitude in order to escape the diseases and agricultural limitations of the lowlands. This has placed most of them on sloping lands. The result has been such dynamic and widespread destruction of the land as is equaled, perhaps, only in China. Millions of acres have already been eroded and the rate of erosion, under increasingly destructive agricultural techniques, is every year accelerating.

The cardinal consideration in Latin American land management is that there exists in this area today *some twenty to forty million ecological DPs.* They are living on, and farming, land of Classes V to VIII, and it is essential that they be moved off the slopes if they are not to destroy their countries' means of existence. Resettlement will be difficult and expensive. But

Latin America has no choice. She must move her DPs—or sink to the most miserable subsistence level.

A Guatemalan Indian—a literate one—summed up the problem well. I had been showing him, for the first time, the meaning of the gullies through the corn- and wheatfields, and of the chocolate color of the river that flowed by.

He watched it a long time, standing with me in the rain; then he said, "Why, my country is a New Atlantis. It is disappearing beneath the ocean." [16]

Chapter 8

Man-Spawn and War-Spawn

Hᴀᴅ ᴛʜᴇ ᴅᴇᴇʀ ᴏғ ᴛʜᴇ Kᴀɪʙᴀʙ ᴘʟᴀᴛᴇᴀᴜ ʙᴇᴇɴ ᴘʀᴏ-
vided with guns and munitions, and a cerebral cortex to free
them from the restraint of instinctive behavior and allow them
to develop a master-race psychology, they might well have
started a campaign of world conquest. They had been forced,
by overprotection and overbreeding, into a situation closely
analogous to that of modern European man; one hundred
thousand stomachs had to be filled every day from land that
could provide for only a fraction of that number. The master-
race idea has seen many rebirths, from the Chosen People
through Urban II and the bearers of the white man's burden
to Joseph Goebbels; it is a convenient sop to the conscience of
peoples on the make.

But the deer lacked the "higher" brain areas—and many of
them died. Man, who is chiefly differentiated from other animals by an ability to learn from the past and to *reject* the past,
is at present deciding whether or not to destroy most of his
tribe. Upon his decision—whether or not to make use of his
special abilities—will his survival largely depend. If, like the
deer, he clings to certain ancient patterns of behavior, there
is no hope for our civilization. The decision is likely to be
most fateful in Europe. For there man has outbred the carrying capacity of his range, and evolved destructive means of
implementing his fears and his hates. In Europe, need is the
fuse that, time and again, has carried the spark.

On the continent as a whole, there are only 0.88 acres of
arable land per person; American nutritionists calculate that

2.5 acres are required for an adequate standard of living. If Europe could not feed on the lands of other parts of the world, millions of her people would die, most years, of cold and starvation. Even before the war, with a high degree of industrialization and imports of millions of tons of food and raw materials, the peoples of Europe endured a living standard far below that of the United States. The average, on Colin Clark's scale, was only 44 per cent of ours.

Every grain of wheat and rye, every sugar beet, every egg and piece of veal, every spoonful of olive oil and glass of wine depends on an irreducible minimum of earth to produce it. The earth is not made of rubber; it cannot be stretched; the human race, every nation, is limited in the number of acres it possesses. And as the number of human beings *increases*, the relative amount of productive earth *decreases* by that amount.

Let us look, briefly, at what is happening to the ratio in Europe: [1]

TABLE 3

	Acres of Arable Land per Person	*Rate of Popu- lation Increase, per 1,000*	*Years Needed to Double Population*
Greece	0.74	11.8	59
Hungary	1.53	5.9	118
Rumania	1.70	10.1	69
Poland	1.33	11.2	62
Italy	0.74	9.4	74
Belgium	0.30	1.2	579
Netherlands	0.27	11.5	61
Germany	0.69	7.6	92
France	1.24	.4	—
Sweden	1.46	3.1	224
Denmark	1.73	7.5	93
United Kingdom	0.27	—	—
England and Wales	—	2.2	314

Kaibab Man

The significance of the third column might be stated another way; it tells the number of years that will be required to halve (approximately) the per capita carrying capacity of the land. Two of the countries we have been most generously aiding—at the expense of our own living standard, it should be remembered—are two that, by failure to control their reproductive rate, are most rapidly reducing their capacity for self-help; they are behaving remarkably like the Kaibab deer.

It is interesting to isolate the European countries on which we have data, and which do not possess rich overseas colonies. If we arrange them according to their living standards, with the highest at the end of the list, and rank the same countries according to their birth rates, with the lowest at the bottom, we find an extremely close correlation.

Living Standard	Birth Rate
Rumania	Rumania
Italy	Greece
Poland	Poland
Hungary	Italy
Greece	Hungary
Germany	Germany
Sweden	Denmark
Denmark	Sweden

Not one country in the above lists even approaches the 2.5-acre minimum of arable land, and of them all only France, with its relatively high standard of living, has enjoyed a period without an increase in population. All these countries expect or will expect to be fed from non-European lands and they expect—even insist on—not falling but *rising* living standards. Indeed, through the Atlantic and United Nations Charters they were all but promised such a rise. How to repeat the miracle of the loaves and fishes the politicians have not told us.

Were the Europeans not superlative agriculturists, their situation and that of the world would be far worse than it now is. We like to think that we are the world's best farmers, yet Belgium produces about 320 bushels of potatoes per acre compared with 110 for the United States. There is only one of the nineteen countries of Northern Europe that has yields of less than 160 bushels per acre.² The production of grain in the United States amounts to 18.6 bushels per acre, whereas in the United Kingdom it is 31, in Denmark 39.3, Germany 29.8, in the Netherlands and Belgium 37.7, etc.

Before the war, Europe imported 14 per cent of her bread grains (including 1,000,000 tons of rice), 43 per cent of her fats and oils, 31 per cent of her sugar, and 15 per cent of feed grains. There had been a considerable shift toward self-sufficiency; in the 1920's Europe bought, at relatively high prices, about 700,000,000 bushels of wheat, but by 1938 had reduced this by one-third, or to the equivalent of wheat produced by *35,000,000 acres of land a year.*

In 1938, the United Kingdom imported a little over 200,000,-000 bushels of wheat, which was a few million less than in the 1920's, despite the considerable population rise. Subsidies to British farmers resulted in a 43 per cent increase in home production in 1932-1937.

Italy was formerly the largest importer of wheat in continental Europe, with an annual net of about 80,000,000 bushels during the mid-twenties. By 1937, Italy had cut its imports to 18,000,000 bushels, a decline of 78 per cent. This was done in part by an increase of production of 25 per cent per acre and in part by an increase in acreage of 5 per cent.

Germany's net wheat imports averaged about 70,000,000 bushels annually, during the twenties, and in the five years ending July, 1937, they averaged only 8,000,000 bushels, or a decline of 89 per cent.

In the mid-1920's, wheat imports into France averaged 53,000,000 bushels, which were cut to 10,000,000 by 1937. In 1934-35 her wheat exports exceeded imports by a considerable extent.

In southern and southwestern Europe, the deficit wheat

producers were Portugal, Spain, and Greece. Even before the outbreak of the civil war in Spain, these countries together had reduced their imports by approximately 8,500,000 bushels a year, compared with imports in the 1920's. Portugal and Greece before the war had increased production until they were supplying 92 per cent of their total requirements, in comparison with 86 per cent in the 1920's.

Reduction in imports does not mean that the gap was being filled from European farms. It resulted, to a large extent, from a deterioration of diet. Corn, rye, and potato flour were increasingly used in attempts to arrive at national and continental self-sufficiency. There was a considerable cut in the use of feed grains, which brought about a decrease in animal foods.[3] This prewar trend was already preparing the way for the Spartan —or Asiatic—measures to which Europe resorted during the war. These were described, in 1944, as follows:

All the countries dependent for a large production of their food supplies on overseas shipments plowed under vast areas of pasture; they reclaimed idle land; they adopted plans for a change in crop acreages, and increased farming subsidies; they drafted people for work in agriculture. These European import countries increased the acreage of potatoes, beets, sugar beets, carrots—the commodities and types of food that yield the highest amount of calories, not per man-hour but per acre. They substantially increased the acreage of oil seeds.

The European farmers stepped up on a large scale the output of another group of foodstuffs—the vegetables. The Germans, for instance, increased their commercial vegetable or truck-crop production by 250 per cent. With the shortage of meat and fats, the vegetables substituted high yields of healthy food.

In the words of Dr. Karl Brandt of Stanford University: "If you face the loss of 20,000,000 tons of food and food imports that came from overseas, and the possibility of starvation, the natural thing to do, of course, is to cut down on the non-essential proportions of the scarcest foodstuffs. These proportions consist mainly of the large amount of animal products and fats that the industrialized people consumed. You kill the chickens first, because the chickens eat what man can eat, namely grain. When you feed chickens, you lose between seven- and nine-tenths of the food energy that we measure in calories. In other words, up to ninety per cent of the energy goes to waste with every pound of animal products eaten, which is not vital in the diet. When it comes to the question of survival or perishing for millions of people, as in Belgium, Denmark and Holland with their tremendous chicken flocks, which existed mainly on the imported feed bags, they slaughtered the chickens right away, down to twenty-five or thirty per cent of pre-war numbers. This was the only intelligent thing to do. The American press which reported these news items created the wrong impression, that this was a sign of starvation. It was quite the opposite. It proved that these nations were on the alert, and did the right thing to avoid starvation. The next step taken was to cut down on the number of pigs, because the pigs compete with man for food. They eat grain, potatoes and skim-milk, which man can eat directly if he wants to, and if he has to, in place of bacon and pork. It was simply the natural economic adjustment to the shortage of feed grain and oil cake." [4] The Europeans did, during the war, essentially what we have been asked to do since the war—degrade our own diet—in order to feed them in the style to which they have become accustomed.

TABLE 4

Food and Income [5]

	Calories Number	Per Capita, Pre-war Per Cent from Cereals	Annual Income Per Capita
Cyprus	2,304	68.1	$—
Portugal	2,461	55.1	—
Greece	2,523	54.5	68
Turkey	2,619	61.3	77
Italy	2,627	61.1	141
Poland	2,702	52.6	81

Czechoslovakia	2,761	45.	159
Spain	2,788	50.8	——
Hungary	2,815	63.8	114
Bulgaria	2,831	75.1	72
Rumania	2,865	69.6	86
Yugoslavia	2,866	72.1	74
Belgium	2,885	41.3	258
Austria	2,933	42.4	303
Finland	2,950	42.	150
Netherlands	2,958	32.7	323
Germany	2,967	37.6	449
Iceland	2,980	39.7	——
United Kingdom	3,005	29.9	478
France	3,012	40.1	257
Switzerland	3,049	34.2	450
Sweden	3,052	29.8	394
Norway	3,129	36.6	349
Eire	3,184	37.8	240
Denmark	3,249	26.4	348
United States	3,249	27.3	555

The trend through the 1930's, and the sharp adjustments made forcibly during the war, lend strong support to the contention that Europe could feed 35 per cent more people—at the Asiatic, or famine, standard.[6] Before the war the average European ate about six times as much meat as the Asiatic, or 94 pounds. In addition he consumed 442 pounds of bread grain, 519 pounds of potatoes, 60 pounds of sugar, and 53 pounds of fat and oil. Unfortunately, however, in spite of the war, the German massacres, and localized malnutrition, the population of Europe, excluding Russia, increased by 11,000,000 people between 1936 and 1946; and the population is expected to reach 404,000,000 by 1955 or *an increase of 10 per cent in about twenty years!* [7] One cannot insist too often on the fact that this population increase is, fundamentally, as much a physical process as though one burned down storehouses containing food. Instead of 370,000,000 empty stomachs to fill three times every day—with food that must be drawn from somebody's land—there will be 404,000,000 empty stomachs, or as many as there were in 1939 in Sweden, Denmark, Holland, Belgium, and Austria combined. This increase in hungry stomachs—and no increase in land! Indeed, the total environmental resistance on the land that is left is rising with the population pressure.

One may understand this situation more clearly by considering physical conditions in certain parts of the Continent.

Northern Europe, comparable to Maine, northern Michigan, Wisconsin, Minnesota, and Washington, was originally covered by spruce, fir, and tamarack. This area included most of Scandinavia, northern Russia, and Scotland. Its soils were of the acid type underlying our own pine forests, and have not produced farms of high carrying capacity. South of the coniferous belt lay great stretches of broad-leaved forests, ranging from Ireland to the Black Sea.

Along the Atlantic, high winds are inimical to the growth of trees and crops alike. While temperatures are mild and equable—with a mean variation in Ireland of less than 15 degrees F—the summer temperatures are too low for corn and the rainfall often too great for wheat; they are also unstable and jeopardize the growing season. The disastrous failure of British and Irish wheat crops in 1947 should have surprised no one. This coastal area produces most successfully oats, root crops, and grass for cattle.

Germany, eastern France, and southern Scandinavia, with more stable temperatures, summer rains, and abundant winter snows, are well adapted to production of cereals and grapes. In both these regions, agriculture has developed over centuries and man has learned the fine arts of rotation, fallowing, fertilizing, etc. Along with parts of southern China, Java, and the Philippines, where human and animal manures are liberally used, Western Europe maintains its agriculture on a sustained-yield rather than an extractive basis. As a matter of fact, during the past few decades, production per acre has been rising over some of this area, with the skills of agricultural scientists being brought increasingly to bear. The biotic potential is more nearly realized. Nevertheless, this is far from being a universal condition and mounting population pressures reverse the trend.

Above all, Western Europe has been spared the cutting rains of the New World. This has at once saved European lands and conditioned European emigrants—"land *is* land"—to expose our soils to the erosion already described.

As one moves inland, two major limiting factors come into play: an increasing altitude and a decreasing precipitation. As one approaches the border of Russia, conditions are more and more like those of our own Great Plains; the eastern side of the Danube is subject to vagaries of climate comparable to those of Montana and the Dakotas.

The Mediterranean region is marked by mild winters with rain, which is of extremely limited use for agriculture because it does not fall within the growing season—and by hot dry summers. The characteristic native plants are the cork oak, cypresses, and cedars. Where these have been destroyed by cutting or fire they are replaced by the brushy maquis, the name of which became famous during the war. This area, through excessive cropping and grazing, especially by the goat, has reared its environmental resistances like great ramparts against the well-being of man. From Spain to Hungary, slopes are washed down to bedrock and, except for intermont and river valleys, the carrying capacity of the land has been brought low. A clue to agricultural productivity is given in the following table:

TABLE 5

Weekly Incomes in Agriculture (1937)[8]

	Small Cultivators	Hired Laborers
Yugoslavia	$1.00 – 2.00	(few hired)
Poland and Rumania	1.40 – 2.40	$1.40 – 2.00
Hungary	2.00 – 3.00	1.40 – 2.40
Belgium	3.60 – 4.60	3.60 – 4.40
Germany	4.00 – 5.00	3.60 – 4.60
Netherlands	4.00 – 6.00	4.60 – 6.00
Denmark	6.00 – 8.00	4.60 – 5.20
Great Britain	8.00 – ?	6.00 – 7.20

The Hungry People

Estimates on food intake in Europe before the war are given in Table 4. Calorie figures are, however, deceptive. For example, Denmark, despite the fact that she was a heavy producer of dairy products, included few of these in her people's diet and substituted sugar and margarine; she also suffered from a lack of fruits and vegetables. Denmark, herself a parasite on the New World that supplied food for her livestock, shipped her converted corn and wheat in the form of bacon, butter, cheese, and eggs to luxury areas such as London—which themselves were parasites on other countries' lands. Trade balances, as symbolized by money, were favorable, so no one bothered too much about nutritional standards or at all about such remote concerns as biotic potentials. Two-thirds of the food of the Italians consisted of wheat, rice, and corn. In some parts of Poland meat was eaten only three or four times a year; although many farmers produced dairy products, they had to sell practically all of these to pay for farm necessities.[9]

The productivity of the land in many parts of Europe, from Spain to the Balkans, has been notoriously reduced by the latifundios, or great estates, held by a few, often absentee, landlords. They were one of the first objectives of Spanish Republican reform. They were rarely cultivated efficiently or fully, and one of the most highly touted Communist measures has been to break up these great areas of land and give or sell them to the peasants. A problem that has received little attention or general discussion is that of the minifundio, or excessively small tract of land, such as has already been described in Latin America. Many farm *families* in Eastern Europe are trying to eke out existences on five, six, and seven acres. These may be broken up into small parcels, separated one from another by as much as three or four miles. The growth of population in that part of the Continent has increased partition, with a consequent rise in the cost of the land, and it is reported that Communist authorities—perhaps as a step toward forcing the people into the mold of collectivized farming—are providing families with less-than-subsistence farms. The limited area of each tract, by making grazing impossible, reduces the supply of manure that is so important to the farmer in France. It also makes rest for the land impossible. As a result, production per acre is falling in much of Eastern Europe. It has been dropping for twenty years in southern Poland.[10]

Generalization about Europe may, of course, be misleading. Each country is unique in productive capacity, economic organization, cultural patterns, etc. Before the war the United Kingdom depended on imports of some 50 per cent, to support 50,000,000 people. Germany imported about 25 per cent of its food. The coastal belt of dairying countries, from Belgium to Denmark, depended largely on overseas grain that they subsequently re-exported in the form of animal proteins. France, nearly self-sufficient in foodstuffs, possessed a relatively high acreage of arable land per capita plus the great advantage of a favorable climate and a sound balance between urban and farm populations.

There is no space here for a detailed consideration of the nations of Europe, but Greece has especial meaning to the people of the United States and has recently been carefully studied by an FAO mission. Since the country shares so many characteristics with other Eastern European countries, and is so firmly intermeshed with American problems, it deserves special attention.

GOAT-GOD'S DOMAIN

Greece is a small country with a total area of 50,100 square miles. The useful agricultural land inside her borders is 12,700 square miles, or 25 per cent of the total. This is the full extent of all lands available for the production of food for 7,500,000 people, whether or not in production at the present time *or susceptible of development*.

The cultivable land lies mostly in valleys or on plains near the coast, at the foot of steep slopes. The remaining 75 per cent consists largely of precipitous mountains that rise to a height of 10,000 feet. This broken terrain, like that of much of Eastern Europe, Asia, and Latin America, creates extremely difficult problems of a physical and economic nature (such as communication and transport) that must be solved if Greece hopes to move toward self-sufficiency. Even under normal peacetime conditions, Greece was able to produce only about 60 per cent of the food she needed.

Her grain production of 13.5 bushels per acre was the lowest in Europe. On the plains of Greece the typical *large* farmer has only 7.5 to 12.5 acres per family. In 1938 the average size of farms, including crop land, fallow, vineyards, and orchards, and not excluding the few big farms and estates, was 9.1 acres. Contrast with this the typical family farms of our own wheat belt—320 to 640 acres—and our corn and livestock farms of 160 to 320 acres!

Like most overpopulated countries, Greece has abused her land. For centuries she has tried to support an impossibly high number of grazing animals, which have destroyed her forests and contributed to erosion and excessive runoff. Like other supersaturated countries, she has turned her land over to the goats. In the common and mistaken notion that it would improve grazing, she has burned her hillsides repeatedly since the Greek War of Independence of 1821; the custom of burning has become deeply seated in the country's folkways.

Because of burning, overgrazing, and the attempt to produce grain, usually without soil-conservation practices, on lands of Classes II to VIII, erosion of these lands is general. Throughout the country examples of serious erosion may be seen, on good land; they could have been prevented if man had been willing to abide by nature's laws. There is some excellent, but local, terracing. Today, the economic pressure is so great that, unless a substitute livelihood can be provided for shepherds and farmers, the practices that encourage erosion will be continued. Like dozens of countries on the other four continents, Greece is confronted with a serious resettlement problem. If potential

carrying capacities are to be realized, hundreds of thousands—
and probably millions—of people must be moved from hillside
areas.

As was described in Chapter 5, the destruction of cover has
had a catastrophic effect on the hydrologic regime. Rivers, as
in the Venezuelan Andes, are "anarchic." They alternate between floods and periods of extremely low water; for example,
the maximum discharge of the Pinios River has been estimated
to be at least 88,300 cubic feet per second, while the minimum
discharge is only 200 cubic feet. Floodwaters are, of course,
characterized by heavy burdens of silt and gravel; these cover
fertile land and block the flow of water to such an extent that
high water is driven back over rich coastal plains, often cutting
new channels. In Greece, as in the United States, attempts at
flood control have been initiated downstream rather than on
the hilltops, with the result that Greek dams, like those of
America, have had their storage capacity sharply reduced.
Estimates of the life of these structures have been as much as
200 per cent wrong! [11]

In short, Greece presents the same complex of pathological
land use as is to be found in overpopulated, mountainous countries throughout the world, and Greece may be expected to
double her population—which means halving the amount of
land per capita—in fifty-nine years.

This is the country, the American people are asked to believe,
that can be "restored" to democratic stability within a few
years! A few hundred million dollars—representing millions of
American working days—are to "raise" the standard of living.
This, despite the fact that prewar Greece had a per capita
income of $68, that it has suffered serious war damage, and
has not reduced its bedroom activities! Greece has never, at
least in recent years, achieved total exports of $90,000,000.
These were largely agricultural products. Now the economists
are going to industrialize Greece, and thus raise her standard
of living. What Greece can sell, and to whom, in competition

with Germany, Britain, France, Italy, and the United States, we are not told. How Greece can be "restored" fast enough even to strike a balance with the new crop of babies, the economists and politicians have not suggested.

Pan, the goat-god, must have reveled these many centuries as his minions took over more and more of Greece. And the goat-laughter surely echoed through the Attic hills, as the strangers from the West began to pay panic tribute, to rebuild what the sharp hoofs had torn down!

The agricultural program developed for Greece by the Food and Agriculture Organization to protect this road block against Communism is hedged about with a barbed-wire entanglement of "ifs." A careful study of the report leaves me with the impression that its authors expect to solve the dilemma at the Greek kalends. There are many references to overpopulation and it is suggested that, if possible, Greece should move her surplus people into complacent countries—if these can be found. (The language, needless to say, is not that of the FAO report.) At no point in the entire report is there any suggestion that a positive effort be made to reduce the breeding of the Greeks. How a group of scientists would justify such an omission on any rational grounds it would be interesting to know; such neglect would disqualify a wildlife manager in our most backward states! Since Greece seems to have planted its hand firmly in the American dinner pail, the question is of more than academic interest to the American taxpayer.

THE VIRILE ITALIANS

Italy, which also begs sweet charity of Uncle Sam, with more than a suggestion that if she does not get it she will move in with Uncle Joe, possesses the same amount of arable land per capita as Greece. In 1946 Count Carlo Sforza, in search of a dumping ground for surplus hungry people, cried, "We are overpopulated. We cannot possibly feed so many mouths!" Yet, if Italy continues to multiply at the present rate, in seventy-four years she will have less than half the productive land per capita that she now possesses.

Hungry people are not likely to be willing to suffer the slow processes of democracy. Freedom seems far less important when one's belly is rubbing one's backbone—and the Man on Horseback, or the man on the red-starred tank, takes on plausibility as a leader out of the wilderness. Democracy, especially in our complex modern world where no part lives unto itself, can scarcely flourish on a diet of ignorance and illiteracy, and mobs of people scratching a bare living from overcrowded, exhausted, eroding land are not in a position to build schools, buy books, and train and employ teachers. It is no accident that authoritarian groups of all stripes consistently oppose freedom of education, and advocate unchecked reproduction.

It is especially in the overpopulated regions that the European land is most vulnerable to erosion, a situation in which cause is an effect and effect at the same time a cause. Serious erosion in Spain was probably initiated during the Moorish occupation. The Moors had ruined much of the southern shore of the Mediterranean and they made a valiant beginning on the same destruction in the Iberian Peninsula. The modern substitution, for small subsistence farms, of large estates owned by absentees and dedicated to grazing (and overgrazing), accelerated the destruction.

There was serious deforestation in the Apennines in Roman times, and even earlier in Greece. Destruction of forests in the Pyrenees and Alps is reported not to have become serious until the later Middle Ages; overpopulation of the valleys, with a growing demand for fields, pastures, and fuel, exerted a catastrophic pressure on the mountainsides. In the French Pyrenees, large areas have been ruined and attempts of the peasants to cope with the erosion are reminiscent of conditions in southeastern Asia.[12] In the Balkans, outside of Greece, peasants resort to what might be called "teaspoon agriculture." They send out their children with teaspoons, to look for fertile soil in rock crevices and any other place it may be found, and use it on their fields as fertilizer.

Before World War II the food situation in Europe was ameliorated by grain supplies available from the Danube Basin, and in some years from the Soviet Union. More than in any other part of the world, the structure of European society has attained the complexity of a living organism, with each part influenced by other parts. This integration makes survival more problematical. Europe reminds one of a dinosaur that has evolved great size and complexity under one set of ecological conditions (1800-1914). Now the environment has been profoundly modified—and the great beast left floundering. In the weakness of the analogy, the miniature size of the reptile's brain, we find hope for Europe: her vast reservoir of scientific knowledge holds the means of escape—if she will take it. It is not to be expected that many European countries, or even Europe as a whole, including the United Kingdom, will become self-sufficient in food.

Twenty years ago one of our foremost crop ecologists wrote: "Someday it may prove fortunate for the peoples of Europe and Asia that there are so few people on American farms, as well as so few in North America as a whole." [13] This was before the explosion of our Dust Bowl, before Hugh Bennett had made the American people begin to see what was happening to their abused, overtaxed land. But Dr. Baker is still right; Europe will take all she can get. Europe is going to continue to expect to draw on the lands of other peoples in far regions of the world; and she is going to expect them to accept the products of her factories in exchange for foodstuffs. Whether or not the rest of the world likes it, it is to a considerable extent a raw material colony of Europe—if Europe can keep it so.

As has been pointed out, economists are of the opinion that Europe could support at an Asiatic level an even larger population than she now has. When Bismarck began to demand for Germany a place in the sun, and Hitler set an entire nation yammering for Lebensraum, Germany's living standard was far higher than that of most of the world, but it was not high enough to satisfy her; she sought to raise it by raping the lands of other peoples rather than by cutting the demands on her own lands and reducing her own needs through decreasing her population. She fought not for survival, as her leaders alleged, but for something approaching the American living standard. She tried to improve her lot through trade—but the rest of the world had the same idea. Naturally, she encountered competition from other industrialized countries. Naturally, they protected their industries by tariffs. Argentina, Brazil, Chile, Peru, El Salvador, Egypt, India, and Australia could scarcely wave the economists' magic wand of industrialization without protection.

The attempt to develop new industries in a nationalistic world and, at the same time, to lower or abolish tariff barriers has created a sort of economic schizophrenia. And Europe is one of the chief victims. Her markets shrink as her need, through growing population pressures, expands. She wants to raise her standard of living—for more people. And in some of her parts she is not above resorting to blackmail to do it.

OUR HOBSON'S CHOICE

We, as the nation with greatest total wealth, are, of course, the number-one victim. We have a great deal that Europe wants, in the form of food, raw materials, and—temporarily—capital goods. But what does Europe have that our labor unions and Chamber of Commerce officials will want strongly enough to accept, in competition with our workers and businessmen? And where is the purchasing power in the "undeveloped," raw-material areas to absorb the competing products of Europe, North America, Japan, and perhaps within a few decades Russia?

Our own living standard was substantially lowered as we fought, provisioned, and armed Europe's war. It has been further lowered since the war, as we have tried to maintain a sort of international WPA. It is undoubtedly going to be low-ered still more in years to come.

We literally have no choice but to accede to the blackmail. (If this term seems too harsh, we should remember "Uncle Shylock," the radiant Strength-through-Nuremburg-Joy, the chants of "Duce! Duce!" as bombs flowered among Ethiopian huts. To assume that the spirit of Jefferson and Lincoln has descended upon the Continent with our dollars would be worse than naïve.) Unless we pay it, we shall leave a vacuum that would suck in the police state from the east; and there would be no more of this self-determination nonsense. Unless we are willing to aid, there can be little hope of avoiding a resurgent militarism. An international WPA is to be preferred to an atomic or bacterial war against which there is no defense. Europe has the potential to wage war, or will have it again within a few years. It has repeatedly shown itself willing to use that potential. We should be stupid, indeed, not to draw the fuse if we can.

But we shall be even more stupid if we do not recognize that the overpopulation that has contributed so much to past Euro-pean disorders is a continuing and growing threat. Our WPA, in Italy, Greece, and elsewhere is actually expanding the threat. A Europe of 450,000,000 in 1975 will be far more dangerous than was the Europe of 370,000,000 in 1935. And it will draw on a good many more acres of someone's productive land. Not Europe's, we must remember. Europe doesn't have it.

To the extent that our aid increases the European population, to that extent do we increase Europe's difficulties and our own danger. Our food and financing and medical care, unless they are a gross failure, will reduce death rates.

Birth rates are falling, but not fast enough to be much help. Vital statisticians solemnly tell us that if we wait long enough population curves will level off and birth rates be adjusted "naturally" to death rates. What may happen to the world meanwhile they seem to regard as one of those bothersome realities which seep into academic cloisters like the essence of leaking drains. Politeness demands that we ignore the stench, if possible. Unfortunately, however, it is rising.

Anything we do to fortify the stench—to increase the population—is a disservice both to Europe and to ourselves. Stabilization and eventual reduction in population in Europe would be one of the longest steps that could be made toward world peace and well-being. A United States of Europe, with one-half or one-third its present population, could probably maintain a standard of living that would equal or exceed that of the United States.

We are in a position to bargain. Any aid we give should be made contingent on national programs leading toward population stabilization through *voluntary* action of the people. We should insist on freedom of contraception as we insist on freedom of the press; it is just as important. And as we pour in hundreds of millions of the American taxpayers' dollars we should make certain that substantial proportions make available educational and functional contraceptive material. Quite as important as the Four Freedoms, which we have made a shibboleth, is a Fifth Freedom—from excessive numbers of children. Far more than much of the world realizes, even the partial achievement of the first four is dependent upon this last.

Chapter 9

Man versus Geography

Few of the phrases of Kipling that have found a currency in our literature are as misleading as his line: "East is East and West is West, and never the twain shall meet." They have met many times, with explosive and frequently with tragic consequences. Hordes from the Asiatic heartland smashed civilizations in both ancient Rome and ancient China. The greatest threat to the civilization of the modern West may well lie buried in the rich, granular soils of the same area.

Peter the Great opened the first modern breach in the Western wall, and the intellectual forces that flowed through that gap are not yet in a condition of equilibrium. Clive and Hastings grafted the riches of the Indies onto the body of the British Empire, and we can still not foresee the results an amputation may bring. When Admiral Perry pried open the gates of Japan less than a hundred years ago he let loose a Pandora's horde that was checked only at the cost of thousands of American lives and billions of American dollars. The horde has quieted down, but since it seems to have firmly seated itself at the American dinner table we can scarcely hope that our troubles with it have ended. The future of the West is inextricably joined with the people and future of Asia, and the direction of the joint future may well depend on the intelligence with which we develop our relationships with that sprawling continent.

Until the West interfered, life on the Asiatic continent was fairly well stabilized except for upheavals growing out of the slow fluctuation of climatic changes. The Asiatics had developed a way of life ecologically suited to their environment. In southern and eastern Asia this had brought into being some of the world's great cultures, and produced art, architecture, literature, and religions that we can scarcely claim have been surpassed. (The music and literature of northern Asia, far superior to anything produced in the New World, are of course deeply rooted in Europe.) One of the most cogent indications of the soundness of some of these civilizations is their duration through more centuries than any western civilization has been able to survive.

It is probable that their power to survive lay largely in the simplicity of their structure. For these Asiatic civilizations were like colonies of that lowly and relatively unspecialized animal, the sponge. If one part were destroyed, the rest lived on unperturbed and re-established itself in the devastated area. Modern, western civilizations may be compared to a more complex animal, such as an anthropoid; if it becomes sick in any one of its members, so interdependent are its parts that it may well die. Some of the sickness of modern Asia is seated in the complexity imposed on it from the West.

The high degree of development of Asiatic civilizations is the more noteworthy because of the unfavorable geographic environment in which they grew. Asia is one of the continents least favorable to human occupancy, where the statistic "number of people per square mile" has little meaning; in the majority of Asia's eighteen million square miles, life for man is difficult or nearly impossible. The total carrying capacity is low.

THE SLOW EQUILIBRIUM

The response of populations to this low carrying capacity was eminently reasonable, and for many centuries they remained relatively small. In the sixteenth century, it is estimated, India had less than 100,000,000 inhabitants—a quarter of what she has today. At the time of Perry's interference, Japan had 26,000,000 inhabitants; in 1800 Russia totaled only about

39,000,000 people. Java, which today is bursting at the seams with 47,000,000, in 1815 had to feed, clothe, and shelter only 4,500,000.

In this brief discussion of Asia I follow the eminent geographer, Dr. George B. Cressey, and include the Soviet Republics. The boundaries between European and Asiatic Russia have never been satisfactorily fixed and the modern unification of the country would seem to be in accord with a sensible geographic concept. It would not occur to many people to include England, Poland, or Rumania in the Asiatic area; there seems to be as little reason for excluding the small area of the western Soviet Union.

Asia includes about one-third of the earth's land mass. From the Dardanelles to western China extends a great wall of mountains that forks and reaches Kamchatka almost unbroken. In the lee of these mountains one finds the world's greatest extensions of desert and near-desert.

Much of the area that is in mountains is so hilly that sustained agriculture can be carried on only with terracing and other practices demanding so much labor that the carrying capacity is inevitably low.

Because of its size and its mountain chains, most of Asia is isolated from the oceans that are the source of the life-giving rains in North America and Western Europe. Interior Asia has no adequate source of moisture and it is probable that 75 per cent of the continent has a rainfall of less than twenty inches. Because it is isolated from the tempering influences of large water masses, it is subject to fierce extremes of temperature. These are high in central Asia in the summer, and as the great land mass heats the air above its surface, this air rises and sucks in winds from around its periphery. In the winter, on the other hand, the continent rapidly radiates its heat and the lowest temperatures known to man are found in Siberia. This cooling of the land creates a high-pressure area into which pours air from the arctic, and powerful cold winds rush out from the edges of the high-pressure area to augment, with their drying effect, the aridity resulting from lack of rainfall. These winds, acting upon a poorly vegetated land, are a powerful erosive force.

As the summer winds are sucked in from the sea and forced to rise above the mountain chains, they cool and drop their tons of water on India, Burma, and southeastern China. Where excessive rains cut away sloping lands, some of the most spectacular erosion to be found anywhere in the world may be seen. On level lands, once the forest has been removed, the rains impoverish the soils by "vertical erosion," or leaching.

The ecologist looks at vegetation as a clue to what may be expected from the land. Most of Asia south to 30 degrees is covered by arctic tundra, with a permanently frozen subsoil; the great taiga, or coniferous forests, comparable to those that sweep across the acid soils of Canada; and semiarid steppe, and desert vegetation. None of these offers favorable agricultural conditions. South of 30 degrees lie the mountains and the torrential, monsoon rains.

In the Soviet Republics, a triangle with its base on the Atlantic extends far eastward. It receives almost unobstructed cyclones that bring life-giving rains from the Atlantic. From India to north China the monsoon zone, receiving precipitation from the Indian and Pacific oceans, again makes agriculture possible. The parts of these areas that are not too hilly or beset by long winters are the areas on which Asia must depend for its food. A glance at a population map will show the response of the Asiatics to these conditions, since it is in the Soviet triangle and south and east of the mountains that one finds the greatest concentrations of people.

Except for these areas of land now so saturated with human populations that living standards are appallingly low, there is little unoccupied good land, except in the U.S.S.R. The Soviet Union is staking her hope of feeding her mounting populations on semiarid lands with rainfall of only twelve to sixteen inches per year. As our own farmers learned to their sorrow, it is the area of deficient rainfall that is most subject to sharp variations.

Five or six years may provide good crops, and be followed by two or three lean years. These semiarid chernozem soils are the most productive in the world but, as Cressey points out, "So long as the natural sod is not destroyed, wind erosion is seldom serious; once the soil is cultivated extensive deflation may take place. Dust bowl erosion has long been critical on the Eurasian steppes." [1]

Into this predominantly hostile environment are crowded more than one and one-third billion people. The highest absolute density is probably found in Java with some one thousand people per square mile. Japan—and the United States, as her custodian—is faced with the problem of how to fill empty stomachs with a population of three thousand per square mile of arable land.

We have had samples of the bitter blows Asia can administer to the western world. Many of the conditions that led Japan to burst her bounds are characteristic of the principal peoples of Asia. In our blindness we are striving—with unquestionable good will—to extend to the rest of Asia the formula that made Japan an explosive mixture. We have apparently learned little from our experience with Japan and would do well to look back at what happened in this extraordinary Island Empire.

THE JAPS WHO CAME TO DINNER

From 1600 to 1867 the population of Japan was apparently stabilized at about 26,000,000. The feudal nation had little contact with the outside world. Births were balanced by deaths, and some factor, be it an innate conservatism or a subconscious ecological awareness, induced the Japanese leaders to hold their people aloof from the rest of the world. Soon after the Americans opened the door the population of Japan began to grow at a rate of more than one per cent per year. What the books refer to as "better" economic and sanitary conditions lowered the death rate. (It would be interesting to hear an economist and a sanitarian defend this word "better," in the light of conditions in Japan today.) Our religious missionaries, bringing with them a promise of life eternal and at the same time an impelling drive to postpone entrance into that life as long as possible, were associated with medical and commercial missionaries. The West helped Japan to exchange the urban slum for a preponderantly rural social organization. Cheapjack imitations of Western machine-made products began to be bartered overseas for raw materials and food for the growing millions. As the death rate went down, the population went up. The birth rate began to decline in the 1920's, but not nearly fast enough.[2]

The Japanese were already living on a far lower material standard than the West. As the population pressure increased, they were faced with the choice of lowering the living standard still further or expanding the means of feeding the people. In all fairness to Japan it should be recognized that for decades she made vigorous efforts to secure more raw materials and food by purely economic means. These were denied her, finally largely through American tariffs. We were eager to sell to Japan but quite unwilling to buy her coolie-made goods. As we raised our tariffs in an effort to protect our own high material living standard, other nations did the same, trade stagnated, and Japan expanded onto the mainland.

The culpability of Japan in seeking this way out of her Malthusian dilemma is a culpability shared by most of the nations that have been self-righteously preaching democracy. We grabbed enormous territories from Mexico, and under Theodore Roosevelt we unblushingly did to Colombia what Russia would now like to do to Turkey. The chief justification for our present attitude seems to be that we did our grabbing several decades ago. We did not have the very eminent excuse of such population pressure as confronted Japan. True, Japan might reasonably have been expected to attack this difficulty with a vigorous, intelligent program of population limitation. As Cressey points out: "No nation has a moral right to allow its population to exceed the productive capacity of its domain unless it is willing to accept a lower standard of living. Mere population pressure does not entitle a country to seize the land of its neighbor, especially when that neighbor is equally pressed. The world is now full, and the regulation of population has become one of the most essential of international problems. Reckless increase without corresponding technological advance can lead only to chaos." [3] We have not been willing, however, to seek this remedy in our own continental slum areas such as South Boston, nor in Puerto Rico, nor have we been willing to advocate it in international organizations, despite the fact that some of our leaders are fully aware of the need for such a step. When we criticize Japan for failing to resort to this obvious remedy, we ourselves are in a highly vulnerable position.

Japan, then, with a population that had mounted to 76,000,000, with trade channels closed to her, and being unwilling or not wise enough to seek a sharp limitation of her population, was faced with the dilemma: starve or fight.*

Unfortunately the dilemma still exists—in an aggravated form. By 1950 Japan will have a population of 79,000,000. She has now lost both Formosa and Korea as well as Manchukuo, from all of which areas she drew substantial amounts of food. If she is to be permitted to regain her place in world trade, she will immediately come into competition with the United States and Great Britain. She will find mounting tariff barriers in many countries that are trying to achieve economic self-sufficiency. With approximately five people per arable acre, it is not likely that she can feed herself at anything more than a bare subsistence level. This is true despite the fact that her management of the land can teach much to most other countries, including the United States. Jacks and Whyte make the statement, "There is no soil erosion in Japan." [4] While this is

---

* Many other factors, such as warmongering by business and military leaders, and Japanese conviction of Manifest Destiny in Asia, contributed; none of them, however, possessed the dominating compulsion of excessive pressure on the means of survival.

somewhat exaggerated, she has kept soil erosion at an admirably low point. Her crop yields per acre were among the highest in the world, though they have fallen during recent years because of decreased fertilizer imports. She made notable strides in forestry, and her protection of watersheds might well be studied by our own engineers, who still think the hydrologic regime can be controlled by dams and levees.

Her progress from a feudal state to an industrial power in less than seventy-five years is a measure of Japan's vigor and intelligence. Unless the country is to be rigidly policed over an indefinite period, it must remain a dangerous focus of infection in eastern affairs. Japan is now being fed, and miserably fed, through American charity. It does not seem likely that the elected representatives of the American people will consent to continue such a program indefinitely. There still remain nearly 80,000,000 Japanese, fully aware of respectable accomplishment in the past and with gnawing hunger every year becoming more demanding.

Expansion of food production within Japan must remain an insignificant possibility. An obvious step toward striking a balance between need and supply would be to reduce the need. So far as the American people have been informed, there has been no vigorous attempt to do this.

THE POOR EARTH!

In China, it is estimated that 100,000,000 people have starved to death during the past century.[5] There is little likelihood that we have seen the end of famine. China possesses less than one-half acre of arable land per person. In 1950, according to estimates of the U.S. State Department, China's population will reach 430,000,000. Some students believe that, given the current rate of increase, the population of China will reach 950,000,000 shortly after the year 2000. It is, of course, extremely unlikely that such a rate of increase can be continued. It would certainly be impossible without help from the outside world, and it is to be hoped that the rest of the world will have too much sense to compound China's demographic dilemma.

It should be pointed out here that statistics on China, as well as on many other areas of the world, are approximations. This is partly because of the absence of satisfactory raw data, and partly because of the many shifts of political boundaries that have taken place during the past three hundred years. Estimates of China's present population vary from 400,000,000 to 600,000,000. In selecting statistics for use in this book I have been guided by a number of factors, the most important of which has been an evaluation of the apparent understanding of the author who is presenting statistics. What has been said about populations is true also, to some extent, of areas. Satisfactory maps, such as would permit scientific land-use programs, exist for few parts of the world. Nevertheless, the approximations in both cases, in view of widespread pathological demographic situations, are certainly close enough so that we may safely use them as guides.

In China there exist nearly one-half billion human stomachs that ought to be filled every day. Level lands on which crops may be easily grown are scarce, except in deltas and along river courses. Like similar ones in other parts of the world, these areas are greatly reduced in effectiveness because of disturbance of the hydrologic regime; they were built by floods and will continue to be covered with floodwaters. Most of the forests of China have been devastated, and its rivers are subject to violent fluctuations of flow.

North China, the wheat-growing region, has soils that are rich in minerals, but the rainfall averages twenty-five inches or less and varies so widely that a high percentage of crop failures must be expected every decade; in this sense it is comparable to our own Great Plains. Furthermore, much of North China enjoys only four to six months free of frost in the year. This combination of deficient, undependable rainfall and short growing seasons acts as a powerful environmental resistance and holds down the region's carrying capacity.

From the Yangtze Valley south, where there is more abundant rainfall, soils are heavy, leached, and far less fertile.

Western and northwestern China, including the large provinces of Sinkiang and Mongolia, are an area of grasslands and desert, characterized by deficient precipitation. Throughout China there is a disastrous lack of organic matter and plant nutrients in the soil.

Despite the unfriendly environment with which they must work, Chinese farmers in many regions, especially the south, have developed a system of agriculture magnificently adapted to their lands, and over millions of acres agricultural output has been maintained between three thousand and four thousand years. This has been done primarily by terracing (in the south) and by heavy fertilization. Human feces, widely used, close the nitrogen cycle and bring back to the soil materials that Europeans and Americans waste by hundreds of millions of tons. James Thorp points out that each city—the source of "night soil"—is surrounded by fertile farms over a distance that a man can go and return in one day in a cart.[6] My father-in-law, James Wallace, reports the interesting fact that night soil from foreign settlements, especially those of the Anglo-Saxons, sold for more than that of the Asiatics, because of its greater nitrogen content, presumably derived from a richer, more varied diet. Green manures are little used, since they are too valuable for other purposes. In a country where each person can count on only some 2,500 square yards to produce his food, fallowing is, of course, impossible.

In many parts of China there are more than two thousand people per square mile. This results in minute farms, which must be cultivated by meticulous hand labor. Woodlots are almost unknown, and in many farming areas land cannot be set aside for grazing. The impossibility of supporting an animal population in most of China, and lack of communication with grazing lands to the west, result in a diet extremely low in animal proteins.

Recent investigators indicate that even the remote western

lands probably suffer as much from excessive use as does interior China. They write: "In many large regions of China grass is the basic resource, and the only satisfactory and economic method of harvesting, of cropping off such land, is to let livestock harvest it.

"One frequently hears of plans to greatly expand the human and livestock populations of the grassland areas, so that these so-called 'waste lands' can be more fully utilized. Such programs cannot hope to succeed except in a few very limited localities. In many areas the numbers of livestock should be reduced, and in only a few areas could any increases be made at present. With the development of adequate methods of range management and control of grazing, the total livestock population could gradually be increased, and with this some increase of human population could be made. But such developments should proceed by adequate development of the range and by development of the small amounts of available adjacent lands that are suitable for cultivation, so that they would supplement the range-livestock industry rather than conflict with it as is now the case.

"The view that livestock numbers are near or in the maximum for existing range conditions is supported by all trained observers who have visited the grasslands and with whom the writer has discussed this problem. . . . In western Manchuria and Inner Mongolia severe droughts are not uncommon, and these when they occur may accentuate the effects of any tendency toward overstocking. . . .

"On this grassland domain, under present economic and market conditions, where the wealth of the inhabitant is measured in livestock numbers rather than long-time net production, there is little economic incentive for livestock producers to expend either financial or human effort to improve production efficiency." [7] In four thousand years Mongolian cattlemen seem to have learned no more than our own in one hundred!

Excessive use of the land, growing out of demands imposed by the mounting number of people, inevitably violates every canon of sound land use. As has been true of every other part of the world where this has happened, serious soil erosion results. China is supposed to have lost all productive capacity from 25 per cent of its land. In the eloquent words of Jacks and Whyte: "The deserts of North China, Persia, Mesopotamia and North Africa tell the same story of the gradual exhaustion of the soil as the increasing demands made upon it by expanding civilization exceeded its recuperative powers. Soil erosion, then as now, followed soil exhaustion. The early home of Chinese civilization in the northwest loessial region now resembles a huge battlefield scarred by forces far more destructive than any modern engines of war. The sculpturing of that fantastic landscape is the greatest work of Chinese civilization. Over vast areas the once deep and fertile soil has gone completely, and as it was washed away it tore gaping chasms, sometimes hundreds of feet wide and deep, through the underlying loess and deposited the eroded material on the valley plains and in the rivers and sea. The Yellow River and the Yellow Sea are aptly named, for they are colored with the yellow subsoil that still pours into them from the now barren loessial hinterland. Hundreds of miles from the eroding region, and for hundreds of miles along its course, the bed of the Yellow River is raised higher and higher above the surrounding country by the continual deposition of eroded soil; the headwaters, no longer absorbed by a porous soil, tear down the hillsides in increasing torrents; and the most disastrous floods in the world, which were once regarded as visitations from Heaven, are now normal and expected occurrences. The Yellow River transports an annual load of 2,500 million tons of soil. There are other rapidly eroding regions and great muddy rivers in China, but the gutted North-West and the Yellow River are the outstanding and eternal symbols of the mortality of civilization." [8]

Authors differ on the rate of growth of the population in China. According to Dr. W. S. Thompson, one of the most careful students of the subject, there has been none comparable to that of other parts of the East, at least during the past four or five decades. That there has been considerable growth during the past two hundred years seems probable. This is attributable to the introduction of such new crops as sweet potatoes, corn, and peanuts as much as to any other factor.

China has practically no new lands into which she can expand. Increased cropping from some existing areas would be possible were the population technologically more advanced, but modern improvements in agriculture are largely unavailable to ignorant, backward peoples. Irrigation and dry farming offer hope of increased food production but advances here are not likely to keep pace with mounting populations.

Champions of mechanization of agriculture see great hope in increasing the production per farmer. This may be possible in regions where enough land is available. With a surplus, the farmer can feed more people and buy the products of displaced farmers in the local Detroit or Chicago. But where land—with a sharply limited carrying capacity—is of insufficient extent, increased production per farmer will not help. What is needed is increased production per farm.

Mighty plans have been dreamed to help China. Blueprints for TVAs, roads, railroads, and industrialization lie upon the desks and drawing boards of both Chinese and western engineers and economists. The possibility of such developments seems remote indeed, until China is able to establish internal peace; and this, in all probability, is a grimly satisfactory outlook both for China and for the rest of the world. For with internal peace and such "improvements" as have been envisioned, China might well suffer such a population explosion as that of India, which increased 15 per cent in one decade. China quite literally *cannot feed more people*. Indeed, with unfavorable climatic conditions, such as a cycle of drought that might occur at any time, she cannot feed the people she has. Foreign areas that can supply food are not likely to buy Chinese products in sufficient amounts to take care of considerably increased numbers of empty stomachs. The greatest tragedy that China could suffer, at the present time, would be a reduction in her death rate.

We have watched Wong die, his agony past, by the side of the road. What he has suffered, what the hundred million like him have suffered, cannot be conveyed in words, even were they the words of a Dante. Millions more are going to die in the same way. There can be no way out. These men and women, boys and girls, must starve as tragic sacrifices on the twin altars of uncontrolled human reproduction and uncontrolled abuse of the land's resources.

THE DEMOGRAPHIC NADIR

India is a land of the limiting factor rampant. Level soils are found only in extremely narrow belts along the coast, along river valleys, and at the northern base of the Indian triangle. Here, millions of people are crammed into the deltas of the Ganges, Indus, and Brahmaputra. Even this triangle peters out to a sterile desert on the west, with three inches of rain. Throughout much of India rainfall is highly seasonal, varies widely from place to place, from year to year, and as to the beginning and end of its prayed-for rainy seasons. In much of the area it falls with a bludgeoning force upon land that has long since been stripped of its plant cover; 425 inches have been recorded at Cherapunji.[9] One inch may fall in ten minutes, forty inches in twenty-four hours.[10] Except for the level areas mentioned, India is principally a land of hills and mountains, where the torrential rains may do their most destructive work.

Fuel is so scarce that tens of millions must do their cooking with dried cakes of cow dung. This gives an illuminating clue to the condition of the deforested watersheds. In many parts of India every available stick, cornstalk, and piece of rice straw is burned as fuel; houses are built of mud, the only available material.

The population has responded soundly to these conditions

and concentrated on level lands. Many millions of acres have been irrigated, but millions have also been ruined by the alkali deposits resulting from bad irrigation practices. Throughout most of India soils are poor because of leaching by tropical downpours and rapid oxidation of organic materials under the fierce tropical sun. The carrying capacity of the land is so low and people are crowded onto such minute tracts that they cannot possibly afford to buy fertilizer.

The life expectancy of the Indian is thirty-two years—less than half that for the United States or England. Forty-five per cent of the babies die before they are ten; 65 per cent of the entire population dies before reaching the age of thirty. According to one of her young economists, "India today is among the poorest countries in the world. Her gross national dividend [income] barely amounts to $19 per capita per year or 5 cents per head per day. For 60 per cent of her total population of more than 400 millions it is not more than 2 cents per head per day. Thus the average Indian's income . . . is just enough either to feed two men in every three of the population, or give them all two in place of every three meals they need, on condition they all consent to go naked, live out of doors all the year round, have no amusement or recreation and want nothing else but food, and that the lowest, the coarsest, and the least nutritious." [11] The average calorie intake is estimated to be less than 1,000 per day.[12]

The British must largely bear the responsibility—not, perhaps, to be interpreted as culpability—for the present situation of India. Before the imposition of the *Pax Britannica*, India had an estimated population of less than 100 million people. It was held in check by disease, famine, and fighting. Within a remarkably short period the British checked the fighting and contributed considerably to making famines ineffectual, by building irrigation works, providing means of food storage, and importing food during periods of starvation. Some industrialization and improved medicine and sanitation did the rest. While economic and sanitary conditions were being "improved," the Indians went their accustomed way, breeding with the irresponsibility of codfish; as Chandrasekhar points out, sex play is the national sport. By 1850 the population had increased over 50 per cent; by 1950, according to State Department estimates, the population of India will be over 432,000,000. The dilemma is neatly stated by Dr. Chandrasekhar, who says:

"India's population today exceeds 400 millions and at the lowest minimum of 1,400 calories she can only feed less than 300 million people! That is, more than a hundred million people or roughly almost as many as there are in this country [the United States] are either starving or are on the brink of starvation. In nearby Australia, for example, people average 3,000 calories a day. The basic reason for this difference is that some 8 million people have twice the area of land that 400 million people in India have today."

India is *increasing her population* at the rate of 14,000 per day. In the decade 1931-1940, this people grew by fifty millions—more than the total population of England, Scotland, and Wales—and to feed and nourish them all, the most optimistic cannot find more than 447,000,000 acres of land even potentially capable of being brought under the plow.

With one-fifth of the world's people, India possesses one-third of the world's cattle. Draft animals are valued and cared for, others are neglected and left free to wander through the countryside and destroy vegetation that is desperately needed for other uses. The "sacredness" of the cow is every day contributing significantly to a lower carrying capacity on India's already overstrained lands, and is an eloquent indicator of her abysmal backwardness. Her people are steeped in superstition, ignorance, poverty, and disease. Mother India is the victim of her own awful fecundity. In all the world there is probably no region of greater misery, and almost certainly none with less hope.

Her very hopelessness may be of good augury for the rest of mankind. India has begun to give expression to a Realpolitik of expansion. One of her leading economists writes: "Where there are vast open spaces, as in Amazonia and Australia, an exclusive policy of restricting immigration militates against the demands of world economy and productivity . . . vast arid areas in North America which are now settled only by cattlemen can be brought under the plough and the harrow if Chinese and Indian immigration is encouraged on a reasonable scale. . . . In the world of the future, a balance of economic resources and populations has to be reckoned with. Standards of living and economic opportunities for all peoples should gradually approximate, if the world is to be saved from recurrent demographic crises and aggressions." [13] In other words, Australia, Brazil, the United States, and Canada should open their doors to Moslems, Sikhs, Hindus (and their sacred cows) to reduce the pressure caused by untrammeled copulation. Our living standard must be dragged down, to raise that of the backward billion of Asia.

Dr. Mukerjee advocates, it is true, a vigorous birth-control policy for India but he is unwilling to wait until it is effective. Since the Indians would not be in their present unfortunate predicament if they had checked their population increase, it is difficult to accede to the conclusion that we must now be its victim.

A heavily industrialized India, backed up by such population pressure, would be a danger to the entire world. Disorders following the British withdrawal seem to be imposing once more the Malthusian checks that held the pre-British population within reasonable bounds. It appears probable that the turmoil will also stultify any considerable industrial development. This is a result piously to be desired—until the United Nations has perfected machinery to prevent war, or until the Indian population is brought within reasonable bounds.

THE OUTSIZE BEAR

One of the most widespread misconceptions current in the world today concerns the wealth of the Soviet Union. While this is undoubtedly one of the richest nations on the face of the earth, "wealth" is a relative term, and some geographers consider that the U.S.S.R. is already overpopulated. If wealth is to be measured in terms of what we like to think of as "The American Standard of Living," Russia is certainly overpopulated; there is little possibility that she can raise her people to our status.

The carrying capacity of the vast majority of Soviet land is low. In this respect she is comparable to Canada—not the United States. She possesses untold mineral wealth, but man can still not eat nickel, tungsten, or petroleum. Millions of square miles of the Soviet Union are subject to a short growing season as well as a scant rainfall. "It has long been a recognized climatic rule that the lower the annual rainfall, the greater the variability from year to year; it appears to be equally true that the lower the annual temperature, the greater the variation in the period between spring and fall frosts." [14] Thus, much of the U.S.S.R. that is not downright unavailable is marginal because of climatic uncertainties.

Only a few areas in the West and in the higher mountains have more than twenty inches of rainfall. Middle Asia and northeastern Siberia maintain their semidesert vegetation on less than eight inches. Variable rainfall has caused repeated famines in some of Russia's most productive areas.

The lack of rainfall is caused by three factors. The first is the great mountain barrier across the southern side; this bars precipitation that might be drawn in from the Indian and South Pacific oceans. North Pacific moisture is unavailable because the sea lies on the wrong side of the continent, and its storms are carried away from Siberia by cyclonic movements. This leaves the Atlantic Ocean as almost the only source of precipitation—and most of the country is so far from the Atlantic that the moisture is gone before the land can benefit from it.

The Koeppen climatic classification shows that approximately one-half of the Soviet Union has short cool summers, with only one to three months above fifty degrees. Another 25 per cent or more consists of steppe or desert.

Well over half of the Soviet Union is dominated by tundra with frozen subsoil, coniferous forest on acid soils, or mountains. It possesses the world's greatest timber wealth, estimated at one-fifth of the total, but much of it is so remote from any means of transportation that it is economically impossible to exploit it, even in a Socialist country (1948). Western Russia imports timber from Finland and Scandinavia!

The great area east of the Caspian Sea is mostly desert. North of this and extending eastward almost to China lie the Russian steppes, an area of short grass and a rainfall of only twelve to sixteen inches. Enormous expanses of productive, granular chernozem soils have developed here, under conditions of low precipitation. They are rich in organic matter and soil nutrients. Their very fertility is an indication and result of the absence of leaching rains. No people on earth has yet successfully come to terms with such an environment. We painfully learned from our own Dust Bowl what happens when the sod cover is plowed. Millions of acres must be included in Class V to VIII land. It may be that with irrigation and scientific planting and cropping, the soil can be kept in place. These measures, however, assume that the population pressure shall not be excessive.

Water tables are deep, but this may be one of the areas in which atomic energy for pumping will be most useful. The extent of these water tables apparently is not known. Replenishment is certain to be slow, and evaporation of surface waters high. This immediately poses the problem of possible exhaustion of stored ground water, and may well create serious difficulties from alkaline deposits on irrigated land. This appears to be the region on which the Soviet government is depending to feed its rapidly growing population. If the gamble on the agricultural productivity of the chernozem soils should turn against Russia, there might well be in store for the world such trouble as it has not yet seen.

It was calculated, in 1928, that the U.S.S.R. possessed 433,000,000 acres of arable land. About 85 per cent of this was under cultivation in 1940, giving an average of 2.2 acres per person as compared with 2.8 acres in the United States.[15] There would not seem to be, here, a great deal of room for expansion.

The Ukraine, the Soviet breadbasket, resembles in climate and vegetation the great plains of Montana and Saskatchewan —hardly the most favorable environment. White Russian agriculture is sharply limited by wet, acid soils; a clue to the backwardness of this region is that both homes and electric plants depend on peat as a source of fuel. Interior Siberia, as has been said, consists mostly of forest and desert. In northeastern Siberia there is good agricultural land, but the possibilities of producing food are limited by the long winters and the dry winds that pour out from mid-continent. Furthermore, there is in this region a not-inconsiderable psychological hazard known as arctic, or Siberian, hysteria. The person affected by it "howls, cries, talks nonsense, laments, often gets cramps, throws himself from corner to corner until, exhausted, he falls asleep. . . . In the northeastern part of Asia . . . all sorts of hysterical phenomena are extremely frequent among natives and often assume an epidemic, contagious character." Contributing factors are said to be climate, mode of life, conditions of work, food, monotony, etc.[16]

Basic to the whole future of the U.S.S.R. and its relationship with the other countries of the world is its ability to cope with agriculture in dry-farming areas. There is no doubt of the scientific genius of the Russian people. No one understands better than their scientists the limitations imposed by their soils and climate. (Whether such understanding has reached the top levels of the Politburo is dubious.) They have long been recognized as world leaders in soil science and they, too, have recognized the scientific imperative, perhaps more than any other people. Reports that came out before the Iron Curtain fell indicated that extremely promising steps were being taken toward the establishment of at least a long-term truce with a hostile environment. For example, fur trappers were using box traps harmless to animals, and freeing the females for breeding purposes. In the United States we have had difficulty even in restricting trappers to the season when pelts are prime. The application of scientific methods might be advanced by a dictatorship which can impose sound land-use practices on people who would ruin the soil under a system of "democratic free enterprise," as has been done over millions of acres in the United States; but this is far from certain.

Despite strict government control and the high value placed on science, reports from travelers coming out of the Soviet Republics indicate that considerable soil erosion exists. As might be expected, Soviet sources tend to suggest that all the damage was done under the pre-Marxian dispensation! And it is no doubt true that serfdom concentrated too many farmers on too little land and, as usual, drove them up erodible slopes.

The long, severe winter of the U.S.S.R. freezes the ground deeply and prevents infiltration of snow water with the spring thaw; this results in severe gully erosion. (Melting snow accounts for about one-third of the total precipitation.)

"In the south and southeast of the U.S.S.R., where the climate is continental, strong, dry, hot winds contribute to the development of wind erosion, dust storms and blowing of sandy and sandy-loam soils. Wind erosion in the winter is widespread. During severe blizzards, the wind tears off the snow cover, destroys the soil and ruins winter crops over large areas. During such winters, snowdrifts mix with dust; the fields are not white but black. . . . Destructive cloudbursts, which erode the soil, are most frequent in the southwestern parts of the U.S.S.R., within the borders of the Ukraine and of Moldavia; in parts of White Russia, in the Caucasus; in Transcaucasia; and in the Far East. Also contributing to the development of erosion is the sharply dissected relief of central Russia." [17] John Fischer reports: "Virtually nothing has been done to check soil erosion . . . I never saw a single terrace or check-dam anywhere in western Russia. Even contour plowing is entirely unknown." [18]

Against the advantage of a scientifically disposed central government must be set the clumsiness of a bureaucracy largely headed by scientific ignoramuses and shot through with terror and politics. During 1946 many rumors emerged that indicated substantial crop failures in the Soviet Union, and the explanation of these places the blame squarely at the door of unwieldy overcentralization. According to these reports, control over the land has been increasingly concentrated in Moscow and has reached the point where the collective farms may not even put in their seeds without orders from on high. Anyone familiar with American bureaucracy can readily imagine what would happen were such a system tried here. In a country where a police spy stands at the shoulder of every worker, such a system could scarcely avoid chaos.

As this book is written, reports are received of a "bumper" Russian wheat crop that may make available to Europe two million tons. If we assume the rather low rate of production of fourteen bushels per acre, this represents the crop from only about five million acres. This, in a country whose population is expanding at an explosive rate, is a rather unimpressive margin of surplus.

It is strange that such pragmatists as the Soviet leaders should not have adopted a more realistic population policy. With their resources they can maintain extremely high living standards for many millions, but certainly not for as many as they will have to feed, shelter, and clothe within a few decades. Without such an inventory of resources as has not yet been made, so far as we know, we can only guess at the optimum, which would probably be 100,000,000 to 150,000,000 people. Anything in excess of this will make too great demands on the carrying capacity and result in a generally lower standard. Moscow has undoubtedly been misled by nineteenth-century economic thought and a Micawber-like faith in technology. It is conceivable that some of her leaders hope to expand through world conquest into other lands. There are, of course, few areas remaining that have not reached the human saturation point.

If the Politburo would consult some of the Soviet's distinguished ecologists, of which it has a number, it might save itself some painful decades in the future.

Southeastern Asia, with the exception of Java, is largely characterized by its low fertility. Here, again, one encounters the familiar tropical pattern of leached soils, organic matter rapidly oxidized by high temperatures, and heavy, concentrated, eroding rains. Theoretically, room could still be made for millions of people throughout large areas of Thailand, Burma, New Guinea, Borneo, etc.

One of the highest stumbling blocks is the traditional system of kaingin, or shifting, agriculture, similar to the milpa agriculture of the Americas. While this plan of burning, cultivating, and fallowing was probably satisfactory enough with an abundance of land to take care of the population, the rise in population now prevents adequate fallowing and land restoration. Land impoverishment, erosion, and floods—destroying lowland rice areas—may be expected to increase rather than decrease for many decades.

The peoples of southeast Asia are confronted with major scientific problems. They themselves have few scientists to solve them, and if they had, decades would be required to untangle many of the knotty problems of tropical environments. Even were the best scientific techniques in the world available, these Asiatics could not for a long time rise above their slough of ignorance and superstition in order to take advantage of them. And any progress they might make would be overwhelmed by excessive numbers of human beings, unless their breeding is curtailed.

In southwestern Asia—specifically Palestine—we find one of the most hopeful areas not only on the continent but in the entire world. On the raddled hillsides and silt-drifted plains, the Jews are repeating the miracle of Lazarus on the dead land. We can have, I think, few experiences so encouraging in the middle of our twentieth century as reading Walter Lowdermilk's *Palestine—Land of Promise*. One aspect of that heartening scene he fails to stress, perhaps even to mention: the fact that the soils of Palestine are unleached. The very harshness of the semiarid climate has preserved the richness of the land until irrigation waters can be brought to it. The potentialities of this area are enormous, though here again it is imperative to remember that area, biotic potential, and environmental resistances impose unavoidable limits.

Once more Palestine demonstrates that "arable land" is as much a function of the farmer as of the farm. The high intelligence and firm character of the modern Jew is restoring productivity to land that has been sterile desert for hundreds of years in other hands. In a world largely peopled by destroyers, this is a thought to dwell on.

Australia has reached one of the world's highest living standards by the well-known methods of the drunken sailor: it is throwing its patrimony to the winds—literally—and having a wonderful time. According to E. S. Clayton, "worse examples of wind erosion are already to be seen in Australia on both grazing and cultivated lands than in the United States or Canada. . . . The position in regard to water erosion is also very serious. It has not progressed so far as in the United States, but the land has only been under cultivation for about one-third of the period."

In Central Australia, western and southwestern Queensland, New South Wales, the north of South Australia, and Western Australia there has been serious deterioration of ranges. The combination of overgrazing, rabbits, and dry seasons has resulted in the gradual degeneration "of hundreds of thousands of square miles of lightly stocked range." In good seasons the responsive growth of the vegetation is followed by an almost explosive increase in rabbits that, in the inevitable dry seasons that follow, sharply cuts back the saltbush and other protective plants. Even the acacias are girdled and killed by rabbits. With a succession of bad seasons, the topsoil blows.

In the Mallee area the sod-breaking plow is the villain. The farmers sow wheat—and their land is swept away. High wheat prices, as in our own West, have caused an expansion of cultivation in wet years, and erosion in dry.

In the semiarid South Australian grazing country, it is calculated that the density of the original protective vegetation has been reduced 75 to 90 per cent. A part of the area, Australian scientists believe, can be restored by a heavy cut in numbers of sheep, but other regions can be saved only by extermination of the introduced rabbit.[19] One measure may prove to be as difficult as the other. The environmental resistance of most of Australia, especially the deficiency and variability of rainfall, is extremely high, and the European's treatment of the land and his excessive demands upon it have raised the resistance still higher. Over vast tracts, the carrying capacity has fallen to almost nothing.

Along with the grasses, the forests, and the soil has gone the water. What does fall from the clouds does not get back into the ground. In many areas the Australians have repeated the folly of the Californians; their windmills have sucked from underground far more water than has gone back into it. The rabbits, the sheep, and the wind have stirred up the dust. Captain Martins, under its yellow cloud a thousand miles at sea, is having an experience that is little different from that of congressmen from Texas and Oklahoma and Nebraska who watched their home soils sift gently down upon Washington.

POPULATIONS VERSUS SURVIVAL

Some population authorities consider that the greatest potential threat to world peace lies in the development of industry—war potential—in India and China. When these spawning millions are considered in relation to their degenerating lands, it is difficult to take such threats seriously. Malthusian forces contributing to internal stresses will probably make impossible any considerable industrial development for decades to come. Large external markets will not be available for the products of

Eastern industry, and an internal per-capita purchasing power of five cents a day is scarcely likely to build a large industrial machine. British withdrawal from India may well result in the reversal of the population trend that this country so badly needs if her people are ever to achieve a reasonably decent standard of living. The spectacle will not be pleasant to watch. How much better it would have been for the people of India if a controlled birth rate could have held her population at a low enough level so that available land could provide not only enough, good-quality food and other products, but a surplus that could support the modern amenities of education and physical well-being. How much better would it be to reduce population by the humane, relatively simple prevention of human fertilization, rather than by the agonies of war, starvation, and disease!

Nathaniel Peffer, one of the Westerners best informed on China, wrote as follows in May, 1947:

"The reasoning of the Communists appears to be that continued war will bring about economic disintegration and then collapse of the Government, after which they will inherit power. The first part of this reasoning is sound. If the war is long, only a miracle can avert economic disintegration. The currency now has only a fictive basis. The cities, cut off from the interior and one another, cannot long continue to live off their own fat.

"It is possible, too, that with economic collapse the Government of Chiang Kai-shek would go down, but it does not follow that the Communists would then succeed to power over the whole country. It is more likely that there would be a breaking up into regional segments, each under a warlord as in the past. There would be a return to the state of twenty years ago, with a satrap rule over what was only officially called a single country. It is even possible that Chiang Kai-shek and his circle could remain entrenched in the lower Yangtze Valley, with its rich industrial cities. In one of the regions the Communists would rule. The one certainty is that neither side can win a decisive victory." [20] Within three days of the publication of Dr. Peffer's article, newspapers were printing reports of rice riots in Chinese cities. There is little hope that the world will escape the horror of extensive famines in China within the next few years. But from the world point of view, these may be not only desirable but indispensable. A Chinese population that continued to increase at a geometric rate could only be a global calamity. The mission of General Marshall to this unhappy land was called a failure. Had it succeeded, it might well have been a disaster.

The much more dangerous areas in Asia would seem to be Japan and the Soviet Union. If Japan is held within the narrow bounds into which we have forced her, and permanently cut off from world trade and the re-establishment of her industries, she can continue to exist as a coolie country, though she too will probably have to face famine unless she takes quick and effective action to check her population increase. If we attempt to raise her to a standard of living that makes democracy possible, she will remain a world threat—unless her population is limited. She does not have the resources at home to feed eighty million people. She does not have the raw materials required by her industry. She has a memory of a remarkable development from preindustrial feudalism to the status of a major power in a period of only seventy-five years. If Japan is to regain anything comparable to her former status as an industrialized world power, she will either have to be subjected to harsh policing to contain her war potential—or her population must be systematically reduced by cutting the birth rate, until her own ability to supply her needs is far nearer to the demand than it has been since 1880. Reduced to a population approximately that of Scandinavia, she might well take an honored place in the world, comparable to that of Scandinavia.

The major threat in Asia—and this is a factor that appears to have been given little public discussion—is mounting population pressure in the Soviet Union. Soviet productivity per man and per acre has never risen above some of the lowest levels recorded by economists. The Soviet Union has suffered a succession of famines, both before the revolution and since. She has deliberately embarked on a planned program of population expansion. This program is undoubtedly conceived, in part, as a means of building the Red Army. But whatever the motivation, it is going to find the Soviet Republics with some 200,000,000 inhabitants in 1950 and 210,000,000 five years later. By the end of this century there may be 300,000,000 Russians. These must be fed on 433,000,000 acres of arable land. As has been pointed out above, this arable land is subject to wide variations in the length of the growing season, to recurrent and devastating drought, and to exceedingly grave hazards of erosion. Should these unfavorable factors happen to combine over a wide area within the next few decades, the entire world may well be painfully convinced of the Soviet overpopulation that is now merely the hypothesis of a few geographers.

The people of the Soviet Union, according to the credible testimony of scores of informed people, do not want war. Now is the time for them to begin control of one of the most powerful causes of war—overpopulation.

Chapter 10

The Dying Land

Fʀᴏᴍ ᴛʜᴇ ʜᴜᴍᴀɴ ᴘᴏɪɴᴛ ᴏғ ᴠɪᴇᴡ, Aғʀɪᴄᴀ ɪs ᴛʜᴇ ᴘᴏᴏʀ-
est of the continents. It possesses the lowest carrying capacity
per square mile. It is involved in difficult problems that have
already had world repercussions. Man has lived in it longer
than most, perhaps than any, parts of the earth. It has felt the
impact of civilization longer than any other continent, except
Asia. If we will read the lesson of its lands, it can teach us much.

All but the extreme northern and southern parts of Africa
lie within the tropics. Its average elevation of two thousand
feet is low enough so that it must endure blazing temperatures.
Its extra-tropical extremes consists mostly of desert—the Sahara,
Kalahari, Damaraland, and Namaqualand. The desert condition is so complete that in parts there is an appreciable rain only
once in seven years; in the southwestern region, the average
rainfall is less than one inch a year. Furthermore, there is some
evidence that Africa is now passing through a climatic cycle
of increasing dryness. Here, even discounting man's activities,
deserts are on the march!

Adjacent to the enormous deserts and semideserts lies the
region of brushy savanna and thorn scrub, characterized by
undependable and scant rainfall—and always the burning sun.

Disregarding these areas of neglible carrying capacity, we
have left only the African heartland, extending from about
15 degrees N. to 18 degrees S., west of Lake Nyasa. Only in
this limited area is there sufficient rainfall for agriculture. And

in the rain forest that covers much of the central belt precipitation is so concentrated in the intensity of its fall, and so abundant, that destruction of the forest inescapably results in destruction of the soil.

Nearly all of Africa is marginal for agriculture. Despite the fact that it comprises 2.7 billion more acres than South America, it is estimated to have only 20,000,000 more acres suitable for agriculture.[1] And its 1946 population was more than 70 per cent greater!

As in most parts of the world, one of the best clues to lands suitable for man's use is given by the native vegetation. A brief study of Africa's plant geography (page 243) will clearly show why Africa cannot support a large population. The area of rain forest suffers from the limitation mentioned above. Surrounding this is the belt of humid forest; here climatic conditions are most favorable for human occupancy, aside from the minuscule, overcrowded areas characterized by Mediterranean vegetation and climate. The transition zone between the humid forest and the semiarid grassy steppe is the wooded savanna, recognizable by its deciduous trees. Their thin understory is open enough to permit the existence of great extensions of parklike grass beneath the boughs. It is comparable to parts of the llanos in Venezuela. This plant association forms one of the favorite habitats of the native African.

Between the wooded savanna and the steppe and desert lies another transition zone familiar to many of us from the motion pictures of Martin Johnson. This is the great belt of hard grass and thornbush, such as the mimosa, over which roam the impressive herds of African antelopes and such associated animals as lions. Finally, we come to the deserts and desertlike steppes, where average rainfall is less than twelve inches a year and the dry season at least nine months long. The climatic conditions that are largely responsible for these belts of vegetation are summarized in the table below:

Formation	No. of Dry Seasons	Mos. of Dry Season	Inches of Rain per Year
Evergreen rain forest	0	0	65
Humid forest	2	3 to 4	44 to 65
Wooded savanna	2	5 to 8	24 to 44
Brushy savanna and thorn scrub	1	8 to 9	12 to 24
Predesert steppe and desert	1	9 to 12	12

Although researches on the complex environment of the Dark Continent have scarcely begun, more is known about it through investigations of the British, French, Belgians, Italians, and Germans than any tropical area of comparable size. Had Latin America been studied even this much, she could avoid much of the misery threatening her expanding populations.

African soils have been rather extensively studied and are an illuminating clue to the carrying capacity of the continent. Beneath the thin grasses of the savanna, in the older part of the continent, soils are largely sandy, worn-out, and poor. Neither flood nor geological erosion has provided new materials and the soils have a great uniformity.

Much of the wooded savanna, such as is found in French and Portuguese Africa, the Belgian Congo, and Rhodesia, is able to exist on poor soils because of high water tables; these, as will be shown later, are generally falling. Here a clearing may be capable of producing several years of good crops, but cultivation is soon followed by a complete degradation of the soils. It is probably this zone that is most seriously threatened at the present time by man's activities.

Another widespread type of African soil is that of the great equatorial forest. Tropical forest soils are often intrinsically poor; it is the thick superficial bed of humus, decayed plant material, slowly built up by the forest itself, that makes possible the existence of one of the most exuberant plant covers in the world. The virgin forest is a system in perfect equilibrium—

PLANT GEOGRAPHY OF AFRICA

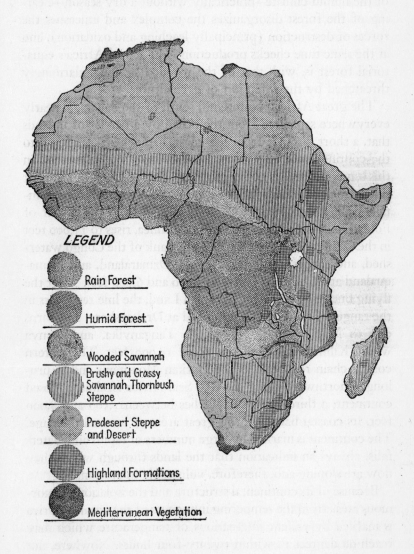

LEGEND

- Rain Forest
- Humid Forest
- Wooded Savannah
- Brushy and Grassy Savannah, Thornbush Steppe
- Predesert Steppe and Desert
- Highland Formations
- Mediterranean Vegetation

characterized by a stable cap of humus, rich in nitrogen and bases. This equilibrium originates in the balance between the forces of production and those of destruction. Partly because of the humid climate—practically without a dry season—clearing of the forest disorganizes the complex and unleashes the forces of destruction (principally leaching and oxidation), and at the same time checks production. The soil of Africa's equatorial forest is, with that of the wooded savanna, alarmingly threatened by the extension of agriculture.

The great African hinterland, south of the Sahara, is nearly everywhere separated from the ocean by a barrier of uplands that, a short distance from the coast, hamper penetration into the continent not only of man but of maritime influences. In this sense, the area is comparable to Central Asia. On the west side of the continent south of the Tropic of Cancer, the mountain wall, interrupted by some breaks, rises in the massif of Fouta Djallon, parallels the Gulf of Guinea, rises to 13,000 feet in the Cameroons, forms the western flank of the Congo watershed, and carries south into Angola, Damaraland, and Namaqualand at altitudes of between 3,000 and 6,000 feet. After the flying buttresses of Great Bushman Land, the line reappears in the ranges of the Great Karroo and at Drakensberg, and turns east to Matabeleland, Nyasaland, Tanganyika, and Kenya where Kilimanjaro climbs to some 18,000 feet. The eastern coastal chain reappears as the Harkan Mountains and is prolonged northward along the Red Sea. Africa is, thus, a closed continent; a third of its surface lies between 1,500 and 8,000 feet. Its coastal barrier forms great areas of internal drainage. The continent is marked by large numbers of rapids and waterfalls, always an indication that the lands through which they flow are sloping and, therefore, vulnerable to erosion.

Because of its continental structure and the isolation of enormous areas from the tempering influences of the oceans, Africa is marked by violent fluctuations of temperature which may reach 68 degrees F. within twenty-four hours. Nowhere, not even in the Amazon Valley, which is to some extent benefited by Atlantic influences, is the importance of plant cover greater. When the African forests have been destroyed, the mean temperature of the surface of the ground will rise as much as 60 degrees. High temperatures stimulate both chemical and biological activity in the soil.

Many of the bacterial activities so important to the richness of the soil find their optimum at about 100 degrees F. When the temperature rises above a certain point, their productivity falls sharply. Direct insolation in Africa has a fatal influence on the bacteria, speeds up chemical actions such as oxidation and laterization, and destroys the colloidal structure so necessary to good soils. Furthermore, concentrated rains reaching a surface cleared of its forest protection, actually break up solid particles, destroy the granular structure. Here again, of course, as in nearly all regions of concentrated rainfall, the absence of plant and humus cover results in the rapid formation of a relatively impermeable layer, reduces infiltration, and accelerates runoff.

Two thousand years ago northern Africa first felt the impact of mechanical man, and the gaunt bones of its civilization are a warning we have still not learned to heed.

"A century or more after the destruction of Carthage by Scipio in 146 B.C.," writes Dr. Walter C. Lowdermilk, "Rome began to colonize North Africa and in the course of time established several important and stately cities. . . . These cities were established at crossroads and along the southern edge of the great agricultural region, devoted principally to the growing of grain and olives." This area, of course, lay in the region of Africa's most favorable climate, the Mediterranean zone.

"The Roman city of Thydrus," continues Dr. Lowdermilk, "at the present site of El Jem, was located in the midst of the great coastal plain of Tunisia. The most conspicuous remnant here is the ruin of a great coliseum to seat 60,000 spectators, which was second in size only to that at Rome. Now a wretched village stands on the site of this great Roman city. This center was supported by intensive agriculture of grain fields and olive orchards; now this plain is sparsely covered with wild vegetation and isolated groves of olives overrun by herds of grazing animals.

"The Roman city of Thamugadi, at the site called Timgad in Algeria, was one of the more famous centers of Roman power and culture. It was established by the Emperor Trajan about A.D. 100 and was laid out in a symmetrical pattern, equipped with a magnicent forum embellished with statuary and carved porticoes, with a public library, with 17 Roman baths adorned with beautiful mosaic floors, with a theater to seat some 2,500 and with marble flush latrines. Timgad was a stately city supported by extensive grain fields in the valley plains and olive orchards on the hills.

"After the weakening of the Roman power by the Vandal invasion in A.D. 430 the Berbers captured the city, and after the Arab invasion of the seventh century it was lost to knowledge for 1,200 years, buried by dust, the product of wind erosion. Only a few columns and a portion of Trajan's arch stood above undulating mounds as tombstones to indicate that once a great city was here. There is no counterpart today of the magnificence of this ancient city. A wretched village of mud-wall houses sheltering a few hundred inhabitants is the only descendant of this center of Roman power and culture. Water erosion as well as wind erosion has been at work on the landscape. Gullies have cut through portions of the city and have exposed the aqueduct which supplied the city with water from a great spring some 3 miles away.

"Ruins of the land are as impressive as the ruins of cities. The hills have been swept bare of soil, a story which may be read throughout the region. The original soil mantle is being washed off the slopes, often showing that the upper edge of the soil mantle is being gradually worked down slope by accelerated run-off from the bared upper slopes. Erosional debris has been deposited on the lower slopes and valley plain. Torrential storm waters cut great gullies into the alluvial plains. Water tables are lowered and rain waters quickly flow off the land leaving it dry and thirsty. The effects of desiccation of the land are brought about even if rainfall has not diminished."

The dynamic panorama described by M. Harroy is of a degenerating continent. Over vast areas of Africa, water tables are falling, rain forest is being invaded by humid forest, humid forest by wooded savanna, wooded savanna by thornbush, and thornbush by steppe and desert. Some authorities disagree with the thesis that Africa is undergoing a climatic change. Lowdermilk says: "The most telling evidence of unchanged climate in the past 2000 years in the successful plantation of olive groves on the sites of ruins of Roman stone olive presses. An experimental grove planted at Timgad by Director Godet demonstrates that olive orchards would thrive today where soil still remains on slopes. The great plantation of more than 150,000 acres in the vicinity of Sfax, Tunisia, which now supports thriving enterprises at Sfax also discredits the change of climate theory. Moreover, in the vicinity of Sousse, Tunisia, there are a few Roman olive orchards which escaped the destructive invasions of the seventh century and survived to the present day. No pulsations of climate have been sufficiently adverse to kill off this remnant of the agriculture of Roman times." [2]

Whether or not Africa is actually undergoing a climatic change must probably remain an open question, because of the lack of meteorological data. As Harroy points out, only the United States, Western Europe, and some small areas such as Japan and New Zealand possess a sufficiently developed net of meteorological stations (one for each thousand square kilometers) to give us statistically significant findings. While South Africa has somewhat more than one rain gauge for each five thousand square kilometers, the rest of the continent, except for Egypt, possesses many less.

About 1890, rainfall was much heavier over all the southern part of the continent. At the same time, the same situation was observed in the same latitudes of Australia. One theory makes this phenomenon coincide with a displacement, toward the south, of the tropical rain belt. After this, however, the dryness was accentuated to such a point that, in 1932-33, 750,000 head of cattle and 7,000,000 sheep perished.

Whether or not Africa is actually suffering a climatic change, man is most effectively helping to desiccate the continent. On the Gold Coast, H. M. Thompson in 1908 mapped the forest, and a comparison of his chart with the present distribution of trees proves without any question that there has been a considerable reduction in the primitive forest. His map shows "not only a great diminution of timber supplies but also the considerable loss of fertility that has taken place, for a very large area marked by him as rain forest is now replaced by the drier, mixed deciduous forest." [3]

Here, as in most of Africa, the destructive weapon is fire. Clearings are made in the forest for agriculture or to secure wood for fire or building. Under the primitive system, after clearings were made there followed a resting period sufficiently long to restore the primitive cover. Today, however, with increasing population pressures, the forest is kept open, permitted to dry, and frequently burned. Repeated fires play an important part in all the natural areas of Africa except in the rain forest which is normally too wet to burn freely; or on the predesert steppes and desert where there is not sufficient vegetation. In the intermediate formations, fire tends constantly to degrade the vegetation toward the lower subclimax.

When the vegetation of a region has disappeared, that which suceeds it is *always* characteristic of a drier region. The rich primitive vegetation gives way to a secondary vegetation, which is composed of fewer species and species of less value. As the Duc de Brabant pointed out in an oft-quoted speech before the African Society in 1933, no one can assay these losses to the human economy. "Before the discovery of the economic treasure that is rubber, a more intensive occupation and exploitation of Brazilian forests, wiping out the rubber trees, might have deprived us today of the pleasure of rolling comfortably on pneumatics! Likewise, excessive deforestation in tropical Africa might have prevented our ever knowing the delights of morning coffee." Many plants have disappeared from the African flora. The destruction of species is, of course, final. There is no possibility that they can ever be brought back.

Another important factor in the degeneration of the African flora has been the introduction of exotic species. Along with these one finds over vast areas such significant indicators of destroyed land as a poisonous bracken of the same genus that is so characteristic of burned-over, eroded areas on both North and South America. This degeneration of the vegetation is not only the cause of increasing dryness, and therefore the development of a less favorable ecology; it is at the same time a result. Once the climax vegetation has been disturbed, a vicious circle is set up, a circle that can be broken only over a long period of time, as in the semidesert lands of northwestern Venezuela. Conditions favorable to the re-establishment of normal vegetation are rare in Africa, and the ecological degeneration is steadily threatening an ever-growing number of areas.

Before the arrival of the European, primitive populations apparently had some empirical understanding of the laws controlling the African landscape. In Madagascar, for example, excessive lumbering was punished by decapitation of the criminal upon the stump of one of the trees he had felled. This is making the punishment fit the crime, with a vengeance! It is an interesting commentary on "civilization" that in the United States the man who commits the same crime becomes one of our wealthiest, most powerful, and most honored citizens. In order to permit periods of forest regeneration up to thirty years, native farmers of the southwestern Belgian Congo forced their people to invade and fell new areas of forest, despite the enormous labor involved.

The Pygmies are zealous defenders of the forest, and dwellers about its edge, known among the Pygmies as "tree-eaters," are thoroughly intimidated by these fierce little warriors. The Belgians have made good use of their attitude and made the Pygmies effective aides to their forest rangers. The Bantu, a nomadic forest destroyer, will not carelessly risk venturing within the Pygmy sphere of influence.

With the destruction of vegetation there has been, of course, a parallel destruction of native animals. Elephants, hippopotami, crocodiles, and associated aquatic and semiaquatic mammals and birds have been driven southward by the advance of the Sahara, giving place to the introduced camel. In many other areas much of the native fauna has disappeared.

Were it intelligently exploited on a basis of selective cutting, the rain forest could provide a great deal of wealth. Less vulnerable to human disturbance than other forest areas, it suffers chiefly through clearings maintained for agricultural purposes, where the cover has been reduced or removed, the soil opened to driving rains and to the exhausting effects of the sun. But as a whole, because of the heavy precipitation, the rain forest tends to re-establish itself, albeit with extreme slowness. Most of it should probably be regarded as Class VII and Class VIII land.

The humid forest, with its three to four dry months each year, is far more vulnerable. Fire destroys the understory and kills young trees. Under human abuse, there is constant evolution toward what has been called "baumsteppe," approximating the savanna. Woody species tend to disappear. (A similar ecological pattern appears in highland Central America.) In this highly unstable environment altitude creates living conditions favorable for human beings—unfortunately, to use Harroy's word. This tends to concentrate man in the humid area and to exaggerate the results of clearing and burning. It is said that this forest in northern Ruanda is disappearing along its entire northern boundary at the rate of more than half a mile a year.

The savanna is probably the plant association most seriously threatened anywhere on the continent. It is one of the healthiest regions for human beings, easiest to exploit, more fertile, and richer in both plant and animal resources than the drier areas. Here occurs the most intense agriculture, and the degeneration of the savanna is largely proportional to the density of population. Under proper management, the carrying capacity would be relatively high; overpopulation, which forces violation of sound principles of land use, makes rational exploitation impossible. The long dry season of five to eight months, with its high rate of evaporation, tends to increase desiccation and make more difficult the re-establishment of a protective plant cover. In this sense, it is very like the degenerating lands of Guanacaste in the New World's Costa Rica.

Fire is normal on the steppe area. The vegetation that has evolved here is able to survive despite the annual passage of the flames. Over thousands of years an ecological equilibrium was established—only to be broken by the arrival of domestic cattle. In much, if not most, of the steppe area overgrazing has brought about the destruction of perennial forage plants, and encouraged the development of annual species or those without much value as cattle feed.

Native big-game mammals have, of course, existed here by the million, as they have on the savanna, for thousands of years. But their herds were part of a complex system of checks and balances that kept their numbers from getting out of hand. If they increased beyond the capacity of the waterholes—formerly, undoubtedly, much more abundant—they died of thirst. Lions and other predators kept the populations from becoming excessive, culled out the weak, the sickly, the old. "Nature red in tooth and claw" was a far kinder nature than that of modern man, who has destroyed indispensable environment beyond any hope of repair.

The little water that falls on the poor plant cover is lost in increasing amounts by runoff and evaporation, and the cover tends to give way to drought-resistant species of small use to stock. In extreme cases, complete devegetation has resulted and sterile rock is exposed.

On the predesert associations, again it is domestic animals that are chiefly responsible for the degeneration of the plant cover. In the judgment of many scientists, they alone are responsible for the advance of the Sahara at the rate of more than half a mile a year. The few trees that exist may be cut down to provide campfires during the cold winter nights. Every bit of vegetation is destroyed by grazing and browsing animals, chief among which is the goat. According to Worthington, "In such dry areas, acacia trees are frequently cut down to provide fodder for camels." In the words of the South African Drought Investigation Commission, "As a result of maltreatment of the land, a smaller quantity of the waters that fall is absorbed by the earth, while the volume of water wasted by runoff is increased to the point where the ability of the soil and the vegetation to resist drought has been sharply reduced."

In Africa a molecule of rain water, after its fall, probably has better than an 80 per cent chance of being returned to the atmosphere by evaporation or transpiration. Destruction of the plant cover is fatal to infiltration, and of course contributes in an equal degree to runoff. On overgrazed areas, according to Jacks and Whyte, the coefficient of runoff may increase from 0.5 to 10-20 per cent. Accelerated erosion is a natural corollary. Under the tropical skies of Africa, infiltration rarely amounts to 10 per cent. (In the North Temperate Zone it is often 50 per cent.) Level cornland, in Pretoria, transpired 66 per cent of its rain. On slopes, runoff, of course, reduces the rate of transpiration. The less rich the soil and the less humus that covers it, the more intensive is the evaporation.

Nearly everywhere on the African continent the water table appears to be continually sinking, as a result of the increased runoff and evaporation. In a region formerly wooded, where an inch of rain kept brooks and rivers alive during several weeks, the same precipitation today is scarcely able to feed them twenty-four hours. Laws has listed twenty important watercourses in the single district of Mombera, in Nyasaland, which have lost their permanent character *since the beginning of the century;* they have disappeared completely or turned into intermittent streams. The headwaters of the Nile, on which the entire economy of Egypt depends, are threatened by deforestation and siltation near their sources. According to Lord Hailey, the level of lakes in Uganda is steadily falling. In southern Libya, Lake Undur, which was still permanent in 1913, is today completely dry from March to July as a result of deforestation of the streams that fed it. Similar examples can be cited for the entire region along the southern margin of the Sahara.

The disturbance of the hydrologic regime has, of course, resulted in widespread disappearance of fishes that were once an important element in the food of the primitive peoples.

Accompanying the degeneration of the cover there is an increase in accelerated erosion. Vertical erosion removes essential plant foods. Sheet erosion, widespread over Africa, is merely a preliminary to gully, or donga, erosion. Hornby estimates that on plateaus in the highlands of Nyasaland five to ten millimeters of soil a year are swept away by sheet erosion. In Kenya, one storm removed an inch of topsoil in a few hours.

Much of Africa, it must be remembered, is arid or semiarid. As Jacks points out, "Nature has arranged that where water cannot punish man for his ignorance and misdeeds, the wind can." In Africa the dry months, notable for high winds, probably take more soil by wind erosion than is cut away by the sharply concentrated rains. Stebbing reports that, in Nigeria, when the rains come too late to hold the soil, young shoots of millet, covered by sand from the desert, must be replanted. In some years, for this reason, it is necessary to replant as many as ten times.

One gains from available literature the impression that Africa is one of the most eroded of the continents. The Belgian Congo is fortunate in having a relatively low population density, but there are alarming signs pointing to its destruction. It is estimated that in the northwest, over 500,000 acres have been "brutally" deforested. In the western Belgian Congo, 50,000 cubic meters of wood are cut a year—and there is no reforestation. The forest is being driven back on many watersheds. In the entire northern Belgian Congo the forest is being cut and burned to make way for more open—more vulnerable—land. The forest has been wiped out in much of the Kivu Basin.

In Angola, the savanna has been invaded by vast coffee plantations, some of which go back to 1853. Every year the native agriculture destroys more of the transition forest and savanna. In the High Bengo the forest has disappeared over great areas, where the native cultures attack in depth more and more of the plant cover of a naturally poor, sandy soil.

On the other hand, in the northern provinces of Northern Rhodesia, the native populations, which have had little contact with the European, have scarcely modified their ancestral way of life. As a result, the forested regions in which they live show little sign of degradation, and erosion is rare except in some of the western districts, where the natives feed themselves by shifting agriculture. In the south, shifting agriculture is common; and, especially near the railroad, the forest has largely been cleared to give place to plantations. Under the local conditions of climate and soil, a long rest would be necessary to regenerate the parts of the forest thus subjected to two or three years of soil-exhausting culture. Unfortunately, the density of the population makes adequate fallowing impossible: in order to rest the land sufficiently, every family would have to possess over a hundred acres. Here, again, we find the modern means of transportation—in this case the railroad—a double-edged sword that, as in Latin America, does more harm than good.

More disturbing is the situation in Southern Rhodesia, where the wooded savanna has been perilously destroyed by the semi-nomadic culture of the natives. To check the degeneration of vegetation that threatens the entire hydrology of the country —in Mashonaland the underground water level has sunk "dangerously" low—vigorous measures have been taken and much of the remaining forests of the territory has been placed in reserves. The right bank of the Zambesi has been intensively cultivated a relatively short time, but exhaustion of the soil and sheet erosion have progressively reduced the extent and value of agriculture. The absence of the tsetse fly has made possible a considerable development of grazing, partly as the normal type of land use following a destructive agriculture. The excess of stock has continued the degeneration of the vegetation, until it now offers little resistance to erosion. Every year, in Mashonaland, sheet erosion carries away an estimated five to six millimeters of topsoil. In Matabeleland and in the native reserves, gully erosion is general.

Along with Madagascar and certain parts of French Equatorial Africa, Nyasaland is one of the regions in which the vegetation has suffered most seriously in an astonishingly brief lapse of time. In 1880 the northern part of Nyasaland was richly forested and irrigated; today this entire forest has been destroyed by native farmers—and the brush that has succeeded it is burned every year. The intense erosion that has resulted has further accentuated the degradation of the plant cover and in places "so much top soil has been removed by wash that mountains and hills are now masses of bare rock, and once forested plains are treeless." [4] Important rivers, such as the Shire, have been filled with silt.

Some of the most effective reforestation work on the Dark Continent has been done in the Union of South Africa. However, it is probable that in no region is the need more critical. In 1923 the Drought Investigation Commission summed up its report as follows:

"(I) That soil erosion is extending rapidly over many parts of the Union.

"(II) That, besides slooting, there is a great deal of surface erosion, both by water and wind, taking place.

"(III) That the soil of the Union, our most valuable asset, irreplaceable and definitely limited in amount, is being removed in enormous quantities annually.

"(IV) That a great part of this soil and valuable plant food is lost for ever, and while the remainder of the eroded material may do good in some instances, it does much harm in others.

"(V) That great damage is done by the eroded material silting up reservoirs and that soil erosion causes greater irregularity in the flow of our rivers, thereby increasing the cost of irrigation works and the cost of producing feeding stuffs.

"(VI) That soil erosion is causing a marked decrease in the underground water supply of the Union, and thereby increases the difficulty of watering stock.

"(VII) Soil erosion is caused by reduction of the vegetal cover.

"(VIII) That soil erosion has a cumulative character which by virtue of the similarity between its cause and effect, always accelerates its rate of growth, in all except a few favored portions of the Union.

"(IX) That prompt action is therefore imperative.

"(X) That soil erosion is caused, mainly by deterioration of the vegetal cover brought about by incorrect veld management, and that all efforts to improve the latter will have a beneficial result on the former." [5]

The Orange Free State, which descriptions of less than a century ago paint as a luxuriant prairie, is today suffering from increasing desiccation. Every year it is ravaged by sandstorms, especially in the western districts. The same situation obtains in the western Transvaal, where the dry steppes adjacent to the predesert areas of the Kalahari are an easy victim of wind erosion, once their plant cover has degenerated. This point, emphasized by M. Harroy, is of great importance. Too many people, even those who live with the open range, fail to recognize that the erosive process has already begun, as Dr. Shantz points out, with the ecological *degeneration* of plant cover, even though actual *destruction* of the cover is some years in the future. There exists a generally unrecognized ecological inertia, the control of which may be difficult once its direction has been established.

In the eastern part of the Union, in the densely populated native protectorates, where wheat culture and sheep raising have been considerably developed during the past forty years, sheet erosion and gullying are general. Three-fourths of Zululand have been affected, while in Basutoland, a region of sharp slopes and the source of important watercourses, the local administration is confronted with extremely serious difficulties.

South Africa is faced with a problem comparable to that of our Navajo reservations, but it is a problem whose complexity is increased a hundredfold.

Tanganyika Territory enjoys two advantages—a low population and sleeping sickness. The former, with less than six inhabitants per square kilometer, has, of course, kept down pressure on the land. There is some overgrazing, but the colony appears to have been administered with unusual intelligence. This has been strongly supported by sleeping sickness, which has prevented the development of overgrazing and overpopulation.

Ecologically ignorant sanitarians, entomologists, and medical men are undoubtedly now making a flank attack on the tsetse fly with DDT or some other insecticide. The environment of Tanganyika is unstable and, unless the land is more carefully managed than it has been in most parts of the world, it will probably be reduced within a relatively few decades to a situation comparable to that of the Union of South Africa. Administrators confronted with the need of resettling displaced persons have looked longingly at Tanganyika Territory. It is to be hoped that before they take action they will carefully examine its limited carrying capacity.

Some authors consider that erosion is today Kenya's greatest problem. Whereas much of the area was once covered with rain forest, today only about 2 per cent remains. About 1910, the Kikuyus, before it was possible to stop them, destroyed hundreds of square miles of forest. The desert of Turkana, southeast of Lake Rudolph, is advancing at the rate of six miles a year. A. M. Champion, in 1909, passed through a verdant region east of Nairobi that, twenty-one years later, he found dried out, abandoned by its inhabitants, and degenerated to the status of scrub with the dominant tree the acacia characteristic of predesert steppe. Cotton, corn, and coffee plantations, often on slopes approaching 7 per cent, have resulted in so much erosion that *many planters have been forced to abandon their land because of falling yields*. Soils from the Mount Kenya area stain the waters of the Indian Ocean some thirty miles about the mouth of the Tana River. The native reserves, often on highly friable soils, offer little resistance to the forces of nature. The great reserve of Kamba in southeastern Kenya has been eroded down to its subsoil over 37 per cent of its extent! The northern reserves of Turkana and Suk are ravaged by sandstorms that every year grow more violent; the inhabitants of the Kamasia reserve have been driven from their homes by famine and misery.

In French Equatorial Africa, even in the rain forest, native lumbering has opened great clearings that are kept by fire from revegetating themselves. The degeneration of the vegetation is such that, as Lecointe points out, "In the equatorial forest itself, in the Gabun and the Middle Congo, the area of savanna is so great in some places, that it may indicate the formation, under the equator, of genuine small deserts of sand." In the wooded savanna, where the French colonial administration has introduced commercialized—plantation—agriculture, the destruction is appalling. Every year, over hundreds of thousands of acres, fire devastates both the savanna and the woodland. Certain districts of Ubangi-Shari are, "without question," among the parts of Africa in which the plant cover has been attacked with the greatest violence. This devastation of the vegetation has, of course, an influence upon the fertility of the soil. In the territory of Chad, both wind and water erosion have worked havoc.

The southern part of the territory has suffered a fate comparable to that of Ubangi-Shari. In the region of Ere, "Every storm transforms the soil into a muddy liquid that flows toward lower elevations . . . as long as the new vegetation is neither sufficiently dense nor heavy to fill its role of protection against water erosion."

In southeastern Nigeria, a relatively hilly region, the dense population farms and warms itself at the expense of the highland forest. As a result, erosion has made its appearance in many sectors and is today a serious threat to the economy of the country. Gullies a hundred feet deep are not unusual, and sheet erosion appears to be general. The valley of the lower Niger and its delta, formerly covered by forest, have undergone severe deforestation. And farther to the west, near the coast, in the province of Ondo, the degeneration of the forest cover is so great that, according to W. D. MacGregor, it is becoming difficult to find a piece of rain forest sufficiently large to justify setting up a forest reserve. In the extreme west, where cocoa plantations have been generally developed, the results of the deforestation are evident in the progressive drying of both the local climate and the subsoil. In the center of the country the vegetation has been degenerated nearly everywhere and has taken the form of a "mixed deciduous forest." It is calculated that the northern and eastern edges of this great central forest area are reduced every year, under the pressure of cultivation, by more than half a million acres. In the north, where a surprisingly narrow belt separates the forest from the predesert associations, agriculture is extensive and repeated fires are the general rule. As might be expected, the vegetation is degenerating rapidly, and the desert is advancing.

In French East Africa, near the sea, where European occupation has a long history, the forest—whether wet or dry—has little protection against the invasion of agriculture. On the Ivory Coast, A. Chevalier estimates that a village of two hundred inhabitants requires seven thousand acres of forest in order to have sufficient territory to permit adequate periods of fallowing. The density of the population continues to make this more and more impossible, and the forests are being progressively destroyed, as in southern Nigeria. Furthermore, cocoa, coffee, rubber, and banana plantations have been developed at an increasing rate during a quarter of a century, and they now suffer wide impoverishment of their soils, upon which sheet and gully erosion has become general.

The story of Africa, since its integration with the European world, is driven by an inner dynamic toward a fate almost as certain as that of a Greek tragedy. Upon an unfavorable environment with a low carrying capacity have been imposed progressive degeneration of vegetation, mounting losses of desperately needed water, and constantly aggravated soil erosion, which turn the spiral toward ever more unfavorable environment. Seen through the understanding of the ecologist, it is not difficult to understand why he has called the Black Continent *The Dying Land*.

The European in Africa has temporarily removed the Malthusian checks. He has put down tribal wars, destroyed predators, moved enough food about the continent to check famine —but he has not substituted constructive measures to balance his destruction of the old order.

From the Sahara to the Union of South Africa, the people of Africa have for many centuries been farmers and pastoralists. Like the tropical forest, they had established an equilibrium with their environment. Integration into the modern world, however, has destroyed the equilibrium and only a willfully blind optimist would attempt to say when it will be re-established.

Agriculture is characteristically of the shifting type. As Lord Hailey wisely pointed out, this "is less a device of barbarism, than a concession to the character of the soil, which needs long periods for recovery and regeneration." But the period of time required for the land to regain its fertility by regeneration of the forest ranges in many areas up to *fifty years*. Almost every policy of the European colonizers has tended to shorten, or abolish altogether, this indispensable resting of the land. Constant propaganda campaigns have been carried on to increase agricultural production.

One response to this may be seen in the Belgian Congo. In 1927 this area had to import 10,000 tons of corn and corn meal to feed its workers. In 1938 it exported nearly 24,000 tons. Corn is, of course, one of the crops most conducive to soil erosion. Thus, the Tyrant of Mexico has been imported into Africa, where, as in the New World, it is tearing down the land at an ever-growing rate. For subsistence agriculture there has been substituted commercial agriculture. Millions of nonproducers, living in African towns, have created a market for the produce of the native farmer. More destructive still has been the growth of European markets that have bought—along with cocoa and cotton—not only the fertility, but even the substance, of the soil.

The incentive to grow a cash crop has often been reinforced by harsh measures. Natives have been required to pay their taxes in farm products, and in many areas to perform forced labor on the land. This entire cultural pattern, it must be remembered, has been imposed upon a primitive people, improvident, fatalistic, and wedded to the ways of its forefathers. Shifting agriculture, because much of the land must be left idle most of the time, imposes a low carrying capacity. When the fallowing is not observed and the land is destroyed, as it has been over millions of Africa's acres, the carrying capacity is forced downward even more rapidly.

Much the same mechanisms that have broken the established pattern of African agriculture have operated on the natives' grazing practices. As land has become scarcer—and there has been a sharp restriction placed upon nomadism as less land has become available—there has been an enormous increase in herds. Colonization has given the natives a sense of security against rustling, and profoundly changed their attitude toward the normal development of grazing.

Population growth, in some places, has increased the number of stock raisers. In Basutoland, for example, in 1898 there were 256,000 herders; in 1931 they had increased to 570,000. The natural resources of protein and fats that the natives formerly obtained from hunting and fishing have considerably decreased, exactly at the time when the food habits of the blacks are tending toward an increased consumption of these products. Finally, the native, with the increased wealth that results from his contact with the white man, has nearly always sought to show off this wealth in the way that is most familiar to him: the possession of cattle. Harroy tells how, in Kenya, attempts to have the cattle raisers convert their herds into cash deposited in the Postal Savings Bank, where the money would earn 2 per cent, drew from the natives the quite reasonable response that they preferred to change profits into cows and goats whose rate of reproduction would be considerably more than the 2 per cent offered by the bank! The black cares little that his choice implies a parallel destruction of his capital, in terms of pasturage, fertility, and available water resources. When the American Cattle Growers Association takes the same attitude, we can scarcely criticize the African native, though he is considered to be more ignorant. The native cattle grower is, of course, as profoundly ignorant of the biology of his cattle as of his environment. Like the Peruvian Indian who sells his largest potatoes and ears of corn and plants the smallest, the native cattle grower often takes his finest animals to the slaughter-house. In 1937 this practice had become so dangerous in the Congo that Belgian authorities were forced to intervene in order to preserve the best bulls.

Against this macabre picture must be set the not-too-satis-factory sketch of the demographic situation. In Africa, as in so much of the world, completely trustworthy census data are not available. Lord Hailey is of the opinion that if the population is growing it is growing slowly. The U.S. State Department, however, with perhaps better facilities for gathering data, is authority for the statement that the population of Africa grew from 151,000,000 to 173,000,000 between 1936 and 1946. According to their best information, by 1955 the population will have reached 191,000,000.

In a colonial economy, exploited for export products, one must go beyond the mere enumeration of the area's occupants. France, Belgium, and England will certainly continue to draw upon African soils. In view of the difficult economic situation of at least two of these countries, demands are likely to increase. Therefore, unless there should be a world-wide economic collapse, in terms of demands made on the carrying capacity, *by 1955 Africa will be supporting far more than 191,000,000 people*. Demands mount as the means of satisfying them gradually disappear. Africa must clearly take her place in the lugubrious procession that includes Asia, Australia, and Latin America.

Chapter 11

The Lion and the Lizard

THIS BRIEF SURVEY OF FIVE CONTINENTS, DIVERSE AND complicated though they are, leads one to a simple—and heartening—conclusion: Man has moved into an untenable position by protracted and wholesale violation of certain natural laws; to re-establish himself he needs only to bring his behavior into conformity with natural limitations. Most of these are, to some extent, understood. In all the vast complexity of the earth, there is little that has been torn down that cannot be rebuilt. The landscape of the Hwang Ho will never again be the same nor, probably, as favorable an environment to man; but an approximation can be restored. We shall never again hear the music of the Eskimo curlew, and with its lost song has vanished a Mozart of the prairies; we shall never again be so rich as before its passing. Most of the wealth that still remains to us can be vastly increased, and man's survival assured. We know almost enough for that—enough so that we may feel confident of filling the gaps in our knowledge.

I do not want to exaggerate the importance of this problem. Conservation is not going to save the world. Nor is control of populations. Economic, political, educational, and other measures also are indispensable; but unless population control and conservation are included, other means are certain to fail. A world organization devoted to search for economic and political solutions that ignores the ecological is as helpless as a bird with one wing. Indeed, it may force the human race deeper into the mire.

THE SANDS RUN OUT

The most critical danger is that we shall not realize how short we are of that one unrenewable resource—time. If we wait until next year, or the next decade, to push our search for a solution, then our fate may well be sealed.

". . . the Lion and the Lizard keep
The Courts where Jamshyd gloried and drank deep . . ."

It has happened to many peoples, to many civilizations. There is no reason why it cannot happen to us. Never before, in history, have so many hundreds of millions teetered at the edge of the precipice.

Ecological health, for the world, requires, above all, two things: (1) That renewable resources be used to produce as much wealth as possible on a sustained-yield basis. We must use these resources well to support as high a living standard as possible; and we must not exhaust them, as there is no substitute. (2) We must adjust our demand to the supply, either by accepting less per capita (lowering our living standards) or by maintaining less people. Since our civilization cannot survive a *drastic* lowering of standards, we cannot escape the need for population cuts.

BEFORE TREATMENT, DIAGNOSIS

The first step toward solution is a clear statement of the problems: What is the relationship of human beings to their many environments? Is it favorable or unfavorable? Both the relationship and the environment must be considered as *processes;* what are national carrying capacities, and how are they trending?

What, for example, are the yields per acre of various crops in various regions of the world, and what have they been over the past fifty years? What were they on virgin soils? To what extent have they been maintained by abandoning wornout

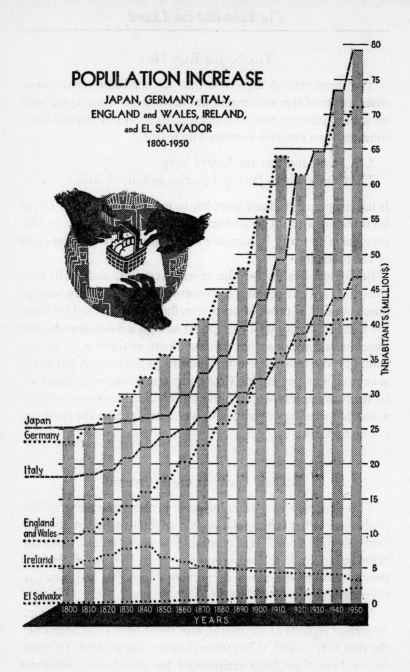

POPULATION INCREASE

JAPAN, GERMANY, ITALY,
ENGLAND and WALES, IRELAND,
and EL SALVADOR
1800-1950

INHABITANTS (MILLIONS)

Japan
Germany

Italy

England
and Wales

Ireland

El Salvador

1800 1810 1820 1830 1840 1850 1860 1870 1880 1890 1900 1910 1920 1930 1940 1950

YEARS

land? How much topsoil has been lost by erosion? How much Class IX land created by man?

What is the carrying capacity of grasslands and how has it changed? If there is overgrazing, how long—under how reduced a yield—will be required to restore maximum production?

What is the trend in water tables? What is the history of siltation over the past fifty years? To what extent has this reduced supplies of drinking water and hydroelectric power? To what extent has it raised river beds? What is the history of floods on the world's watersheds, and how have these floods been affected by deforestation, overgrazing, bad agricultural practices, and siltation?

What species of wildlife are in danger of extermination? What species exist in excess numbers, as a result of environmental mismanagement?

What is happening to human numbers, in each country—and the world? How many calories per capita will be available ten years hence? Twenty years? Fifty? How much protein, milk, cheese, fruits, and green vegetables?

With such information as is available, only a generalized definition of the problem, in these terms, can be achieved; to arrive at a clear understanding will require continuing research, a sort of ecological bookkeeping.

With understanding of national carrying capacities we can finally arrive at a comprehension of the global carrying capacity—know how much surplus, always on a sustained-yield basis, the United States, Canada, Argentina, and Australia can deliver to overcrowded Britain, Germany, Belgium, Japan, India, and China. It is impossible to overstress the necessity of getting away from year-to-year improvisations, prayers for good weather, and *destruction of the world's resource capital*. We already have a fair idea of what every country needs, and is going to need, until populations are controlled and reduced. We must also know how much of the need can be supplied. All nations can reasonably expect to share our surplus products;

no nation should be expected to go into its resource capital to feed excessive populations elsewhere.

Here, in the United States, as we more clearly define the problem, we must come to recognize the ecological imperative, the fact that our environmental resistances are being continually and rapidly increased by excessive lumbering, forest fires, overgrazing, bad agricultural methods, overcropping, the breaking down of soil structure, loss of water tables, extermination of wildlife, etc. Until we clearly see the growth of these environmental resistances we are not likely to do much to control them.

A conservation program, my experience shows, inescapably rests like a tripod on three legs: research, education, and action on the land. These must function simultaneously if the structure is not to collapse.

No Substitute for Knowledge

Without research we shall not know what we are doing. We shall make costly and destructive mistakes, we shall waste millions on ill-planned forestry, soil-conservation terracing, dependence on chemical fertilizers, the introduction of insect pests and other animals that may get out of hand, or waste millions of dollars—as we have in the past—trying to import species that cannot survive. We shall try to transplant a system of land management from one environment (where it has succeeded) to another (where it cannot). We shall promote unsound emigration. We shall fail to make the best use of the land, such as the dedication of Class VIII land to watersheds and wildlife. By our ignorance we shall neglect vast riches, such as are probably locked in tropical forests.

Co-operative research is important. Costa Rica, with an annual national budget of $11,000,000, obviously cannot support agricultural experiment stations, a wood products laboratory, a soil-conservation service and research stations, forestry stations, wildlife investigations, etc. Countries and states should pool their resources. Co-operative investigations should be made, for example, of the grasshopper outbreaks that, from the Dakotas to Argentina, every year cost the farmers of the Americas millions of dollars; in areas of climatic and cultural similarity, it is highly probable that similar factors influence the numbers of these insects. Comparable investigations of the biology of rodent outbreaks would seem sensible. The studies that have recently been initiated on the breeding of improved types of Northern Hemisphere trees would, in view of the enormous extent of northern climax forests, appear to promise considerable wealth to the Soviet Republics, Scandinavia, Germany, the British Isles, Canada, and the United States. A sufficient number of primitive areas, to be used as research stations, can obviously not be set up in overpopulated countries such as Haiti and El Salvador, which have unquestionably extirpated important plant associations. Neighboring countries, like Costa Rica and the Dominican Republic, with their smaller populations, can set aside undisturbed lands, and it will be to the advantage of the entire world to have these studied internationally. A number of stations, such as Barro Colorado Island in the Canal Zone, and national parks in North and South America and Africa are already available for studies.

The scientists of many nations are walled off from the main currents of thought, and even from their own disciplines, by barriers of language and poverty. One of the most useful and practical developments imaginable would be the establishment of an international clearinghouse and translation center, to digest and summarize the results of land-use research and make them available in English, Spanish, French, and one or more Asiatic languages. Such journals as *Biological Abstracts*, *Chemical Abstracts*, and the *Experiment Station Record* (recently suppressed in the name of economy) have been literally invaluable tools to scientists receiving them. Developments of the last ten years in microfilm reproduction make the distribution of scientific publications at low cost a simple matter.

It is important that scientific advisory services be made available, both to international organizations and to national governing bodies. They are needed as a means of evaluating work done by scientific bureaucrats. In the United States, for example, scientific and other learned societies would undoubtedly co-operate with Congress by the appointment of part-time committees, which would change every three or four years. It is important that these committees include men under the age of forty; minority reports should be encouraged. A large part of the responsibility of such scientific advisers would be to evaluate the publications and field operations of their governmental colleagues, in part by digests of criticisms in both foreign and domestic professional journals. Such evaluation, free of political control and the influence of vested interests, ought to give short shrift to the pork-barreling and shocking incompetence of such organizations as the U.S. Army Engineers and Reclamation Service.[1] Some of the scientific publications of government bureaus have been of extremely low quality, so low in fact that they are not even reviewed in scientific journals. Work of this caliber, fortunately, represents a fairly small percentage of the total output.

The same, unhappily, cannot be said of the so-called scientific work done in some of the poor countries. Many of their workers are badly trained; they suffer from lack of contacts with scientific colleagues; and they are usually, as has been pointed out, miserably paid. One of the chief functions of any conservation organization, from the local Audubon Society to the United Nations, should be to educate employers in the realization *that there is no such thing as cheap brains.* A badly prepared scientist, of mediocre intelligence, may not only waste the funds with which he is working and lose irreplaceable time; he is very likely to arrive at dangerously misleading conclusions. To cope with the complex and critical problems facing the world today, we need the best intelligence we can find. To our attempts to save ourselves, no one can contribute more than the scientist. Few scientists care about wealth, but they do want reasonable security, educational opportunities for their children, etc. If men of high ability are to be attracted to scientific careers, they must be decently compensated. When we pay physicists, biologists, and chemists less than truck and bus drivers—as we often do—we have no excuse for looking down our nose at Latin America because most of its countries starve their scientific workers.

In the United States, the National Science Foundation, if it is established, should give substantial support to land-use research through universities, agricultural schools, state governments, museums, etc.

It is imperative that research be extended from the natural sciences to the social sciences; if conservation is to be effective, they are inseparable. There are, unquestionably, dangerous peaks ahead, midway of our course. The social sciences are the radar that can avert disastrous crashes. Only through anthropological, psychological, general semantic, and other investigations can we learn how to make ecological health so important to the world's people that they will not only accept it but demand it. The U.S. Soil Conservation Service, with characteristic vision, has already sponsored extremely important and promising work in this field. The findings may be expected to speed up considerably the application of sound practices to the land.

Economic research is indispensable in fitting land-use practices to diverse social groups in diverse total environments, whose carrying capacity is *always* limited. Such research must be given ecological orientation, since the North American economic measuring rod cannot be applied to the Kurds nor can El Salvador hope for an Argentine living standard. Such research must be, in a word, non-Aristotelian; so far as possible it must relate the whole man to the total environment, recognize the uniqueness of peoples and environments, and the fact that relationships between man and environment, and environment and environment, are constantly changing. Sound, adequate research results in vast savings of time and wealth.

Operation without research is almost certainly wasteful, and may be disastrous.

LET THE PEOPLE KNOW!

Quite as necessary as research is education. At present there is a frustrating lack of trained and educated men to manage land resources. It is important not to confuse technical training and education. The United States has many highly trained technicians who are far from being educated. They can do their own limited job, and do it well; but because they are ignorant of history, literature (as a key to human behavior), economics, geography, sociology, mathematics, languages, etc., they are unable to relate their specialty to the total environment. Dr. Sears reports that "one of the engineering officials of a major American corporation, speaking before the alumni council of an excellent technical school, said bluntly that from his experience he would rather have engineers trained in the liberal arts atmosphere of a small college, which he named, than the crack professionals from this technical school. He went on to say that men with a liberal arts background were more resourceful, more flexible, and more imaginative in their approach, all of which more than compensated for their lack of specialized technical courses." [2] Sir Richard Livingstone defines a technician as "a man who understands everything about his job except its ultimate purpose and its place in the order of the universe." As technicians face a changing world or must operate in a foreign environment, they are often disastrously inadequate.

To cope with resource problems on a world basis will require the education of tens of thousands of men and women. There is intelligence in abundance, if it is put to work. We must broaden and improve our own training, train people from other lands, and send them home to work both on the land and as teachers. International, regional education should be developed. The Balkan countries might combine, as well as the tropical nations. The Inter-American Institute of Agricultural Sciences, at Turrialba, Costa Rica, is a step in the right direction. It has the advantage of training Latin-American students, in a tropical environment, where the language problem is far less serious than if they were studying in the United States or Europe.

A large proportion of the required training will be given at the functional level, as is being so well done at the United Fruit Company's agricultural school in Honduras. This will require much less preparation on the part of the men and women involved, and wherever possible should be carried out in their own countries, or at least in an environment with which they are thoroughly familiar. Robert Pendleton has compared training an Oriental boy in an American agricultural school to sending an American to northern Scotland to study the raising of oranges in southern California.[3] Here, again, it is important to emphasize the value of a non-Aristotelian approach, in order that the idea of a unique, dynamic environment-as-a-whole be firmly understood.

Effective conservation has been made impossible, in many parts of the world, by man's failure to recognize the indispensability of scientific treatment. When a man is sick, he usually goes to a highly trained general practitioner who may send him to an orthopedist, psychiatrist, specialist in eye-ear-nose-and-throat diseases, specialist in circulatory diseases, genito-urinary or gastro-intestinal diseases, etc. A sick river valley is vastly more complicated than a sick man, if only because the man is one of the most important parts of it; diagnosis and treatment of the illness should, in many cases, require the particular skills of climatologists, pedologists, hydrologists, botanists, zoologists, agronomists, soil conservationists, foresters, grazing experts, sociologists, economists, etc. In some parts of the world the sick valley may be subjected to the blundering management of a lawyer. In the United States we are likely to turn it over to an Army engineer. Is it any wonder that, on all continents, flood peaks are steadily rising?

The education of conservation workers is not enough. The

leaders in all countries must understand the ecological imperative, and in the democracies this understanding should
reach all the people. Many years ago Thomas Henry Huxley
wrote:

"Suppose it were perfectly certain that the life and fortune of every one of us would, one day or other, depend upon
his winning or losing a game at chess.

"Don't you think that we should all consider it to be a
primary duty to learn at least the names and the moves of the
pieces; to have a notion of a gambit, and a keen eye for all the
means of giving and getting out of check? Do you not think
that we should look with a disapprobation amounting to scorn,
upon the father who allowed his son, or the state which allowed its members, to grow up without knowing a pawn from
a knight?

"Yet it is a very plain and elementary truth, that the life,
the fortune, and the happiness of every one of us, and, more or
less, of those who are connected with us, do depend upon our
knowing something of the rules of a game infinitely more difficult and complicated than chess. It is a game which has been
played for untold ages, every man and woman of us being one
of the two players in a game of his or her own. The chess-
board is the world, the pieces are the phenomena of the universe,
the rules of the game are what we call the laws of Nature.

"The player on the other side is hidden from us. We know
that his play is always fair, just, and patient. But also we know,
to our cost, that he never overlooks a mistake, or makes the
smallest allowance for ignorance. To the man who plays well,
the highest stakes are paid, with that sort of overflowing gen-
erosity with which the strong shows delight in strength. And
one who plays ill is checkmated—without haste, but without
remorse."

A nontechnical conservation education must be in two
phases, short-term and long-range.

The first is designed to reduce destruction and to begin
restoration, to check the epidemic that has already started.

It should be pointed at control of forest fires, plowing on the contour, protection of wildlife, etc. To get such ideas across to the public as rapidly as possible, all suitable media should be used: posters, movies, broadcasts, newspapers, pamphlets, etc. Advertising and publicity techniques that have girdled the globe with American tooth paste should sell sound land-use and ecological awareness; instead of promoting an American standard of living, they should promote a rational, national standard. So far as possible, adult groups, such as labor unions, churches, military forces, prisons, service clubs, conservation organizations, parent-teacher associations, etc., should be used as targets for the educational material. Such institutions as the Audubon Nature Camp, where teachers not only learn how to live with the earth, but how to teach others to do it, should be multiplied a hundred—or even a thousand—times. Juvenile material should be distributed through schools, Boy and Girl Scout organizations, 4-H clubs, etc.

If the democratic way of life has any long-range justification, it must prove that it has survival value. This, I am convinced, it can do. Better than any other system of government that now exists, it can bring to *all* its people the realization that their lives and their civilization are profoundly shaped by their environment. The town meeting, the grange, the garden club, the women's organization, the soil-conservation district, are all inevitably influenced by environmental impacts. Their recognition of this relationship, their development of a program leading ever more rapidly to a more favorable relationship, may give democracy the survival value it has certainly lacked through most of the past hundred and fifty years. We have been skidding down the road toward national suicide by destroying the environment that permits our survival; a reversal of our direction is unthinkable in any but democratic terms. Here may well be the most fruitful opportunity democracy has ever had.

Long-range efforts in education should be designed to give man a sound ecological orientation. They should operate through teachers' training schools, colleges and universities, and eventually in all primary and secondary schools. Courses should be given in human ecology, including ecological orientation of history, economics, agriculture, literature, engineering, medicine, international politics, and the arts. It is at least as important that American children understand what the uncontrolled raindrop has done to their country as what happened at Bull Run or in a seven-gabled house in Salem. (Incidentally, this understanding of the world about them is far easier to teach most children than are many other subjects. And adults, as I have discovered in lectures from Boston to Osorno, rarely fail to appreciate the fascination and importance of man's relationship with his environment.)

If doctors are going to keep people alive, they should be aware of the effects of their activities. If engineers are going to build roads, they should be taught the place of these roads in the landscape, and in the human culture pattern. Students of history and literature should be brought to a realization of the influence, on these fields, of land use and abuse; of the improbability that an impoverished land, like modern Greece, could develope an Age of Pericles.

It is strange but, I think, true that in all of history there have been almost no great landscape painters. By this, I mean that they have not done for landscape what men like Rembrandt have done for human portraiture. They have not given us pictures that would tell us the real character of the land—whether it is good or evil, exhausted or vitally productive—or help us to understand the forces that have made it what it is. (I should like to see a painting of a farm that would be as revealing as Franz Hals's "Laughing Cavalier.") Likewise, the poets have been extraordinarily blind to the earth, and man's relationship to it. Here are drama and beauty of deeper import than anything to be found in Milton, more profound tragedy than was ever achieved by Sophocles. If man is to be aware of his Antaean dependence, we need the support of the arts to bring that awareness alive.

One of the most promising educational devices, which up to the present has scarcely been experimented with, is the national and state park. These should be used—and where they do not exist they should be created—to foster an appreciation of nature and to enlarge the understanding of natural processes. Here in all their fascinating complexity and interest can be seen the great plant climaxes, associations, competitions, the movements of the hydrologic cycle, the building of the soil by which we live, the environment and interactions of wildlife. Every year between twenty and twenty-five million Americans visit our national parks alone. Were the National Park Service given the funds, there is no reason why every one of these millions of people should not learn something important about the earth that supports them—and find out, at the same time, how much fun they can have doing it. What the Park Service has accomplished, with extremely limited means, is admirable; in terms of the need for such education and what might be done, its results are pathetic.

ACTION ON THE LAND

Education and research are futile unless they result in an action program that, like spring rain, sinks well down among the grass roots. Throughout the world there must be control of the hydrologic cycle, through protection of forests and reforestation, controlled grazing, and improved farming methods. These last should include not only the conventional crop rotations, fallowing, fertilization, contouring, strip cropping, terracing, etc., but a fresh approach to the management of arable land. When row crops, such as corn and soybeans, increase erosion as much as a thousand times, it would seem obvious that clean tillage *must* give way to some sort of cultivation that will leave enough plant cover between the rows to hold the soil in place. This problem was widely discussed after the appearance of Faulkner's *Plowman's Folly* but, as one can plainly see in fields from Canada to Chile, the effects have thus far been negligible. There is need for a far wider application of genetic improvements to agriculture, in order to increase production per acre and in this way to make possible the retirement of hundreds of millions of acres that should never have been plowed. One of the most immediate needs is resettlement. Tens of millions of people, as has been pointed out, must be moved off eroding slopes. Such a program can be considerably advanced through the development of small industries, and this should be one of the principal goals of planned economic reform.

International control of resource exploitation, in order to protect technologically retarded nations, is indispensable. Latin-American countries should be shielded against conscienceless exploitation by North American fishermen and lumbermen. Colonial lands should be placed under an ecological trusteeship, just as the treatment of "natives" is safeguarded. International bodies of scientists should make periodic evaluations of land use, insist on sustained-yield practices, and hold trustees responsible for resource destruction. The United Nations, and associated organizations, should maintain an ecological commission, cutting across organization lines, to assay the influence of all UN activities on the relationship between human beings and their indispensable environment.

A world-wide campaign should be carried out to stop waste, including so-called "productive" waste. Simply because a nation possesses great stores of resources is no justification for throwing them away merely to create jobs and pseudo wealth. The more prosperous countries should be made as conscious of the immorality of waste in a world of want as are the poorer countries, where people will pay for a discarded tin can with a dozen of the eggs that they, themselves, can scarcely afford to eat. Particularly important is the conservation of sanitary wastes, both garbage and sewage. Reclamation of organic materials for fertilizer and other products is yearly becoming more imperative. Reclamation of sewage and industrial wastes would keep them from poisoning our rivers.

The action program, it is not necessary to point out, must be developed within the framework of nature's laws. Management of the land must start with the hilltop, and not the river bottom. The frequently repeated suggestion of a world dotted with TVAs ignores the weaknesses of the original TVA, and the fact that what may be sound in some parts of the United States may be inapplicable under different conditions. When a country is not able to protect her capital's hydroelectric reservoirs against fire, deforestation, farming, erosion, siltation, and flash floods, an attempt at anything as complicated as a TVA would be like children playing house with a skyscraper. Perhaps nowhere outside of Western Europe, Palestine and North America has there been sufficient technical and social progress to permit the development of TVAs; simpler forms of land management should be used as the starting point. Certainly, countries whose governments are rotten with corruption and nepotism should not be encouraged to involve themselves with such an expensive and, to invent a word, graftable, machinery. Above all, we should not finance them.

OUTWITTING THE LIBIDO

All possible conservation measures are futile unless human breeding is checked. It is obvious that fifty years hence the world cannot support three billion people at any but coolie standards—for most of them. One-third of an acre cannot decently feed a man, let alone clothe him and make possible control of the hydrologic cycle. When numbers mount, land abuse, as has been shown, mounts with them. Unless population increases can be stopped, we might as well give up the struggle.

A primary need is a completely new approach to contraception. Charles Goodyear's treatment of rubber provided invaluable interim control and through reduction, though not complete stabilization, of populations has contributed mightily to world peace; if for no other reason, Goodyear deserves a place in the Hall of Fame. But old methods are no longer good enough. In areas like Puerto Rico, where three-quarters of the houses lack running water, current contraceptive techniques cannot possibly be effective; Hindus, with their $19 annual income, more in need of birth control than any other people, cannot possibly afford contraceptive devices. A cheaper, dependable method that can easily be used by women is indispensable. If the United States had spent two billion dollars developing such a contraceptive, instead of the atom bomb, it would have contributed far more to our national security while, at the same time, it promoted a rising living standard for the entire world. If such an amount is required to develop a satisfactory contraceptive, it will be a sound investment.

Once more we return to $C = B:E$. When excessive numbers of people increase the environmental resistance, as they inevitably do, the carrying capacity falls; and with the carrying capacity fall educational levels, health levels, general cultural levels, the possibility of social order and stability, etc.

Effective population control must reckon with folkways that in some cases, as in China, may prove extremely difficult to change. For peoples under control of such beliefs infinite misery lies in store. Some religions may also set up obstacles. These, however, may not be so insurmountable as has been thought.

It is not generally recognized, for example, even by many Catholics, that the principles of population control have been approved by the Church. In a book published with the imprimatur of Cardinal Hayes occurs the statement: "As regards the end of marriage, we must assiduously keep in mind that the end of this institution was not that children should or even could be born *in every family*, but that through this institution the conservation of the species should be sufficiently provided for. As long, therefore, as this preservation is not endangered, it cannot be shown that this or that couple must have intercourse at the times that are propitious for fecundation and pregnancy, nor that they must positively intend generation."[4]

This same volume points out that "The overcrowded population of Japan has rendered that portion of the East a very unsettled region and likely to prove dangerous for the rest of the world." Since the Japanese situation has been extended to the rest of the world and *overpopulation is in itself a danger to* "*conservation of the species*," there would seem to be a logical compulsion toward control of fertilization. In another volume, published "With Ecclesiastical Approbation," it is asserted: "Broadly speaking, married couples have not the right to bring into the world children whom they are unable to support, for they would thereby inflict a grievous damage upon society." [5] Italian newspapers, please copy.

Complete approbation is given by the Church to the so-called rhythm method of birth control. While an impressive array of medical authorities supports this method, many non-Catholic physicians and biologists doubt its reliability. However, it would seem without question to reduce the frequency and probability of conception. In the books quoted there is still a rigid proscription of chemical and mechanical methods of contraception. Whatever the doctrines of the Church, and whatever the means used, Catholics in the United States are producing smaller families, as they are in France and other European countries. Dr. Latz's book reports that 36 per cent of the clientele of birth-control clinics in New York, Chicago, Newark, and Cleveland were Catholics. In Catholic Puerto Rico, women who already have children have been, in large numbers, seeking sterilization.

The United States should lead in making available to all the peoples of the world the most modern information on contraception, and the services of its health and educational experts in organizing birth-control campaigns. So far as possible, these should parallel, if not surpass, the other health programs of the World Health Organization. Where FAO finds overpopulation, its conservation and food-production programs should include contraception programs. It should not ship food to keep alive ten million Indians and Chinese this year, so that fifty million may die five years hence.

Population "experts" say that, given time, populations will level off and stabilize themselves. To this the obvious answer is, *there is not time*. The modern world has gone down twice—and only extraordinary measures can keep it from going down again.

These same experts assert that people cannot be educated to desire birth control. To this the answer is, we have never really tried. In the guano islands, off the coast of Peru, I have watched Andean Indians, many of them unable to read or write, faithfully brush their teeth twice a day. Tens of millions of people the world around have adopted the custom of boiling their polluted water, in self-defense. These things have been learned at extremely low cultural levels. Given the love of children and the devotion to their welfare that is so marked among the so-called backward people, family limitation in the interest of family welfare and eventually in the interest of national and world welfare could be given a cogent appeal. The strong advocacy of organized birth-control programs on the part of leading Hindu intellectuals is evidence of their confidence that birth control can be effective among their people.

Vigorous birth-control campaigns, using all educational and advertising techniques, should also be organized by individual countries. Contraception should, of course, be voluntary. There is more than a little merit in the suggestion, made many years ago by H. L. Mencken, of "sterilization bonuses": small but adequate amounts of money to be paid to anyone—especially the males—who would agree to the simple sterilization operation. This does not interfere with sexual pleasure, nor with physical satisfaction. Since such a bonus would appeal primarily to the world's shiftless, it would probably have a favorable selective influence. From the point of view of society, it would certainly be preferable to pay permanently indigent individuals, many of whom would be physically and psychologically marginal, $50 or $100 rather than support their hordes of offspring that, by both genetic and social inheritance, would tend to perpetuate the fecklessness.

On Our Way!

These suggestions are not offered as a blueprint, nor as a complete program. I do not have the space nor the requisite knowledge to prepare either. Different environments and different times will require varying operations. I have merely tried to outline general procedures based upon many years of conservation work in many countries. I have suggested definite, important, and—above all—*practicable* steps that are so completely within the reach of human accomplishment that they should convince us the task is anything but hopeless. If we will but start to execute these projects we shall have begun to resolve our dilemma.

The question remains: Who is to do the job? The ideal answer would be: Everybody. For these are problems that, involved as they are with all human life, require the understanding and participation of as many people as possible, from the humblest shepherd and peasant to the most powerful ruler and fruitful thinker.

But action, to achieve full effectiveness, must be organized. The United Nations and affiliated groups can find here not only one of their greatest opportunities, but perhaps the unifying principle they have seemed, at times, sadly to lack. Obviously, much of the responsibility must fall upon national and state governments. However, private persons and private organizations such as foundations must also play their part. Until the march toward disaster is halted and the direction of the procession is reversed, there cannot be too much help.

Chapter 12

History of Our Future

BY EXCESSIVE BREEDING AND ABUSE OF THE LAND
mankind has backed itself into an ecological trap. By a lopsided
use of applied science it has been living on promissory notes.
Now, all over the world, the notes are falling due.

Payment cannot be postponed much longer. Fortunately,
we still may choose between payment and utterly disastrous
bankruptcy on a world scale. It will certainly be more intelligent to pull in our belts and accept a long period of austerity
and rebuilding than to wait for a catastrophic crash of our
civilization. In hard fact, we have no other choice.

When I write "we" I do not mean the other fellow. I mean
every person who reads a newspaper printed on pulp from
vanishing forests. I mean every man and woman who eats a
meal drawn from steadily shrinking lands. Everyone who
flushes a toilet, and thereby pollutes a river, wastes fertile organic matter and helps to lower a water table. Everyone who
puts on a wool garment derived from overgrazed ranges that
have been cut by the little hoofs and gullied by the rains, sending runoff and topsoil into the rivers downstream, flooding
cities hundreds of miles away. Especially do I mean men and
women in overpopulated countries who produce excessive
numbers of children who, unhappily, cannot escape their fate
as hostages to the forces of misery and disaster that lower upon
the horizon of our future.

If we ourselves do not govern our destiny, firmly and courageously, no one is going to do it for us. To regain ecological
freedom for our civilization will be a heavy task. It will fre-

quently require arduous and uncomfortable measures. It will cost considerable sums of money. Democratic governments are not likely to set forth on such a steep and rocky path unless the people lead the way. Nations with lower educational standards than ours, nations that are technologically retarded, are still less likely to move. In our own interest we must accept the responsibility for this leadership, as we have in the spheres of economics and politics.

Drastic measures are inescapable. Above everything else, we must reorganize our thinking. If we are to escape the crash we must abandon all thought of living unto ourselves. We form an earth-company, and the lot of the Indiana farmer can no longer be isolated from that of the Bantu. This is true, not only in John Donne's mystical sense, in the meaning of brotherhood that makes starving babies in Hindustan the concern of Americans; but in a direct, physical sense. An eroding hillside in Mexico or Yugoslavia affects the living standard and probability of survival of the American people. Irresponsible breeding makes amelioration of the condition of the Greeks—or the Italians or Indians or Chinese—difficult, if not impossible; it imposes a drain on the world's wealth, especially that of the United States, when this wealth might be used to improve living standards and survival chances for less people. We cannot escape our responsibility, since it is a responsibility to ourselves.

We must equally abandon any philosophy of "Sufficient unto the day—." We are paying for the foolishness of yesterday while we shape our own tomorrow. Today's white bread may force a break in the levees, and flood New Orleans next spring. This year's wheat from Australia's eroding slopes may flare into a Japanese war three decades hence. Comic books from the flanks of the Nevado de Toluca in 1948 may close Mexico City's factories in 1955. The freebooting, rugged individualist, whose vigor, imagination, and courage contributed so much of good to the building of our country (along with the bad), we must now recognize, where his activities destroy resources, as the Enemy of the People he has become. The exploiting lumberman of Madagascar was beheaded; we should impose at least as effective, if kinder, controls. We must develop our sense of time, and think of the availability of beefsteaks not only for this Saturday but for the Saturdays of our old age, and of our children and grandchildren's youth. The day has long since passed when a senator may callously demand, "What has posterity ever done for me?" Posterity is of our making, as is the world in which it will have to live.

Above all, we must learn to know—to feel to the core of our beings—our dependence upon the earth and the riches with which it sustains us. We can no longer believe valid our assumption that we live in independence. No longer can we rest secure in the certainty that somehow, from somewhere, our wants will be supplied. We, even we fortunate Americans, are pressing hard on our means of subsistence. Our neighbors on five continents know what it means to find their cupboards bare. There is no phase of our civilization that is not touched by wasting dearth. There is hardly an aspect of human activity, through all the complex span of our lives, that does not, in some open or occult manner, feel the chill of scarcity's damp breath.

We must—all of us, men, women, and children—reorient ourselves with relation to the world in which we live. We must learn to weigh the daily news in terms of man's subsistence. We must come to understand our past, our history, in terms of the soil and water and forests and grasses that have made it what it is. We must see the years to come in the frame that makes space and time one, that will keep us strong only as, like Antaeus, we draw our strength from the earth. Our education must be reshaped, as the story of our existence in an environment as completely subjected to physical laws as is a ball we let drop from our hands. Our philosophies must be rewritten to remove them from the domain of words and "ideas," and to plant their roots firmly in the earth. Above all, we must weigh our place in the society of nations and our future through the decades to come in the scale of our total environment.

The history of our future is already written, at least for some decades. As we are crowded together, two and a quarter billions of us, on the shrinking surface of the globe, we have set in motion historical forces that are directed by our total environment.

We might symbolize these forces by graphs. One of them is the curve of human populations that, after centuries of relative equilibrium, suddenly began to mount, and in the past fifty years has been climbing at a vertiginous rate.

The other graph is that of our resources. It represents the area and thickness of our topsoil, the abundance of our forests, available waters, life-giving grasslands, and the biophysical web that holds them together. This curve, except for local depressions, also maintained a high degree of regularity through the centuries. But it, too, has had its direction sharply diverted, especially during the past hundred and fifty years, and it is plunging downward like a rapid.

These two curves—of population and the means of survival—have long since crossed. Ever more rapidly they are drawing apart. The farther they are separated the more difficult will it be to draw them together again.

Everywhere, or nearly everywhere, about the earth we see the results of their divergence. The crumbling ruins of two wars mark their passing. The swollen bellies of hungry babies, from San Salvador to Bengal, dot the space between them. Parching fevers and racking coughs, from Osorno to Seoul, cry aloud the cleavage between these curves. The angry muttering of mobs, like the champing of jungle peccaries, is a swelling echo of their passing.

The direction of these curves and the misery they write across the earth are not likely to be changed in the proximate future. Their direction is fixed for some decades. Great masses of people have a preponderantly young population; as they come into the breeding age we must, despite all possible efforts short of generalized slaughter, expect human numbers to increase for a time. The drag imposed by ignorance, selfishness, nationalism, custom, etc., is certain to retard, by some decades, any effective or substantial improvement of resource management.

So that the people shall not delude themselves, find further frustration through quack nostrums, fight their way into blind alleys, it is imperative that this world-wide dilemma be made known to all mankind. The human race is caught in a situation as concrete as a pair of shoes two sizes too small. We must understand that, and stop blaming economic systems, the weather, bad luck, or callous saints. This is the beginning of wisdom, and the first step on the long road back.

The second step is dual—the control of populations and the restoration of resources.

Unless we take these steps and begin to swing into them soon—unless, in short, man readjusts his way of living, in its fullest sense, to the imperatives imposed by the *limited* resources of his environment—we may as well give up all hope of continuing civilized life. Like Gadarene swine, we shall rush down a war-torn slope to a barbarian existence in the blackened rubble.

References

Chapter 2

[1] Gottschalk, L. C. "Effects of Soil Erosion on Navigation in Upper Chesapeake Bay." *Geographical Review*, XXXV, No. 2, April, 1945.

[2] Harroy, J. P. *Afrique, Terre qui meurt.* Bruxelles: Marcel Hayez, 1944, p. 72.

[3] Gaffron, H. "Photosynthesis and the Production of Organic Matter on Earth," in *Currents in Biochemical Research.* New York: Interscience Publishers, Inc., 1946, p. 26.

[4] Ackerman, Edward A. "The Geographic Meaning of Ecological Land Use." *Journal of Soil and Water Conservation*, I, 2, October, 1946.

[5] Harroy, J.-P. *Op. cit.*, p. 52.

[6] Pearson, F. A., and F. A. Harper. *The World's Hunger.* Ithaca: Cornell University Press, 1945.

[7] Pearson, F. A., and Don Paarlberg. *Starvation Truths, Half-Truths, Untruths* (pamphlet). Ithaca, 1946.

[8] Ritchie, James. *The Influence of Man on Animal Life in Scotland.* Cambridge, 1920.

[9] Clark, Frances N. "Measures of the Abundance of the Sardine, *Sardinops caerulea*, in California Waters." Sacramento: Bull. 53, Bureau of Marine Fisheries, Division of Fish and Game, 1939.

[10] Murphy, R. C. *Conservation—VI.* New York: Garden Club of America, 1941.

[11] Gurney, Senator Chan. Letter to the *New York Times*, July 27, 1947.

References

Chapter 3

[1] Korzybski, Alfred. *Science and Sanity*. Lancaster: Science Press, 1941.

Chapter 4

[1] Pearson, Frank A., and Don Paarlberg. *Starvation Truths, Half-truths, Untruths*. Ithaca, 1946, p. 12.

[2] Cited in Burch, Guy Irving, and Elmer Pendell. *Population Roads to Peace or War*. Washington: Population Reference Bureau, 1945.

[3] Clark, Colin. *The Conditions of Economic Progress*. London: Macmillan, 1940.

[4] Pearson and Paarlberg. *Op. cit.*

[5] Walford, Cornelius. *Famines of the World: Past and Present*. London: Edward Stanford, 1879.

[6] Cited in Burch and Pendell. *Op. cit.*

[7] Donnell, E. J. *Chronological and Statistical History of Cotton*. New York, 1872, p. 19.

[8] Harris, Seymour E. "The Economist's View of Land Use." *Journal of Soil and Water Conservation*, I, No. 2, October, 1946.

[9] Moulton, Harold G. *The Formation of Capital*. Washington: The Brookings Institution, 1935.

[10] Kelly, Tom. "There's More to Dirt than Gets in Your Eye." *Outdoor America*, 12, No. 4, March, 1947.

[11] Harris, Seymour E. *Op. cit.*

[12] Dublin, Louis I. *Population Problems*. Boston: Houghton Mifflin, 1926.

[13] Clark, Colin. *Op. cit.*

[14] Burch, Guy Irving. In *Population Bulletin*, III, No. 1, March, 1947. Washington: Population Reference Bureau.

[15] Senior, Clarence. "Population Pressures and the Future of Puerto Rico." *Journal of Heredity*, 38, No. 5, May, 1947.

[16] Burch, Guy Irving. In *Population Bulletin*, II, No. 5, May, 1946. Washington: Population Reference Bureau.

[17] Burch, Guy Irving. *Op. cit.*

Chapter 5

[1] Ackerman, Edward A. *Op. cit.*

[2] Ritchie, James. *The Influence of Man on Animal Life in Scotland.* Cambridge, 1920.

[3] Weaver, J. E., and F. E. Clements. *Plant Ecology.* New York: McGraw-Hill, 1938.

[4] Leopold, Aldo, Lyle K. Sowls, and David L. Spencer. "A Survey of Over-populated Deer Ranges in the United States." *Journal of Wildlife Management*, 11, No. 2, April, 1947.

[5] Hesse, R., W. C. Allee, and K. P. Schmidt. *Ecological Animal Geography.* New York: John Wiley & Sons, 1937.

[6] Sears, Paul B. "Man and Nature in Modern Ohio." *Ohio State Archaeological and Historical Quarterly*, 56, No. 2, April, 1947.

[7] Pelzer, Karl J. *Pioneer Settlement in the Asiatic Tropics.* New York: American Geographical Society, 1945.

[8] Musgrave, G. W. "The Quantitative Evaluation of Factors in Water Erosion—A First Approximation." *Journal of Soil and Water Conservation*, 2, No. 3, July, 1947.

[9] Shantz, H. L. In *Conservation of Renewable Resources.* Philadelphia, 1941, pp. 37-39.

[10] Graham, Edward H. "The Ecological Approach to Land Use," A Symposium, The Biologist's Viewpoint. Reprinted from the *Journal of Soil and Water Conservation*, I, No. 2, October, 1946, p. 58.

[11] Cited in Lotka, A. J. *Elements of Physical Biology.* Baltimore: Williams & Wilkins, 1925.

Chapter 6

[1] Craven, Avery O. "Soil Exhaustion As a Factor in the Agricultural History of Virginia and Maryland, 1606-1860." Urbana: *University of Illinois Studies in the Social Sciences*, XIII, 1, 1925, pp. 1-179.

[2] Watts, Lyle F. "Timber Shortage or Timber Abundance in the U.S.A." *Unasylva*, I, No. 1, Food and Agriculture Organization of the United Nations.

[3] *Problems and Progress of Forestry in the United States, Report of the Joint Committee of Foresters of the National Research Council and the Society of American Foresters* (Washington, D.C.), 1946, pp. 1-112.

[4] Foster, Ellery. *America's Log Jam and How to Break It*. Washington: C.I.O. Department of Research and Education, n.d.

[5] Dewhurst, J. Frederick. *America's Needs and Resources*. New York: The Twentieth Century Fund, 1947.

[6] *The Western Range*. Senate Document 199, 74th Congress, 1936.

[7] Allred, B. W. "Viewpoints on Conservation of Grazing Lands." *Journal of Soil and Water Conservation*, 2, No. 1, January, 1947.

[8] The Washington *Sunday Star*, Jan. 5, 1947.

[9] Gottschalk, L. C. *Op. cit.*

[10] Gottschalk, L. C. *Op. cit.*

[11] Sears, P. B. *Op. cit.*

[12] Jacks, G. V., and R. O. Whyte. "Erosion and Soil Conservation." Aberystwyth: *Bull.* 25, Herbage Publication Series, March, 1938.

[13] Washington, *Conservation News*, Aug. 1, 1947.

[14] Bird, John A. *Western Ground Waters and Food Production*. U. S. Department of Agriculture, Miscellaneous Publication 504.

[15] Sears, P. B. *Op. cit.*

[16] Jackson, H. H. T. "Conserving Endangered Wildlife Species." In *Smithsonian Report*, 1945.

[17] Allred, B. W. *Op. cit.*

[18] *Iowa Conservationist*, Aug. 15, 1946.

[19] Bunce, A. C. *Economics of Soil Conservation.* Ames: Iowa State College Press, 1942.

[20] Pearson and Harper. *Op. cit.*

[21] Whelpton, P. K. "Population Policy for the United States." *Journal of Heredity*, XXX, No. 9, September, 1939.

Chapter 7

[1] Vogt, W. "Mexican Natural Resources—Their Past, Present and Future." In *Report on Activities of the Conservation Section, Division of Agricultural Cooperation.* Washington: Pan American Union, 1946.

[2] Vogt, W. *The Population of Venezuela and its Natural Resources.* Washington: Pan American Union, 1946.

[3] Allen, Robert S. *Our Fair City.* New York: Vanguard Press, 1947.

[4] Cooke, M. L. *Brazil on the March.* New York: McGraw-Hill, 1944.

[5] *Venezuelan Report.* Washington: The Venezuelan Embassy.

[6] Osorio Tafall, B. F. "El Destino Marítimo de México." México, D.F.: *Revista de Economía*, X, No. 8, Aug. 31, 1947.

[7] Vaillant, George C. *Aztecs of Mexico.* New York: Doubleday, Doran & Co., 1941.

[8] Vogt, W. *Op. cit.*

[9] *Population Index.* April, 1947. Princeton. Data from FAO and U.S. Bureau of the Budget.

[10] *Foreign Commerce Weekly*, Aug. 2, 1947.

[11] Vogt, W. *The Population of El Salvador and Its Natural Resources.* Washington: Pan American Union, 1946.

[12] Vogt, W. *The Population of Costa Rica and Its Natural Resources.* Washington: Pan American Union, 1946.

[13] Vogt, W. "Informe sobre Aves Guaneras." In *Boletin de la Compañía Administradora del Guano.* Lima, 1942.

[14] McBride, G. M. *Chile: Land and Society.* New York: American Geographical Society, 1936.

[15] Elgueta G., Manuel, and Juan Jirkal H. *Erosión de los Suelos de Chile.* Boletín Técnico, No. 4. Santiago: Ministerio de Agricultura, 1943.

[16] Vogt, W. "Hunger at the Peace Table." *Saturday Evening Post,* May 12, 1945.

Chapter 8

[1] Data from *Report of the FAO Mission to Greece.* Washington: Food and Agriculture Organization of the United Nations, 1947, p. 155; *Population Bulletin,* III, No. 1. Population Reference Bureau, Washington.

[2] Pearson, Frank A., and Don Paarlberg. *Op. cit.*

[3] Wheeler, Leslie A. *European Wheat Requirements and Policies.* Washington: USDA, 1938 (mimeographed).

[4] Brandt, Karl. *Feeding the World.* Chicago: The Chicago Council on Foreign Relations, 1944 (mimeographed).

[5] *Population Index.* April, 1947, Princeton. Data from FAO and U.S. Bureau of the Budget.

[6] Pearson, Frank, and Floyd Harper. *Op. cit.*

[7] *World Population Estimates.* OIR Report 4192. Washington: Department of State, March 1, 1947.

[8] Yates, P. Lamartine, and D. Warriner. *Food and Farming in Post-War Europe.* London: Oxford University Press, 1943.

⁹ Bourne, Geoffrey H. *Starvation in Europe*. London: George Allen and Unwin, 1943.

¹⁰ Yates and Warriner. *Op. cit.*

¹¹ Much of the above material from *Report of the FAO Mission to Greece*.

¹² Jacks, G. V., and R. O. Whyte. "Erosion and Soil Conservation." In *Bulletin* 25, Herbage Publication Series. Aberystwyth, March, 1938.

¹³ Baker, O. E. In *Population* (Lectures on the Harris Foundation, 1929). Chicago: University of Chicago Press, 1930.

Chapter 9

¹ From the book, *Asia's Lands and Peoples*, by Dr. George B. Cressey, published by Whittlesey House, copyright, 1944, by McGraw-Hill Book Company, Inc.

² Thompson, W. S. *Population and Peace in the Pacific*. Chicago: University of Chicago Press, 1946.

³ Cressey. *Op. cit.*

⁴ Jacks, G. V., and R. O. Whyte. *Vanishing Lands*. New York: Doubleday, Doran & Co., 1939.

⁵ Cressey. *Op. cit.*

⁶ Thorp, James. *Geography of the Soils of China*.

⁷ Phillips Ralph W., Ray G. Johnson, and Raymond T. Moyer. *The Livestock of China*. Washington, 1945.

⁸ Jacks and Whyte. *Op. cit.*

⁹ Shirole, M. K. "Soil Conservation—Nation's Foremost Need in India." *Journal of Soil and Water Conservation*, 2, No. 2, April, 1947.

¹⁰ Cressey. *Op. cit.*

[11] Chandrasekhar, S. *India's Population*. New York: The John Day Co., 1946.

[12] Cook, R. "Mother India's Starving Children." *Journal of Heredity*, 8, No. 37, August, 1946.

[13] Mukerjee, R. *Races, Lands and Food*. New York: The Dryden Press, 1946.

[14] Cressey. *Op. cit.*

[15] Cressey. *Op. cit.*

[16] Novakovsky, S. "Arctic or Siberian Hysteria as a Reflex of the Geographic Environment." *Ecology*, V, No. 2, April, 1924.

[17] Sobolev, S. S. "Protecting the Soils in the U.S.S.R." *Journal of Soil and Water Conservation*, 2, No. 3, July 1947.

[18] Fischer, John. *Why They Behave Like Russians*. New York: Harper & Brothers, 1947.

[19] Jacks, G. V., and R. O. Whyte. "Erosion and Soil Conservation." *Bulletin* 25, Herbage Publ. Series. Aberystwyth, March, 1938.

[20] *New York Times Magazine*, May 4, 1947.

Chapter 10

[1] Pearson and Harper. *Op. cit.*

[2] Lowdermilk, W. C. "Lessons from the Old World to the Americas in Land Use." Washington: *Smithsonian Report*, 1943, pp. 420-421. Reprinted from *Proceedings of the Eighth American Scientific Congress*, Vol. 5.

[3] Source of material for this chapter, unless otherwise indicated: Harroy, J. P. *Afrique, Terre qui meurt*. Bruxelles: Marcel Hayez, 1944.

[4] Hailey, Lord. *An African Survey*. London: Oxford University Press, 1938.

[5] Union of South Africa. *Final Report of the Drought Investigation Commission*, October, 1923. Capetown: Cape Times Limited, Government Printers, 1923, pp. 14-15.

References

Chapter 11

[1] Terral, Rufus. *The Missouri Valley*. New Haven: Yale University Press, 1947.

[2] Sears, P. B. "Importance of Ecology in the Training of Engineers." *Science*, 106, 2740, July 4, 1947.

[3] Pendleton, R. L. *Training for Agricultural Research in Humid Tropical Asia*. New York: Southeast Asia Institute (Educational Memorandum), n.d.

[4] Coucke, V. J., and J. J. Walsh, M.D., Ph.D. *The Sterile Period in Family Life*. New York: Joseph F. Wagner, Inc., 1933.

[5] Latz, L. J., M.D. *The Rhythm of Sterility and Fertility in Women*. Chicago: Latz Foundation, 1932.

Reading List

The thoughtful reader will recognize that ecological understanding must take into account all human and environmental processes (these are in reality inseparable), that an adequate ecological picture must be both vast and intricate, and that a comprehension of environmental relationships must inevitably lead to many fundamental changes in our "thinking" and "feeling" about many human activities. This book has stressed two aspects of these relationships—population pressures and the wise use of resources—because of their critical and immediate importance if our civilization is to survive. But the implications of ecological wisdom are far wider, as rich and interesting and all-pervasive as life itself. No one book, especially a pioneering effort such as this essentially is, could adequately deal with the subject.

In the hope that readers will be interested in traveling farther down the ecological road, a number of books are suggested. This is not an exhaustive bibliography. It does not attempt to cover the field; there is no literature that will do this. In recommending these titles, readability has been given considerable weight. There are some important omissions, simply because we know of no book to fill the gaps. A literature, even a technical literature, remains to be developed in this field.

Human Breeding and Survival by Guy Irving Burch and Elmer Pendell. Penguin. This little book, originally published as *Population Roads to Peace or War*, is an excellent introduction to the world population problem. It is sponsored by the Population Reference Bureau, 1507 M Street, N.W., Washington, D.C., which periodically issues valuable and lively population bulletins covering such subjects as the relationship of population growth to the Marshall Plan.

The World's Hunger by Frank A. Pearson and Floyd A. Harper. Cornell University Press, 1945. Rarely has so much of significance been so clearly stated in so few words. The authors relate the pressure of population to land resources—but neglect destruction of resources—with a clarity and succinctness any author might envy.

The Soils That Support Us by Charles E. Kellogg. Macmillan, 1941. A layman's book, written by one of the greatest living soil scientists, that manages to convey the fascination that lies in an understanding of the earth's surface. Anyone who reads it will live in a more interesting and meaningful world.

Natural Principles of Land Use by Edward H. Graham. Oxford University Press, 1944. There is rarely justification for calling a recent book a classic, but we feel confident that this will become one. The author, Chief of the Biology Division, U. S. Soil Conservation Service, shows how man on the land can adapt himself to nature's laws. Don't let the textbookish title discourage you; it's good reading.

Deserts on the March by Paul B. Sears. University of Oklahoma Press, 1935. An extremely well-done book by one of the world's foremost ecologists, this has never had the wide recognition it deserves. If ten million Americans would read it, we could feel much more secure about the future of our country.

Soil Exhaustion as a Factor in the Agricultural History of Virginia and Maryland, 1606–1860 by Avery O. Craven. University of Illinois Press, 1926. One of the few eco-historical studies ever made, it paints our forefathers in a truer light, and presents a more meaningful history, than most of the better known works of American historians.

Vanishing Lands by R. O. Whyte and G. V. Jacks. Doubleday and Co., 1939. A thoughtful discussion of soil erosion as a world problem. Somewhat uneven in reliability and coverage, and in our opinion unduly pessimistic as to the possibility of control, it is, nevertheless, an important survey, especially valuable in its interpretation of the social and economic implications of erosion.

Soil Conservation by H. H. Bennett. McGraw-Hill, 1939. This is one-volume library on soil conservation, by the world's foremost authority. Primarily a reference work, it treats the subject in virtually all its phases. Useful alike for the man who wants to know what happened to the soils of the ancient Mediterranean area, and the man who has a gully through his cornfield.

The Missouri Valley by Rufus Terral. Yale University Press, 1947. A description and analysis of this great area in terms of history, geography, and use-capabilities, and the problems of management. Unlike most advocates of the valley authority idea, Terral views TVA critically and recognizes the modifications necessary to fit the authority technique to this unique and varied region. Perhaps does not give full weight to the difficulty of problems to be solved.

Heaven's Tableland by Vance Johnson. Farrar, Straus and Co., 1947. A journalist's highly readable and intelligent discussion of our failure to adapt our behavior to natural laws in the Dust Bowl, and what it has cost us—and will continue to cost us—in terms of total environment.

Is Utah Sahara Bound? by Walter P. Cottam. University of Utah, 1947. (Pamphlet.) An extraordinarily well-written story, by a distinguished botanist, of what we Americans have done and are doing to one of our states. Must-reading for everyone concerned with the future of our country.

The Natural Resources of Mexico—Their Past, Present, and Future; The Population of Costa Rica and Its Natural Resources; The Population of El Salvador and Its Natural Resources; The Population of Venezuela and Its Natural Resources by William Vogt. Pan American Union, 1946. These are surveys written for the respective governments, but couched in layman's language, of the resource-human-being relationships in four countries. They are nearly unique in their ecological treatment of the region south of the Rio Grande. They have provided some of the material in this book.

Asia's Lands and People by George C. Cressey. Whittlesey House, McGraw-Hill Book Co., 1944. This is a college text, but it is so well written and organized, so thoroughly geared to the relationships between man and his environment, that we unhesitatingly recommend it to the general reader. The ecological understanding it displays is all-too-unusual in geographies.

Races, Lands, and Food by Radhakamal Mukerjee. Dryden Press, 1946. In this little volume, written by an economist with an unusual knowledge of the land and ecological processes, are set forth some of the clearest analyses of the dilemmas arising from excessive breeding, insufficient dying. It also gives some idea of what Asia is going to try to get from the rest of the world if it can.

Reading List

Population and Peace in the Pacific by Warren S. Thompson. University of Chicago Press, 1946. In this book, one of America's foremost population experts relates population trends to the land areas in which they are taking place. While, in our opinion, the book makes an over-optimistic estimate of the tropics' capacity to absorb populations, it tells us much we should know about our far-western frontier.

Afrique, Terre qui Meurt by Jean-Paul Harroy. Marcel Hayez, Brussels, 1944. This book is difficult to secure and not yet available in English, but we include it in this list because it is a magnificent portrayal of ecological trends over an entire continent. Its first hundred pages include a summary of tropical ecology that should be read by everyone who mistakenly believes that Africa and Latin America can absorb the world's surplus of humanity.

Animal Ecology by Charles Elton. Macmillan, 1927. This is the closest thing we have to a satisfactory text on the subject. A real classic in its field, and technical in its treatment, it is fascinating reading for anyone interested in animals. Many of the principles it develops are applicable to the problems of human populations.

Soil Conservation, an International Study. Food and Agriculture Organization of the United Nations, 1948. An admirable summary of the situation, with especially fine photographs; it tends, however, toward elementalism, and on its map of the world puts the land of the eastern United States in the same category with that of the Amazon basin and the southern half of Africa!

Science and Sanity by Alfred Korzybski. Science Press, 1941. This is the most important, most rewarding, and most difficult book on our list. As an introduction to the new science of general semantics, it is profound in its interpretation of our relationship to the world in which we live, and of the impact on that relationship of what we "think" and "feel" and say. For the intellectually vigorous, it offers high adventure.

Language in Action by S. I Hayakawa. Harcourt, Brace and Co., 1941. *People in Quandaries* by Wendell Johnson. Harper Bros., 1946. These are not substitutes for *Science and Sanity*, but many people have found Korzybski's book easier going after reading one or both of them. Worth reading in their own right, both are interesting and stimulating aids to living in our modern world.

Index

A–horizon, definition, 26; destruction, 101; erodability, 27; formation, 85; recovery from erosion, 101 ff.; productive capacity, 102; *see also* soil, *and* topsoil
Abraham, of Ur, 19
absentee ownership, in Africa, 37; in Europe, 202; in Latin America, 37; in Spain, 207
Adirondack mountains, and subsoil erosion, 102
Africa, absentee landlordism, 37; agriculture, 241, 244, 250 ff.; area, 241; aridity, 23, 253; bananas, 259; belts of native vegetation and human occupancy, 241 ff.; big-game mammals, 241, 249, 251; carrying capacity, 30, 240, 242, 257, 260 ff.; climate and vegetation belts, 242; cocoa, 259; coffee, 254, 257, 259; corn exports and imports, 260; corn production, 257, 260; cotton, 257; death of livestock through drought, 248; degeneration of vegetation, 248 ff., 258, 260; disappearance of fishes, 253; disappearance of watercourses, 252; deserts, 240 ff., 251 ff.; ecological equilibrium and domestic cattle, 251 ff.; erosion, 242, 244, 246, 249, 252 ff.; European influence on Malthusian Checks, 260; European markets, 261; exports of lobster to United States, 36; exports of raw material, 68; famine, 258, 260; forests, 241 ff.; forest control measures in Southern Rhodesia, 254; forest destruction, 245, 248, 253; forest management, 250; forest protection through Pygmies, 249; game herds, 86; geography, 244;

goats, 252; grazing, 254; illiteracy, 47; internal drainage, 244; land abuse, 250; land destruction, 258 ff.; land destruction since Roman colonization, 245 ff.; meteorological data, 247; native grazing practices, 261 ff.; olive groves, 247; *oncocercosis*, 28; overcultivation, 258 ff.; overgrazing, 30; overgrazing and the advance of the Sahara, 251 ff.; overpopulation, 251; plantation agriculture, 258 ff.; population, 254, 256, 258 ff.; population concentration, 250; population data, 241, 257, 262 ff.; possibly changing climatic cycle, 240, 247; precipitation, 240 ff.; primitive populations and native laws, 249; railroads, 254; reforestation, 255; resettlement, 257; rubber, 259; scientific research, 242; sheep, 248, 251, 256; shifting agriculture, 254, 260 ff.; sleeping sickness as check on overpopulation, 257; soil, 242, 254; soil structure, 245; South African Drought Investigation Commission, 252, 255 ff.; taxes, 261; temperature and importance of plant cover, 244 ff.; tsetse fly, 30; unfavorable environment, 259; waters, 244; water tables, 242, 246 ff., 252 ff.; wheat, 256; wildlife destruction, 33; *see also* country references
Agrarian Society, of New World, 60
Agricultural Experiment Stations, 51, 123; and cooperative research, 268
Agricultural Extension Service, 123
agricultural land, versus arable land, 27; cropland destroyed in United States, 121; in Great Plains, 23;

resource management, 161; "roaring forties," 84; siltation of ports, 189; siltation of rivers, 189; soil, 187 ff.; standard of living, 74; steel production, 167; topsoil destruction, 188; tourist trade, 189; vegetation, 85, 188; water tables, 158; wheat yields, 188; *see also* Latin America

China, agricultural practices, 224; agriculture, 220 ff.; amount of arable land per capita, 219, available land, 244; birth control and folkways, 280; birth rate, 74; carrying capacity, 220, 224; climate, 220 ff.; Communist economic policy, 237, diet, 221; erosion, 223; famine, 57, 219 ff., 224 ff.; fertilizers, 110, 221; in fifteenth century, 14; floods, 220, 223; General Marshall's mission, 238; grazing lands, 221 ff.; industrialization, 224; industrialization as threat to world peace, 236; internal per capita purchasing power, 237; introduction of new crops and population growth, 224; livestock populations, 221 ff.; loss of productive capacity, 223; malaria, 13; and meaning of history, 19; overpopulation, 74; population data, 219 ff.; precipitation, 215, 220 ff.; railroads, 224; range management, 222; rate of population increase, 219; rational population policy, 77; rice riots, 238; soil, 220 ff.; standard of living, 74 ff.; TVA possibilities, 224; Yellow River Valley watersheds, 99; *see also* Asia

cities, and centralized government in Latin America, 154 ff.; creation through Industrial Revolution, 59; expansion in United States, 64 ff.; labor pools, 147; and need for conservation education, 148; population data, 148; rise of, 41 ff.; and rural social organization in Japan, 217; and scarcity of water in Mexico, 174; trend from rural concentrations as obstacle to rational land use, 148

Civil War, and land destruction, 117
climate, in Amazon Basin 83 ff.; in

Asia, 214 ff., 220 ff., 234; in Canada, 21; in equatorial lowlands, 23 ff.; in Europe, 200 ff.; influence of, 24; in Latin America, 153 ff.; as limiting factor, 23 ff.; present possibly changing cycle in Africa, 240 ff.; *see also* country references

climatological research, in Latin America, 159 ff.; as means of solving regional resource problems, 159 ff.

climax, checks and balances, 89 ff.; definition of, 87; destruction of, 89 ff.; effects of destruction, 90; influence of man, 87; United States grasslands, 87; variations, 87 ff.

coal, in England, 5 ff., 166; and hydroelectric power in Latin America, 166; and solar energy, 18

coffee, in Africa, 254, 257; in Brazil, 63; in Central America, 24; in El Salvador, 75, 154; in Guatemala, 63; in South America, 24

Cofre de Perote National Park, 171

collectivized farming, in Europe, 203; and Russian government control, 233

Colombia, calorie intake and annual income per capita, 172; carrying capacity, 25; Santa Marta Mountains, 25; siltation of ports, 158; *see also* Latin America

colonization, and concepts of urban man, 81; in Peru, 183 ff.; as population control in Greece, 58; *see also* immigration, *and* resettlement

commercial combines, in U.S., 37

commercial fishermen, and reduced fish populations, 35 ff.

commercial groups, destruction of National Forests, 119

Communist Manifesto, 53

Compañía Administradora del Guano, *see* Guano Administration

compartmentalism, as applied to research and action programs, 142 ff.

competition, 36 ff.; as animal population control, 92; balanced, 109; export, 70 ff.; and industrialization of Greece, 205 ff.; Japan versus United States and Great Britain, 218; manufacturing, 78, 209; shipping, 71;

United States versus postwar Europe, 209

Congress, appropriation cuts, 140; and non-Aristotelian concept, 51; attitude toward conservation education, 149; cattle and sheep interests, 31; committees, 121; complacency and resource management, 112; conservation appropriation cuts of 80th Congress, 124; inadequacy in scientific matters, 140 ff.; and land legislation during Civil War period, 117; and proposed landownership legislation, 144; and research expenditure, 142; and scientific advisory services, 270; and Valley Authorities, 127

conservation action on the land, 277 ff.; adequate management of arable land, 277; campaign against waste, 278; conservation of sanitary waste, 278; control of hydrologic cycle through protection of forests and reforestation, 277; controlled grazing, 277; ecological trusteeships, 278; improved farming methods, 277; international control of resource exploitation, 278; and land management within nature's laws, 279; planned economic reform, 278; resettlement of populations, 278

conservation education, non-Aristotelian approach, 273; attitude of Congress, 149; development of international regional education, 272; diagnosis of problems, 273; expenditures in Latin America, 157; expenditures in United States, 137; function of conservation organizations, 270; lack of trained resource managers, 272; of leaders, 274; man's relationship to his environment, 276; nontechnical short-term and long-range, 274 ff.; relationship to arts, literature, disciplines, etc., 276; role of Audubon Nature Camp, 275; role of national and state parks, 277; in schools, universities, etc., 276; technical training versus education, 272; techniques and media, 275 ff.; and

work of government agencies, 148 ff.

conservation expenditures, in Costa Rica, 182; in Latin America, 157; in United States, 137, 157

conservation program, 268 ff.; action on the land, 277 ff.; development through civic organizations, 275; education, 272 ff.; research, 268 ff.

conservation research, barriers of language and poverty of scientists, 269 ff.; in cooperation with countries of similar climate and culture, 269; economic research and ecological orientation, 271; expenditures in United States, 137; natural sciences versus social sciences, 271; as part of conservation program, 268 ff.; scientific advisory services, 269 ff.; see also research

continence, and population control, 63

Convention on Nature Protection and Wild Life Preservation in the Western Hemisphere, 109

contraception, see birth control

cormorant, producer of guano, 185

corn, African exports and imports, 260; culture on slopes, 170; in El Salvador, 75; exports from New World, 60; influence on Latin American history, 157; in Iowa, 22; prizes for increased Mexican production, 170; production in Africa, 257, 260; production in Mexico, 22; as soil-destruction force, 97 ff., 115 ff.; the "tyrant," 157; see also agriculture

corruption, and national parks in Mexico, 163; of governments and government officials, 155; and resource management, 155

Costa Rica, agricultural land, 180; area, 180; attitude of farmer, 180; calorie intake and annual income per capita, 172; climate, 180 ff.; conservation expenditures, 182, 268; education, 182; erosion, 180 ff.; extractive exploitation of forests, 181 ff.; floods, 181; forests, 180 ff.; highway expenditures, 182; hydroelectric power, 180 ff.; Inter-Amer-

and immigration, *and* resettlement distillation of water, 20 ff.

Dominican Republic, calorie intake and annual income per capita, 172; cooperative research, 269; and immigration, 191; *see also* Latin America

DPs, *see* displaced persons

drought, *see* climate, *and* country references

dust bowl, 21, 24, 208, 230; possibility in 1947, 140; and precipitation in Missouri Valley, 83; and railroads, 39; recurrence, 67

Dutch elm disease, 28

ecological degeneration and actual destruction, 256

ecological DPs, and European DPs, 107; in Latin America, 191 ff.; and resource destruction, 107; *see also* displaced persons

ecological equilibrium, 86 ff.; and African environment, 260; and balanced agriculture, 110 ff.; and economic thinking, 146; in Latin America, 191; and present European food situation, 208 ff.; value of wildlife, 132 ff.

ecological fifth column, 143 ff.

ecological health, 265, 271

ecological incompetents, 145 ff.

ecology, and Aristotelian logic, 49 ff.

economic laws, and land management, 37

economic pressure, 31, 69; *see also* industrialization

economic research, and ecological orientation, 271; non-Aristotelian, 271

economic and social councils, and elementalistic thinking, 54

economic systems, erroneous concepts of, 81

economic thinking, as cause of ecologic imbalance, 146; money evaluation versus biophysical evaluation, 146

economists, and concept of biotic potential, 63; and the land, 42 ff.; and Malthusianism, 55, 63

economy, balanced, 43; depression recovery in 19th century, 64 ff.; effect of farmer's purchasing power, 64 ff.; effect of shrinking purchasing power, 80; expanding and contracting, 67; extractive, 110, 157; in Latin America, 157; pioneer, 115 ff.; planned reform, 278; Russian expansionist, 233 ff.

Ecuador, annual income per capita, 172; exploitation of fish, 35; *see also* Latin America

education, Aristotelian cast, 141 ff.; in Latin America, 160 ff.; need in a democracy, 151; and relationship between man and his environment, 143; and teachers' salaries, 7 ff.; in United States, 79 ff., 125; *see also* conservation education

Egypt, birth rate, 74; meteorological stations, 247; overpopulation, 74; protective tariff, 209; siltation of Nile and national economy, 252; standard of living, 74 ff.; *see also* Africa

eighteenth century, American farmer, 40 ff.; cotton exports to Old World, 60; famine, 58; timber, 113

Eire, birth rate, 74; calorie intake and annual income per capita, 199; population decrease, 74; and former starvation, 74; *see also* Europe, *and* Great Britain

Ejido, definition of, 163; as destroyer of land, 163; *see also* Mexico

elementalistic thinking, and economics, 54; and Economic and Social Councils, 54; and international affairs, 54; and international organizations, 53; and land-use problems, 54; and multiple-use concept, 54; and national affairs, 54; and population problems, 53 ff.; and sociology, 54; and "soil erosion," 124; and United States Army Engineers, 54

El General Valley, 181

El Salvador, agriculture, 177 ff.; amount of cultivable land per capita, 76; area, 177; calorie intake, 76, 178; calorie intake and annual income per capita, 172; carrying ca-

pacity, 75, 178; character of people, 75, 179; coffee, 75, 154, 178;
compared to Costa Rica, 180, 182;
corn, 75; death rate versus birth
rate, 179; deforestation, 177 ff.; diseases, 178; exports, 75; extirpation
of important plant successions, 269;
fuel, 157, 177; government, 179; illiteracy rate, 177 ff.; industrialization, 75; lack of land surface, 106;
land abuse, 75; land classification
of cultivable area, 177; malnutrition, 76; overpopulation and adjustment to land-use capabilities,
106 ff.; population data, 177 ff.;
population per square mile of arable land, 161; possible increase in
agricultural production, 178; as
possible leader in Latin America,
179; railroads, 157; resource management, 161; significance to North
Americans, 75; standard of living,
75, 178; starvation, 15, 75 ff., 152,
177 ff.; *see also* Central America
Emergency Conservation Committee,
and resource restoration, 137
emigration, to New World, 59 ff.; as
population control in Greece, 58;
see also immigration
energy, from earth to man, 18 ff.
England, agricultural practices, 71;
amount of arable land, 71; arable
land per capita and rate of population increase, 194; area, 6; coal, 5 ff.;
colonies, 57 ff.; exports, 61; export
competition, 70; famine, 57 ff., 72;
in fifteenth century, 14; food and
available land, 6; free trade, 63;
hunger, 6; imports from Denmark,
202; imports from New World, 60;
and Industrial Revolution, 58 ff.;
manufacturing, 60 ff., 64, 70 ff.; and
meaning of history, 19; population,
57, 63, 71; precipitation, 84; purchasing power, 70; during Queen
Victoria's reign, 6; shipping, 71;
and Socialist Government, 71 ff.;
standard of living, 71; subsidies to
farmers, 196; withdrawal from
India, 237; *see also* Great Britain,
and Europe

environment, in Africa, 259; and
breaking of hydrologic cycle, 96;
exhaustion by man, 110; genetic
changes within, 87; influence on
soil types, 85; limitations, 16; versus
"political" and "economic" means,
80; present modifications in Europe, 208 ff.; relationship to man,
143 ff., 276; and research, 271; and
shifting agriculture, 93 ff.; stabilization, 94; understanding for human
adjustment, 109 ff., 158 ff.; variations in Latin America, 158 ff.; and
water, 81 ff.; *see also* country references, *and* environmental resistance
environmental resistance, and Civil
War, 117; definition, 16; and destructive weapons, 33; effect of
ecological DPs, 107; formula, 16;
and grazing lands, 31; and increased
cost of living, 129; as increased by
stockmen, 120; increasing in Europe, 200; after Industrial Revolution, 59 ff.; and land productivity,
21 ff., 93 ff.; and modern agriculture, 42; in Palestine, 235; and
practical ceiling, 22; and precipitation, 102 ff.; under primitive conditions, 31 ff.; and resource losses,
125; and role in solution of resource
problem, 268; in rural Georgia and
South Carolina, 45
erosion, in Africa, 244, 246, 249,
252 ff., 256; and agricultural crops
versus natural plants, 97; and
American standard of living, 67;
and angle of repose, 94; in Asia,
215 ff., 223; in Australia, 235;
in Canada, 125; cause and effect,
100; and change in soil structure,
96; control methods, 97, 103 ff., 124,
125, 232 ff.; effects, 121 ff.; in Europe, 84, 201, 204, 207; geological,
94; gravity, 99; gully, 99, 170, 232,
253 ff.; of human nervous system,
38; induced, 100; and land classification, 105 ff.; in Latin America,
153 ff.; losses from, 121 ff.; "moral"
erosion in Latin America, 155; of
range land, 120; rate of increase,
99; relationship with cropping prac-

fauna, *see* animals *and* wildlife

fertilizer, 37; and balanced agriculture, 110; in China, 110, 200, 221; Japanese imports, 219; in Java, 200; need in Latin America, 162; in the Philippines, 200; in "teaspoon agriculture," 207 ff.; *see also* guano resources, *and* menhaden

fescue bunchgrass, an example of induced erosion, 100 ff.

field mice, and the food chain, 19

fifteenth century, relationship between human populations and natural resources, 14

Fifth Freedom, 211

Finland, calorie intake and annual income per capita, 199; timber exports to Russia, 230; *see also* Europe

fire, influence in plant successions, 87 ff.; as limiting factor, 28, 32; *see also* country references, *and* forest fires

fire protection, in Alaska, 140; and failing water supply, 128; in United States forests, 139 ff.

fish, in colonial United States, 112; costly effects of siltation on fishing, 123; disappearance from African waters, 253; fisheries and the TVA, 39; international treaties, 36; overexploitation by American fishermen, 35; and pollution of waters, 34; production data, 35 ff.; reduced populations, 35; value of fishing industry in United States, 132

flax, as soil-destruction force, 115

flood control, by beaver dams, 150; through engineering methods, 125 ff.; in Greece, 205; siltation of reservoirs, 121 ff.; and the TVA, 38 ff.; and United States Army Engineers, 54; value of ground cover, 99

flood plains and human occupation, 126 ff.; of Missouri and Mississippi Rivers, 126

flooding, and hydroelectric developments, 38; of productive land, 126 ff.

floods, in Africa, 30; in Asia, 234; in China, 220, 223; in colonial

United States, 112 ff.; in Greece, 205; in Mexico, 171 ff.; Missouri River floods of July, 1947, 124; in United States, 21, 126 ff.

fog, ocean, 25 ff.

food, and annual income per capita in Europe, 198 ff.; and annual income per capita in Latin America, 172; as political weapon, 140; and practical ceilings, 22; present situation in Europe, 208 ff.; present world demands, 140; prices, 34 ff.; storage in Europe, 58; surpluses, 78, 176; synthesized, 18

Food and Agriculture Organization of the United Nations, agricultural program for Greece, 206; and contraception programs, 281 ff.; mission to Greece

food chain, 19; example of, 19; and pyramid of numbers, 91 ff.; within various plant associations, 91

forest destruction, 32 ff.; as cause of increased rate of runoff, 140; effects in Latin America, 158; effects of Mexican highways, 170 ff.; in Europe before Middle Ages, 207; through expanding economy, 67; in nineteenth century, 39; results of, 121 ff.; watersheds, 119; Wisconsin's legal measures against, 89 ff.; throughout world, 79; *see also* country references

forest fires, in Alaska, 140; in Chile, 158; in Mexico, 172; in United States, 139 ff.

forest land, area in United States without organized fire protection, 139 ff.; private versus government ownership; total area in United States, 118

forest products, need for, 118 ff.; *see also* lumber, timber

forestry, American mission to Chile, 164; and cooperative research, 268; Latin American Departments, 157; obstacles to rational program, 144; sustained-yield, 136; TVA programs, 39

forests, in Africa, 241 ff.; and Agricultural Revolution, 42; in Asia, 215; in colonial United States,

Gold Coast, forests, 248; fire and agriculture, 248; population increase, 248; *see also* Africa

Good Neighbor Policy, 165

government, centralized, 154 ff.; corruption, 155; Latin American conservation activities, 155; local versus national, 155; responsibility in conservation programs, 269 ff., 275, 277 ff., 281 ff.; *see also* United States Government

government policies, and effect of water, 103

Graham, E. H., 47

grasshoppers, and destruction of vegetation, 24; in Latin America, 159; and need for cooperative research, 269; *see also* insects, *and* pests

grasslands and grazing lands, in Africa, 251 ff., 254, 261; in Argentina, 31; in Australia, 31; in China, 221 ff.; classification, 106; in colonial United States, 113 ff.; control, 277; destruction and expanding economy, 67; development of soils, 86; in Ireland, 200; overexploitation in United States, 31; preservation measures, 109; in national parks, 31; *see also* country references

gravity erosion, *see* erosion

Great Britain, birth rate, 73 ff.; disparity between populations and carrying capacity, 70 ff.; hydroelectric power, 166; industrial competition with Latin America, 168; industrialization, 72 ff.; influence on economic and sanitary conditions in India, 226; lack of adequate productive land, 73; manufacturing production, 61 ff.; as near-monopolist in industry on international scale, 75; purchasing power, 78; skills, 5, 70 ff.; timber imports, 113; weekly incomes in agriculture, 201; *see also* country references *and* Europe

Great Plains, climate, 201; destruction through railroads, 149 ff.; and mechanized agriculture, 147; precipitation 23, 84; soil, 21; temperature, 23; wind erosion, 21

Greece, agricultural production, 197, 204 ff.; and the American people, 203; American WPA and militarism, 210; amount of agricultural land, 203 ff.; arable land per capita and rate of population increase, 194; area, 203; average farm, 204; birth control, 58, 206; calorie intake and annual income per capita, 198; carrying capacity and resettlement, 205; erosion, 204 ff.; exports, 205; FAO mission, 203; flood control, 205; forest destruction, 204, 207; geography, 203 ff.; goats, 204 ff.; hydrologic regime, 205; imports, 197; industrialization, 205 ff.; land destruction, 204 ff.; land-use capabilities, 106; land-use practices, 204; modern Greece versus Age of Pericles, 276; overpopulation, 106, 204 ff.; population, 205 ff.; population data, 203; prewar per capita income, 205; resettlement problem, 204 ff.; standard of living and American taxpayer, 205 ff.; standard of living and birth rate, 195; starvation, 15; storage dams, 205; topography, 204; waters, 205; *see also* Europe

Guanacaste, Costa Rica, 181

Guano Administration, of Peru, 155; as conservation organization, 186; government and private management, 186; increased guano production, 186

guano resources, 183 ff.; and alteration of microclimates, 24; bird population control, 92; cormorant, 185; management, 184, 186; production data, 36 ff., 185 ff.; protection of birds, 186

Guatemala, annual income per capita, 172; carrying capacity 40; coffee. 63; disastrous effects of milpa agriculture, 156; forests, 25; fuel, 177; populations, 40; soil, 25; *see also* Central America

Gulf of Maine, and disappearance of menhaden, 36

Gulf of Mexico, 140; American topsoil versus grain exports, 69; and

Index

Manchuria, 222, *see also* Asia
Manchukuo, 218, *see also* Asia
markets, domestic, 64; rural, 66; world free, 77; *see also* country references, *and* industrialization, *and* purchasing power
Marshall, George C., mission to China, 238
Maryland, effects of tobacco exploitation, 115 ff.
meat, and higher standard of living, 140; importation of, 31
mechanization of agriculture, 42; in Dakotas, 45; and effect of petroleum famine, 147; influence on nation's economy, 66; influence on per capita output, 147; *see also* country references
medical profession, and expanding populations, 48; health campaign in El Salvador, 179; and malaria, 12 ff.; and present overpopulation in Europe, 210; United States government measures, 76 ff.; work in Latin America, 163 ff.
Mediterranean Sea, and oil, 68
menhaden, as fertilizer for New England corn, 185; production, 36
meteorology, 82; lack of data in Africa, 247; research in Latin America, 160; stations, 247
Mexico, agriculture, 169; alkaline dust diseases, 174; and American culture, 168; biotic potential, 22; birth control, 74; calorie intake and annual income per capita, 172; carrying capacity, 40; charcoal and deforestation, 171 ff.; climate, 175; climatological research, 160; corn yield per acre, 22; cultivation data, 169; deforestation and graft, 161; destructive effects of the ejido, 163; disastrous effects of milpa, 156; erosion, 163, 169 ff., 170; fish, 35; floods, 172; forest destruction, 170; forest fires, 172; forest production, 161; fuel, 157; highways, 70 ff.; industrialization, 167, 173; infant mortality, 176; internal markets, 167; land abuse, 152; land destruction, 170 ff.; land hunger, 163; land productivity, 175 ff.; land-use

patterns, 163; life expectancy of Mexican, 175; Mexican Revolution and landholding, 173; national parks, 171; national parks and political corruption, 163; overpopulation, 74; population, 40, 169 ff.; population data, 175; population growth, 169 ff., 175 ff.; population pressure and resource poverty, 176 ff.; potential arable land per capita, 169; precipitation, 24, 175; pre-Conquest resource destruction, 169 ff.; present reform administration, 163; railroads, 157; resource destruction, 175; resource management, 161; soil, 22; soil conservation service, 169; standard of living, 74 ff.; State of Michoacán, 4, 171; State of Oaxaca as future desert land, 171; and Swedish colonization, 45; topographic influence, 25; water resources, 174 ff.; water supply, 128, 171; watersheds, 174 ff; *see also* Latin America
Michoacán, State of, 4, 171
microclimates, 24
microfilm production, 269
microscopic fauna and flora, 28; in formation of soil, 85
Middle West, in colonial United States, 114; iodine deficiency in soils, 26; floods, 125 ff.; waterfowl sanctuaries, 108
migration, as wildlife population check, 131
milpa, 28, 47, 93; description of, 156 ff.; effects of, 156 ff.; origin of, 156
minifundio, definition of, 202; in Europe, 202
Mississippi Valley, flood plains, 126; watersheds, 99
Missouri Valley, Dust Bowl, 83; flood plains, 126; watersheds, 99
Missouri Valley Authority, 126 ff.; irrigation, 126; flooding of fertile land, 126; as possible national liability, 126; versus Tennessee Valley Authority, 126 ff.
moldboard plow, as destructive tool, 33
Mongolia, 222, *see also* Asia

117; dynamic interrelationship of factors, 86; erosion in British Isles, 84; of Europe, 200 ff.; formation, 84 ff.; of Great Plains, 21; iodine deficiency, 26; as limiting factor on land productivity, 26; loss in fertility, 124 ff.; microscopic fauna and flora, 28; organic content, 26; under primitive conditions, 94; as real capital, 44; research, 108 ff.; structure, 26; surveys, 159; types, 85 ff.; unprotected, 98 ff.; volcanic, 26; *see also* land, *and* country references

Soil Conservation Districts, 136; and conservation farm planning, 122

South African Drought Investigation Commission, 252; report of, 255 ff.

South America, calorie intake and annual income per capita, 172; coffee, 24; malaria, 13; national parks and cooperative research, 269; pests, 159; plant diseases, 159; sanitary habits, 64; Santa Marta Mountains, 25; *see also* country references

South Carolina, cotton, 45; tobacco, 45; rural living standard, 45

Southern Rhodesia, agriculture, 242, 254; grazing, 254 ff.; gully erosion, 255; resource-control measures, 254; savanna, 242, 254; sheet erosion, 254 ff.; soil, 242; water tables, 242, 254; *see also* Africa

Soviet Union, agricultural land, 231; agricultural practices, 230 ff.; agriculture, 215; amount of arable land, 231, 239; area, 214; areas of population concentration, 215; aridity, 23; climate, 215, 229; cooperative research, 269; erosion, 232; expansion economy, 233; famine, 239; forests, 230; forest reserves, 79; geography, 215; government control of land and land-use practices, 232 ff.; grain exports, 208; Koeppen climatic classification, 229 ff.; land productivity, 238; marginal land, 229; minerals, 229; overpopulation, 239; population data, 233, 239; population expansion program, 239; population increase, 230; precipitation,

215, 229 ff., 232; serfdom and concentrated farming, 232; Siberian hysteria, 231; soil, 26 ff., 215 ff., 230; standard of living, 233; timber imports, 230; transportation, 230; wind, 24; *see also* Russia

soybean, as soil-destruction force, 97

space-time, four-dimensional, 49

Spain, agricultural production, 197; calorie intake and annual income per capita, 199; erosion, 207; imports, 197; influence of 16th century culture in Latin America, 152 ff.; land destruction during Moorish occupation, 207; landownership patterns, 207; and meaning of history, 19; overpopulation, 207; *see also* Europe

Spanish Republican reform, 202

spoils system, and Latin American science, 160

standard of living, 8; and adjustment of human needs to resources, 158 ff.; amount of arable land required, 194; and Aristotelian thinking, 53 ff.; in Asia, 215; in Australia, 235; and birth rates, 74; and carrying capacity, 23 ff., 67; in ecological health, 265; effect of angle of repose, 103; in Europe, 57 ff., 195 ff., 208 ff.; and food surpluses, 176; and increased national meat consumption, 140; and industrialization, 70 ff.; influence in England of American GIs, 71; and land management, 111; and land-use capabilities, 107; in Latin America, 75; and material progress, 37 ff.; as "multi-ordinal term", 56; in pioneer economy, 115 ff.; versus resettlement, 192; and runoff, 103 ff.; subsistence level, 147 ff.; symptoms of lower standard, 79; *see also* American standard of living, *and* country references

starling, as introduced species, 89

starvation, as animal populations check, 89; in China, 219 ff., 224 ff.; in Eire, 74; in El Salvador, 152, 177 ff.; in Great Britain, 57 ff., 72 ff.; in Haiti, 152; in modern Europe,

culture, and conservation education, 149; and new Dust Bowl, 67; world arable land estimates, 27

United States Department of the Interior, and Congressional appropriation cuts, 140; and conservation education, 149

United States Department of State, 42, 219, 227

United States of Europe, population and standard of living, 211

United States Fish and Wildlife Service, 123; and conservation education, 149; and resource restoration, 136 ff.

United States foreign policy, 15

United States Forest Service, 123; and conservation education, 148 ff.; and controlled lumbering on rangeland, 136; establishment of, 139; and resource restoration, 136 ff.

United States Geological Survey, 123

United States government, and benefit payments, 43; foreign aid, 77 ff., 79; loans to farm tenants, 148; nutrition measures, 77; sanitation measures, 76 ff.; and taxes, 7 ff., 69; *see also* Congress

United States Maritime Commission, 42

United States National Park Service, and conservation education, 148 ff., 277; and resource restoration, 137

United States Navy, 42

United States Soil Conservation Service, aims of, 104; conservation education, 148 ff.; conservation farm planning, 122; conservation measures, 124; establishment of, 139; and resource restoration, 136 ff.; and social science research, 271; and the TVA, 38 ff.

UNRRA, *see* United Nations Relief and Rehabilitation Administration

Ur, as former seaport, 19; 151

Urban II, 58, 73

urban man, concepts of colonization, 81; lack of comprehension of influence of natural resources, 81; *see also* cities

Uruguay, calorie intake and annual income per capita, 172; *see also* Latin America

USDA, *see* United States Department of Agriculture

Vaillant, George, 169 ff.

Valley Authority, concept of, 126; and sheepmen's subsidies, 127; *see also*, Missouri Valley Authority, Tennessee Valley Authority

vegetation, in Amazon Basin, 83; and angle of repose, 103; blackberry as substitute, 88; in Chile, 85; destruction of, 24; in formation of soil, 85; and the hydrologic cycle, 83, 96; under primitive conditions, 94; protective, 83; quantity and quality of, 21; *see also* country references

Venezuela, annual income per capita, 172; carrying capacity, 25; erosion, 165; oil development, 165; precipitation, 154; Santa Marta Mountains, 25; subsistence agriculture, 165; *see also* Latin America

vertical erosion, *see* erosion

Virginia, effects of tobacco exploitation, 114 ff.

volcanic soil, 26; in Costa Rica, 180

Von Tschudi, estimate of Peruvian guano resources, 185

Vosges Mountains, erosion, 104

war, 12; atomic, 48; bacterial, 48; and overpopulation, 239; war contracts, 9

Washington, George, and soil conservation, 116

waste, of natural resources, 66 ff.

water, absorption capacity and erosion, 98; condensation, 82; desiccation of wells and springs in Mexico, 171; destruction, 66 ff.; effects through angle of repose, 103; evaporation, 83; failing supplies in Mexico, 173 ff.; in formation of soil, 84 ff.; infiltration, 97; as limiting factor, 27; limitations on use, 103; management practices, 104; for municipal and industrial purposes,